Technical
Communication

Sidney W. Wilcox

Assistant Professor of
Technical Communication
Arizona State University

Technical
Communication

International Textbook Company

Scranton, Pennsylvania

To

Thomas Whitfield Davidson of Dallas

*My lifelong friend
and source of continuing inspiration*

Second Printing, April, 1968

Preface

When the engineering school at Arizona State University was organized in 1955, the dean and faculty, all of whom had recently been in professional engineering or scientific jobs in industry, decided to make communication a core course on the senior level. They were convinced (and still are) that the professionally trained engineering graduate must have basic communication skill in addition to his mathematics and science. It was decided in the early planning for the new course that it should be a practical one, aimed as directly as possible toward achieving minimum goals in effective writing and speaking rather than toward developing specialized skills in technical report writing. The results have been so gratifying in terms of employer demand for graduates who have taken this course that it is believed a textbook incorporating the subject matter and teaching methods of the course will serve a useful purpose.

The scope of the text has been made somewhat broader than the usual one-semester course so that the instructor may have some choice in developing his own course plan. If all the materials are used, the text will serve for a two-semester course. In that case the first semester might be planned to end with Chapter 8, and the second semester could be devoted to research and professional writing projects. Although the text is intended primarily for teaching a basic communication course to technical people, it can serve as a text for a creative writing course involving an accurate, objective use of the language. This text offers a practical approach to developing the craft of communication. The mechanics of expression and technical style are the tools of the craft. The writing assignments begin with simple problems of paragraph length and end with a professional-level communication project.

Experience has shown that a course in basic communication designed to reach technical students must begin fairly close to the point where the subject got shelved when specialization in mathematics and science began. For some otherwise bright young men this is below high school level in the mechanics of expression. Instruction in mechanics (not included in the text) begins with an inventory of skills in basic English; this is accomplished by giving nationally standardized tests. From these tests the instructor can decide how much time he should give to grammar review and which individuals will need most help.

The approach to the mechanics of expression is informal (non-school-marmish). Only those errors which the instructor believes are the most damaging to communication and to the reputation of the engineer are emphasized. The whole class is required to reach a certain minimum achievement level through the combined incentives of the short assignment and the privilege of revising for credit. It has been found that students are challenged to make their greatest effort on a closely controlled, one-paragraph paper. Mastery of the paragraph speeds up mastery of the longer forms. The paragraph is assigned because it is the shortest or smallest sample which demonstrates the kind of writing assigned. A larger sample would serve better but would take too much of the student's time. The short practice papers done outside the classroom should carry relatively little credit toward the semester grade, for it is to be expected that some students will get outside help in editing these short papers. But the student soon becomes aware that editorial help for papers done outside of class may actually hinder his learning and cause a failure when he is thrown upon his own resources in the controlled written assignments done in the classroom.

In general, the class lectures follow assigned reading matter in the text, though frequent examples from technical periodicals and from student papers are also used. Those who have made exceptionally low scores on the standard English tests may be asked to systematically review basic English in the areas of weakness indicated by the tests. For this a high school grammar is recommended. The first few weeks will turn up most of the basic problems in mechanics of expression. Once the technical student begins to understand a few things well and loses some of the fear or dread or boredom which he expected to experience in a writing class, he learns rapidly. Technical people by reputation (and as confirmed by observation) tend to express themselves cryptically or to string unrelated ideas together in choppy sentences. The first step in overcoming this fault is to develop coherent sentences and paragraphs. The writing of eight or nine unified paragraphs usually smooths out the student's style and improves his thinking processes.

From the length of the assigned paragraphs, one might think the author is opposed to the short paragraph. But this is not so. The longer paragraph assignments are effectively used to correct the engineer's habit of stopping before he has developed his topic to the satisfaction of the reader.

When the student has shown that he can communicate effectively within precise form and content limits, with relatively no mechanical errors, he gets a change of pace by making a short speech or writing a letter of application for a job. Application letters, though included late in the text, should be assigned early in the course when most undergraduates are sending out such letters. But if this text is used for sophomore or junior students, application letters may better be reserved for later assignments.

The speech is useful at this point not only for the diversion afforded, but because the same subject can be continued in the next exercise involving the five-paragraph assignment. For the five-paragraph paper the student chooses a subject which he must discuss from two points of view: the *pro* viewpoint and the *con* viewpoint. Through this exercise he develops skill in handling the techniques of unity and coherence in the longer composition and in objectively analyzing his subject. In doing this he also learns how to write introductory, transitional, and concluding paragraphs.

After the five-paragraph assignment, and before a full-length report is attempted, the instructor may wish to present the material on technical style. Adequate understanding of style is assumed when the students are able to demonstrate the various levels of formal and informal (popular) style. After the study of technical style, the full-length report should be attempted.

The short recommendation report was selected for class instruction because it gives the student a chance to analyze a technical problem and at the same time to show his knowledge of style and the techniques of presentation. The difference between a convincing report and an inadequate report will be obvious when the class studies the samples they produce. It will be clearly demonstrated that a sharp eye, a discerning mind, and a passion for accuracy are absolute necessities in writing effective recommendation reports. Writing the report as if the student were already on the job gives a real-life earnestness to this assignment.

If the instructor is following somewhat closely the sequence of topics in the text, he will be ready at about this point to begin the term project. For the majority, the term project will be a technical research paper, though several other interesting options are encouraged: an article for publication, an on-the-job assignment, or a departmental laboratory research report in which the student may have assisted. Other options include technical society contest papers, applications for patents, and any other special project which in the opinion of the instructor is of sufficient merit to qualify as a professional readiness check (see Chapters 9, 10, and 12 for details on term project options). The term project options are provided to permit the individual to select whatever appears to offer the most useful and practical means of furthering his own special training. This is indicated by the three criteria established for the selection of a subject: the subject must be current, it must be significant, and it must be of interest to the student.

In the writing of these projects the instructor may wish to suspend formal class lectures during the two or three weeks of peak activity and to make himself available for office conferences as needed. Usually one or two conferences per student can be expected. In this way he becomes personally acquainted with the projects and the level of student effort. The requirement that no project will be accepted until the note cards and the original draft are seen by the instructor has been found pretty discouraging to the one or two percent who try to "beat" the course.

In the last weeks of the course the emphasis is shifted to oral communication to give the instructor time to fully evaluate the longer papers. A guest speaker from industry initiates the constructive study of public speaking for technical people by telling the class what his company expects in communication skills from the graduating engineer. After the guest speaker, experience in oral reporting similar to that which the student may soon have on the job is provided by a ten-minute report on some aspect of his term project. A 3 by 5 inch card outline is permitted, but technical notes are discouraged. These may help the speaker, but they have little value for the audience. However, the student is permitted to use posters, slides, or the blackboard for illustrations. After the speech the student remains before the class for five to ten minutes to answer questions from the group. There is little doubt that a student has done honest and thorough work if he presents some interesting angle of a technical subject without notes and if he shows poise and confidence under further questioning from his classmates and the instructor.

Finally, in Chapter 12, the student is given a brief introduction to some special forms of business communication which involve sales brochures, engineering proposals, letters, and telegraphic messages. The letter of application for employment contained in this group, if it was not assigned before, is recommended. The patent application discussed in Chapter 12 may be used as a term project. Otherwise Chapter 12 may be omitted without disturbing the continuity of the basic class assignments.

Learning will be more rapid if students are given a chance to re-write inferior papers. It has been found that the incentive to revise can be greatly increased by providing a 10 percent reduction in possible points for each revision; thus, an unsatisfactory paper revised by the next class meeting could be worth as much as a B; by the second meeting, a C; and by the third, a D. On the other hand, the unrevised substandard paper would bring no credit whatever. The additional writing practice which revision entails also provides a means of bringing the slower students up to the minimum performance without boring the faster ones.

Another assignment contributing to the enduring benefits of the course is that requiring the student to make an analysis of his own progress. This assignment may come at the end of the course or after the first eight or ten short assignments. By making a chart of his errors the student sees where his weaknesses are. He is then required to explain what is necessary to correct errors and poor usage (by category, not individual errors) and to suggest the more acceptable forms and practices.

The young scientist or engineer is considered to be eligible for graduation when he has learned to write within the assigned limits of form and content (with no outside assistance except a dictionary) without making more than three serious errors per page (see the section entitled Numbered Errors near the end of Chapter 1). Failure to complete any of the major assignments can also result in a failing grade for the course.

The author is deeply grateful for the helpful suggestions of students and friends in the preparation of this text. Student contributions, however, except the research paper at the close of chapter 9, the contest paper at the close of Chapter 10, and the geological survey at the close of Chapter 12, are not acknowledged by individual name. Quoted passages from copyrighted sources are acknowledged by footnotes.

SIDNEY W. WILCOX

Tempe, Arizona
September, 1962

Contents

Technical Communication

1
General Concepts

To begin a text with a sales pitch when the subject is already sold would be a waste of words. Technical communication is already high on the priority list. It is a required course of study for all branches of engineering at Arizona State University, and it is either required or recommended in most other accredited technical and preprofessional schools. Inadequate communication is a generally acknowledged barrier in our accelerated technology race for national survival. Better communication in all areas of industrial and scientific activity could well become a national goal. Money spent to improve communication would stretch the dollars spent for research. Through better communication, what is known by a few could be known by many. For the higher the general level becomes (in a republic, that is), the more support is given to the research scientists. Training a few thousand technical writers will help, but this is not enough. Engineers and scientists must do a better job of communicating with each other and the general public. This author's experience has shown that a little effort in that direction while the future engineer or scientist is still in the classroom can be immensely rewarding.

By the time a technical student reaches his junior or senior year he has begun to see that the ability to express himself clearly and to comprehend what others have said is more important than he had perhaps thought a few years before when he gave up his interest in English for the more robust and challenging mathematics and science courses. He might profit a little by retaking freshman English or advanced composition, but conventional courses in English, helpful as they are, do not prepare the technical student for the communication problems he will soon face on the job. The practical course presented in this text does provide the specialized knowledge and skills a technical man needs. A serious study of what is said here, and the successful completion of the prescribed exercises, will give the technical student a new outlook on the whole area of communication. He will

1

be able to perform with confidence the technical communication assignments normally encountered by new employees. He may not know exactly how to write certain company reports, but he will know enough to ask questions and to express his ideas effectively once he is shown the kind of report to be written.

Before a serious effort is begun to improve the student's technical communication skill, some general concepts ought to be understood and accepted as a sort of common base upon which the student and instructor can work. Such concepts are presented briefly in this chapter, as follows: standard usage, technical style, and mechanics of expression. The idea that all writing must be adapted to the needs of the occasion is not new, but it should be reexamined from the technical writer's viewpoint. Technical style is a new concept for most students. Its general structural differences are pointed out here; a full treatment is reserved for a later chapter. The chief purpose now is to develop the idea that a thorough understanding of certain basic mechanics of the language is a prerequisite for effective communication.

STANDARD USAGE

One does not speak of *correct* English any more. It is now *standard usage*. The best writers and speakers in a technical field set the standard, and the others follow. But the failure to follow standard practice in grammar or word use is just as damning as it ever was (perhaps even more). The ground rules and the instruction are intended to bring one's practice within the bounds of standard usage. Words and modes of expression not customarily used in a given situation are, by this definition, substandard.

It follows that standard usage in one situation can be poles away from standard usage in another situation. If, for example, one is at a stag party with close friends, the level of polite conversation, even for educated men, may plummet a surprisingly great distance. Still there are subjects and language which would not be in good taste even at a stag party. Violations of confidences or discussions of the private affairs of one's friends are taboo. To discuss these subjects would be substandard practice for the occasion.

Now to extend the example. If one of the gentlemen who attended the stag party is later engaged in a normal family discussion at home, what was standard usage at the party will undergo considerable modification. He will now use the modes of expression and the vocabulary of the home. One can call a neighbor a *snake*, a child a *brat*, and a screwdriver a *doohickey* and still be following standard usage in the home. On the other hand, if someone refers to the coffee brewing equipment as an *electrically heated percolator*, he will be using language that is nonstandard for the home. It is just as natural to say *coffeepot* in the home as it is to say *it's me* or *bust* or *knucklehead* or *broad* (meaning a woman) at the stag party.

The language of the home, though, is not appropriate for conversation with one's associates in business. Standard usage on the job is quite another thing. When a man speaks to the boss or a fellow worker, his speech is somewhat more reserved. He chooses his words more carefully to denote the exact idea he wishes to express. He will not stand at a conference table and say, "I'm gonna tell you about this here gadget I made," when what he means to report on is an efficient new filter he has designed for removing suspended silicon dust from a grinding coolant. In making such a report he cannot shout or bang the table; he speaks with dignity and restraint. He may feel like swearing, but he probably will not. He takes his cue from the practices of competent technical people on such occasions and acts accordingly. If he did not use standard language, his audience might be more concerned with his mode of expression than with the ideas presented.

But there is a still further level of usage. No matter how polished and effective an oral technical report may be, it is rarely suitable for publication without rewriting. Written communication on a technical subject demands the most precise word use of all communication. The best speech or the best dictated transcript will require many revisions before it becomes the printed page. The preparation of a technical article for a journal or popular magazine may require months of checking, rewriting, and polishing. The difficulty comes in saying precisely and concisely what one means, and nothing more.

As one can see, the term "standard usage" does not mean grammatical license. As one moves through the various areas of oral and written communication in business, in social gatherings, and in the home, standard usage controls word choice and the way thoughts are expressed in sentences as surely and as arbitrarily as conventional rules of grammar. Though one may not refer to substandard usage as incorrect English, failure to write and speak in the manner appropriate to the occasion is just as confusing and socially unacceptable as it ever was.

TECHNICAL STYLE

In their attempts to use the verbal language to communicate mathematical and scientific ideas, writers, especially during the past twenty to twenty-five years, have taken a few pragmatic shortcuts. Collectively, these changes have resulted in a new mode of expression characterized by its distinctive style—concise statement, objective viewpoint, and a highly specialized vocabulary.

Said another way, technical style is characterized by a denotative (one meaning) use of words, somewhat shorter sentences, and the absence of subjective or emotion-packed words. The unnecessary words have been removed. Nothing remains which is not needed to convey the technical ideas. This kind of writing is at the opposite pole from the novel, which purposely involves the reader's emotions and gives little heed to concise expression. Technical writing is objective and compact.

One readily apparent characteristic of technical style is the frequent use of abbreviations, figures, formulas, symbols, and graphic art. Standard abbreviations are used without periods, except as shown in the list of abbreviations in Appendix A. Other abbreviations can be used as needed, provided they are spelled out and explained to the reader on first use. Numbers above 10 referring to definite quantities are written in figures; numbers 10 and below are spelled out, except when used in combination with others above 10. Indefinite quantities are also spelled out. One should write, "About twenty students were present to see the demonstration." Numbers must always be spelled out when they begin a sentence. Fractions as adjectives are hyphened if they are compounded: a three-quarter-inch gap or a ¾-in. gap. But fractions are not hyphened if they are used as nouns: three quarters of an inch across or ¾ in. across. Whole numbers are hyphened if used as adjectives: a ten-foot pole, but a pole ten feet high; a 10-ft pole, but a pole 10 ft high. Whole numbers from twenty-one to ninety-nine are also hyphened.

Formulas are simplified or omitted in popular technical style, but they occur frequently in more specialized writing. They are usually centered on the page and explained immediately below, as follows:

Make the pumping signal a strong microwave signal at

$$f_p = f_1 + f_2$$

where f_p = pump frequency,
f_1 = signal frequency,
f_2 = idler frequency.

One learns, then, to recognize technical style by its form and contents. Its form is concise, its viewpoint objective, and its language specialized. These characteristics are easily recognized in technical journals, but they are less obvious in popular technical articles where technical style merges with literary style. When technical style is analyzed as shown in Chapter 7, it will be found that it takes more than jig-saw-puzzle technique to achieve the precision and compactness of technical style. A knowledge of English is required.

MECHANICS OF EXPRESSION

The experience at Arizona State University has shown that written communication proceeds at a snail's pace until the student has mastered the sentence and the paragraph. Almost the whole of English grammar is related in some way to the sentence, and almost all that must be learned about technical style and methods of presentation can be learned from a mastery of the paragraph. It has been observed, moreover, that the basic English practiced by most employers tends to be conservative rather than liberal or modern. This is probably because most people in management today went to school at a time when students were taught to follow arbitrary rules of *correct* usage. For this reason the conventional standards in mechanics of English as they can be observed in business and industry are preferred, and the review is limited to a few fundamental trouble spots. The stress is laid on those items which are considered most helpful to the technical student: the essential elements of the sentence, the paragraph, verbs and verbals, subordination devices, and a few other items. But this is not enough for the student who may be weak in English. For a full grammar and composition review the student should purchase or borrow an authoritative English handbook.

Sentence Sense

A sentence is a subject-verb relationship that says something or asks something. This is only slightly more precise than saying that a sentence is a group of words expressing a complete thought. It is entirely possible to have a verb (a finite verb, that is) and a noun and still not have a sentence, because it is also necessary that the subject and predicate be in a logical relation to each other before a statement is made. One may even prefer a definition from grammar school days:

A sentence is a group of words containing a subject and a predicate which makes a statement or asks a question. For technical writing any of these definitions is quite adequate, provided it is clearly understood.

The sentence is the vehicle of all communication. It will be recalled that a sentence has two or three basic elements, depending on the kind of verb used. Some predicates are complete in meaning, requiring no receiver (direct object) upon which to perform their action. This sentence, for instance, needs only a subject and predicate: The baby walks. But a sentence containing a verb which must have its action received by an object (a verb not complete in meaning in itself) possesses three essential elements—subject, verb, and direct object—as in the example Jim stuck me. A transitive verb (the kind of verb which must perform its action on someone or something before its meaning is understood) always requires a noun or pronoun as a receiver of its action.

The complete sentence, then, must possess at least two essential elements if the verb is already complete in meaning (intransitive) and at least three essential elements if the verb action must be carried across (transitive) to an object. The verbs in the clauses I smile, I laugh, and I walk are complete in meaning without a direct object. But if one says, I stick, no assertion is made, though the verb may convey a general idea of action; hence, the sentence is incomplete. But if the transitive verb is given a receiver for its action, this time an assertion is made: I stick John. The sentence is now complete, and the meaning of the verb is clear. One may observe how the meaning of a transitive verb can change with a different direct object by comparing the preceding example with the meaning of stick in the following sentence: He stuck his head out.

A transitive verb is one which is not complete in meaning until the receiver of the action is named. An intransitive verb is one that has complete meaning without any transitive (carry-over) action implied. One must not, however, regard the action quality itself of the verb as constituting the difference between intransitive and transitive verbs. Intransitive verbs may be quite active; it is just that the action simply is *not* (in + transitive) carried across to a receiver. The action of a transitive verb, though, is not completely understood until a receiver is named.

With an intransitive verb, then, it is possible to have a sentence with only the *two* essential elements of subject and verb. If the verb happens to be transitive, however, the group of words cannot be called a sentence unless it has the minimum of *three* essential elements: subject, verb, and direct object. (This is not true in the passive voice. Why not?) All the other words, phrases (related groups of words), and dependent subject-verb relationships (dependent clauses) in the sentence are nonessential elements. The nonessential elements also include modifiers of various kinds (dependent clause, single word, and phrase modifiers), independent adverbs, appositives, indirect objects, retained objects, subjective complements, adverbial nouns, words of address, interjections, conjunctions, and prepositional phrases. Constructions which affect the meaning of nouns and pronouns are said to modify as adjectives; words, phrases, and dependent clauses which change, qualify, or in any way affect the force or meaning of verbs, adjectives, and other adverbs are called adverbial modifiers.

The point of discussing sentence elements is more readily seen when it is realized that at times it may be necessary to shift subordinate ideas from one grammatical function to another. Or when deciding whether a sentence makes complete sense, a participial modifier can sometimes be mistaken for an asserting verb form (predicate). Inverted order—shifting of any of the essential elements—may also confuse the student and result in the writing of an incomplete sentence. A sentence fragment in this course may be defined as a group of words lacking one of the essential elements; a command having the second-person pronoun subject, *you*, understood is the only sentence fragment permitted in technical writing. Modifiers alone, no matter how arranged, can never make a sentence. It takes a name word and a verb in some kind of subject-verb relationship to make a sentence. Once the sentence form is mastered, it can be recognized in any number of variations. Because sentence elements can be shifted in so many ways to obtain the desired effect, there is no reason why one should get into a subject-first-forever habit or always have the same monotonous sentence pattern.

Independent clauses may be joined to make longer thought spans when the ideas are closely related. The problem here becomes one of judging whether the clauses are more effective when joined and of deciding which conjunction (connecting word) most accurately shows the relationship between the main clauses. This is the coordinating step; the subordination of clauses will come later.

Punctuation Between Independent Clauses

Punctuation between main clauses is emphasized in this course because showing the relationship of main clauses by the use of standard punctuation is so necessary to the reader's understanding of the writer's precise meaning. Failure to use standard punctuation (comma and semicolon) between main clauses is likely to confuse the reader. Technical communication demands that both writer and reader know the difference between independent and dependent thoughts. The conjunction and the punctuation mark show this quite well, provided, of course, that both reader and writer operate by the same standards. The accompanying chart will help explain the common relationships which occur between main clauses and the kind of punctuation needed for each.

For a complete punctuation review one must refer to an English handbook; it should be a practical grammar, however, not a radical departure from what was generally taught twenty-five years ago. Practice in the recognition of clauses and in the punctuation of compound sentences is also recommended.

In the chart, the various relationships between the main clauses

CoordinATING ConJUNCTIONS

Additions ; then ; also ; besides ; furthermore	,and	,or	Choice or Alternatives ; otherwise
Contrast ; however ; still ; nevertheless	,but	,for	Inference or Consequence ; consequently ; hence ; therefore

are graphically shown. Starting with the relationship of alternatives, explanation of the chart will follow a clockwise direction. In a choice between two independent thoughts, no subordination occurs. The expression of alternatives, or of a choice between two main clauses, does not affect the rank of either. It is just as if one placed an *or* between this lieutenant and that lieutenant; one still has two lieutenants of equal rank, unless one of them decides to disobey the captain's orders. The conjunction *or* (inside the triangle) introducing an alternative is preceded by a comma; *otherwise* (outside the triangle) is preceded by a semicolon.

Continuing in the clockwise direction, when two or more independent clauses are joined with inference or consequence conjunctions, such as *for, hence, therefore, thus, consequently, moreover, on the other hand, notwithstanding,* the rank of the clause joined is still the same. Sometimes the conjunction *so* may be observed doing the work of a coordinating conjunction. When used thus in technical writing, it should be preceded by a semicolon and treated as *therefore*. But since *so* has questionable standing as a coordinating conjunction, it should be used sparingly. In the next group, where the contrast relation exists between two independent statements, the conjunctions *but, however, still,* and *nevertheless* are used. These conjunctions are likewise coordinating because they do not change the rank of the clause joined.

In the upper-left position of the chart one encounters the most abused and misunderstood conjunction of all. Here the ruts are far deeper and harder to climb out of. Beginning writers still cling to the childish "and" habit and lose effectiveness by forcing *and* into almost every joining situation. *And* is sometimes called a pure addition sign, but it should never be used to join words, phrases, or clauses which are not equal in rank and parallel in structure. To the intelligent reader *and* indicates a coordinate relationship. *And* may join words, phrases, and clauses in pairs or in series, provided the elements joined are equal in rank, parallel in structure, and logically admissible in the same sum. If two clauses do not have equality of rank, *and* is illogical and cannot properly join them. Any attempt to make *and* serve such a purpose only succeeds in destroying the intended meaning and confusing the reader. Because the reader understands *and* as a plus sign, he naturally tries mentally to add the ideas. If they cannot be added, the reader is confused. To have one's exact meaning understood, one must choose *and* only for purely additive relations. In technical communication the precise conjunction is just as necessary as calling an object by its technical name.

Besides the short, pure *and*, other words which may serve as additive coordinating conjunctions include *also, besides,* and *furthermore*. These, like the other longer coordinating conjunctions used between main clauses, are always preceded by the semicolon. This is the one juncture on which nearly all grammarians (even the modern ones) agree: main clauses joined by coordinating conjunctions must be separated by either a comma or a semicolon, depending on the conjunction used and on the nature and relationship of the clauses. Main clauses joined without a conjunction are always separated in technical writing by a semicolon. But in no instance—and this will be invariably true in this course—will main clauses be joined without punctuation, regardless of the close relation of the clauses or the coordinating conjunction used.

The use of semicolon or comma between main clauses follows these practices:

1. A comma is used between main clauses joined by *and, but, or, for, nor, yet.*
2. A semicolon is used between main clauses joined by the other coordinating conjunctions.
3. A semicolon is used between main clauses not joined by a conjunction.
4. A semicolon is also used before *and, but, or, for, nor,* and *yet* when the clauses joined are broken by internal commas; a comma may serve, however, if the internal commas are not near the juncture of the main clauses. When they are, clarity demands that the semicolon be used to separate the clauses even though the conjunction used would normally require only a comma.

The foregoing are the generally encountered main-clause situations in technical writing; and though one may find exceptions in good writing, the prescriptions given should be carefully observed in this course. When the course is completed and the student has demonstrated an unerring sentence sense, he may then follow the practice he thinks best. Rigid restrictions at this time on the punctuation between main clauses give the instructor a chance to see whether the student is confusing a prepositional phrase, a participle or an infinitive, an independent adverb, or a parenthetical statement with a main clause. In other words, when the sentence syntax (the way the sentence goes together) is mastered, punctuation between main clauses ceases to be a problem.

Other Punctuation Problems

The punctuation of dependent clauses, and of interrupters such as independent adverbs and parenthetical constructions, should be discussed here briefly. Commas are used to set off interrupters and parenthetical elements, and in some instances a comma is used to separate dependent from main clauses. A semicolon is never used to separate an item of inferior rank from one of greater rank; and semicolons are never used to enclose interrupters. Comma practice in technical writing is generally conservative, with some relaxation only where the meaning is unmistakably clear.

Commas to enclose are always used in pairs, never singly, when the nonessential elements occur within the sentence. If the elements occur before or after a main clause, one comma alone separates the nonessential or nonrestrictive element from the main clause. The primary consideration in the use of the comma, other than its use between main clauses as previously described, is to help the reader understand what the writer intended to say.

Some words of caution are now due:

1. A comma (or any other mark) is not used without a good and justifiable reason.
2. The only time a comma is used before *and* when it is not joining main clauses is before the *and* which joins the last item of a simple coordinate series.
3. A semicolon must never be used to replace a comma, except between certain main clauses and between the items of a complex coordinate series (when the items are very long or are complicated by internal commas).
4. A semicolon is never used to separate a dependent clause from a main clause; it is never used to separate any but coordinate items of equal rank.
5. When in doubt one should check the standard uses for the comma and the semicolon as set forth at the front or back of a college dictionary.

Thus it must be concluded that punctuation cannot be practiced intelligently without main clause and dependent clause recognition, and clause recognition depends upon the student's ability to recognize the essential elements of the clause: subject, verb, and direct object. Some further distinctions should now be made with respect to clause recognition. One of the surest symptoms of muddled thinking is the failure to distinguish between dependent and independent clauses. Muddled thinking is revealed by such obvious boners as a semicolon between a main clause and a dependent clause, no punctuation at all between main clauses, commas separating the subject from its verb, and commas separating a pair of words, phrases, or dependent clauses.

Dependent Clauses

The term *clause* refers to any subject-verb relationship. If it can make sense standing alone (that is, if it depends on no other element for its meaning), it is said to be independent, and it could stand alone as a complete sentence. If, on the other hand, a subject-verb relationship is preceded by a connective which conditions its meaning or in any way relates the clause functionally with some other element, it is dependent. Clauses which are not preceded by an introductory or connecting word are nearly always independent. The clause is likewise independent if it is preceded by any of the *coordinating* conjunctions.

The term *sentence* is a broader term than *clause*. A sentence may contain a single main clause (simple sentence), a main clause and one or more dependent clauses (complex sentence), two or more main clauses (compound sentence), or two or more main clauses and one or more dependent clauses (compound-complex sentence). In technical writing there are fewer of the longer types of sentences.

One can recognize a dependent clause in a subject-verb combination (a) by its introductory or joining link with another clause in the sentence and (b) by its function (use) in the sentence. Clause recognition can be sharpened by a further look at the essential elements. A name word about which a statement is made can usually be recognized as the subject, though sometimes, when a verbal noun (gerund) is used as a subject, this may not be detected at once. An infinitive, such as *to see,* may also be used as a subject. But neither a gerund nor an infinitive can ever serve as a predicate. The student should study these examples:

1. *Gerund Subject:*
       Balancing the equation is the first step.
2. *Participle Modifier:*
       The *varnished* screw holds better.
3. *Infinitive Subject:*
       To balance the equation is the first step.
4. *Infinitive as Adverb:*
       He filtered the solution *to remove* the precipitate.
5. *Infinitive as Adjective:*
       The switch *to pull* is located behind the door.

From these examples it can be seen that gerunds, participles, and infinitives do not assert action, being, or a state of being. For that reason these verb forms cannot serve as predicates. They can function only as nouns, adjectives, and adverbs.

Once the subject and its predicate are isolated and the entire clause is recognized, the next step in determining whether the clause is independent or dependent is to observe the word which introduces it or joins it to the remainder of the sentence. The common subordinating conjunctions (see list) used to introduce dependent clauses should be memorized and their meanings clearly understood.

Subordinating Conjunctions

Cause, Reason, Purpose, Result	because; since; that; lest; so that; in order that
Place or Time	where; wherever; when; while; until; after; before; since; whenever
Degree, Manner, Comparison	than; as; as if; as though; as well as
Condition	if; unless; provided
Concession	though; although

The presence of a subordinating conjunction is positive proof that the clause is dependent. Sometimes, however, in noun clauses the introductory word is omitted:

I know the survey was made, because I was at home the day the survey interviewer came by.

In this example the first dependent noun clause underlined (a noun) serves as a direct object, an adverb clause (double line) follows *because,* and an adjective clause (wavy line) describes the noun *day.* The independent clause contains a noun clause as direct object, and the subordinate adverb clause contains an adjective clause as a modifier of the noun *day.*

Finite Verbs

Predicate (finite verb) recognition, however, is not enough to satisfy the needs of technical writing. In order to achieve the objective, impersonal handling of subject matter demanded in some technical writing, one must know more about verbs. If his instructor or a future employer should require a report to be written in the third person, indicative mood, active voice, present or past tense, the technical man must be able to do so. Or if the student wishes to employ more verbals to make his report move smoothly and accurately, without resorting to excessive predicates, he should be able to do so. One must not only be able to choose the mood, tense, and voice of the predicates which serve his purpose best but he must be able to recognize and use the other verb forms—infinitives, participles, and gerunds—as functioning verbals.

The finite verb (predicate) of a sentence is limited by tense, person, number, voice, and mood. Each of these characteristics will be touched on briefly. All action occurs in *time*. Action at this instant is called present. This is of course only a convenience; there is no such thing in practical everyday life. Before one can measure the time, it is already past. But men of old who gave us the tenses were not concerned with such nice distinctions. For practical purposes the present means now, the past any time before now, and the future any time after now. These are the simple tenses. The perfect tenses—meaning completed actions—are times which imply duration and completion. The *present perfect* refers to an action which was begun in the past and is either completed or continuing at this moment. The *past perfect* tense is used to denote an action which was begun in the past and completed in the past. The *future perfect* tense is used to show action which will begin at some point in the future and be completed at some more distant future time.

It is in his effort to express these various times (tenses) that the student encounters the conjugation of the verb. Children have difficulty at first with verb forms but soon become accustomed to a change in spelling of the word (*write, wrote, written; ring, rang, rung*) as a means of showing a change in the time of action. For a while a child may even wonder why one does not use *brang* and *brung* as the past and past perfect forms of bring. Normally these forms are mastered in grade school, where they are simply lumped into one irregular class. In college one may make further distinctions, such as using the terms *weak* and *strong* for regular and irregular verbs. A class in the history of language may reveal even more precise distinctions: Anglo-Saxon, for instance, recognized seven classes of strong verbs, three classes of weak verbs, and many anomalous, in-between classes.

The verb pattern is easier understood when the student realizes that, as new verbs were added to the language, only the weak pattern of tenses was used so that eventually almost all verbs were regularly conjugated by -*ed*. Still, some of the older weak verbs, as well as strong verbs, of early English have proved too hardy and useful to lose. Altogether, about 75 or 80 of each class (strong and weak) have remained. They are easiest learned by memorizing the principal parts.

Principal Parts of Verbs

The principal parts of verbs can be used as a formula to produce any tense form needed. If one knows that *see* changes to *saw* in the past and to *seen* in the perfect tenses, he need only remember *see, saw*, and *seen*. A further aid for calling up the standard form when the principal parts are known is to use the elementary but valuable *ear guide:* Using the principal parts as predicates, one may say, "I see now, I saw yesterday, and I have seen."

Some verbs do not have all their tense forms. The verbs *ought* and *must,* it will be noticed, have only a present tense in modern usage, hence only one principal part. *Can* has only a past tense (*could*), which gives it two principal parts. Other verbs may have all their tenses, but the perfect stem is the same in form as the present. For example, though *run* has three principal parts, the spelling of the third is the same as the first: *run, ran, run.*

In the accompanying list most of the troublesome verbs in the language are given with their principal parts.

Using a card to cover the second and third principal parts of the verb, the student should go through the list until he has complete recall. If ever in doubt, he should consult a standard dictionary, which will list the principal parts. If none are listed, the verb forms its principal parts in the regular way: *radio, radioed, radioed.* Further review as needed on verbs should be done with the aid of an English handbook.

The Verbals

Verbals are depth, or 3-D, words. They make handy communication forms. In these forms some of the original verb action is retained, with descriptive and naming qualities added. Such powerful verbal modifiers as *sizzling* steak, *boiling* water, *snarling* dog, *gnarled*

Principal Parts of Some Troublesome Verbs

arise	arose	arisen				(gotten)
bear	bore	borne	get	got	got
beat	beat	beaten	give	gave	given
begin	began	begun	go	went	gone
bend	bent	bent	grind	ground	ground
bet	bet	bet	grow	grew	grown
bid	bade	bidden	hang	hung	hung
(to order)			(an object)		
bind	bound	bound	have	had	had
		(bit)	hear	heard	heard
bite	bit	bitten			(hid)
bleed	bled	bled	hide	hid	hidden
blow	blew	blown	hit	hit	hit
break	broke	broken	hold	held	held
breed	bred	bred	hurt	hurt	hurt
bring	brought	brought	keep	kept	kept
build	built	built	kneel	knelt	knelt
burst	burst	burst	know	knew	known
buy	bought	bought	lay	laid	laid
can	could	—	lead	led	led
cast	cast	cast	leave	left	left
catch	caught	caught	lend	lent	lent
choose	chose	chosen	let	let	let
cling	clung	clung	lie	lay	lain
come	came	come	(to rest)		
cost	cost	cost	light	lighted	lighted
creep	crept	crept	lose	lost	lost
cut	cut	cut	make	made	made
deal	dealt	dealt	may	might	—
dig	dug	dug	mean	meant	meant
dive	dived	dived	meet	met	met
do	did	done	must	—	—
draw	drew	drawn	ought	—	—
drink	drank	drunk	pay	paid	paid
drive	drove	driven	plead	pleaded	pleaded
dwell	dwelt	dwelt			(proven)
eat	ate	eaten	prove	proved	proved
fall	fell	fallen	put	put	put
feed	fed	fed	quit	quit	quit
feel	felt	felt	read	read	read
fight	fought	fought	rend	rent	rent
find	found	found	rid	rid	rid
flee	fled	fled	ride	rode	ridden
fling	flung	flung	ring	rang	rung
fly	flew	flown	rise	rose	risen
		(forgot)	run	ran	run
forget	forgot	forgotten	say	said	said
forsake	forsook	forsaken	see	saw	seen
freeze	froze	frozen	seek	sought	sought

Principal Parts of Some Troublesome Verbs (*continued*)

sell	sold	sold	split	split	split
send	sent	sent	spread	spread	spread
set	set	set		(sprang)	
		(sewn)	spring	sprung	sprung
sew	sewed	sewed	stand	stood	stood
shake	shook	shaken	steal	stole	stolen
shall	should	—	stick	stuck	stuck
shed	shed	shed	sting	stung	stung
shine	shined	shined	stride	strode	stridden
(to polish)			string	strung	strung
shine	shone	shone	swear	swore	sworn
shoe	shod	shod	sweep	swept	swept
shoot	shot	shot	swim	swam	swum
		(shown)	swing	swung	swung
show	showed	showed	take	took	taken
	(shrunk)		teach	taught	taught
shrink	shrank	shrunk	tear	tore	torn
sing	sang	sung	tell	told	told
sink	sank	sunk	think	thought	thought
sit	sat	sat	throw	threw	thrown
slay	slew	slain	thrust	thrust	thrust
sleep	slept	slept	tread	trod	trodden
		(slidden)		(woke)	(woke)
slide	slid	slid	wake	waked	waked
sling	slung	slung	wear	wore	worn
slink	slunk	slunk	weave	wove	woven
slit	slit	slit	(cloth)		
smite	smote	smitten	wed	wed	wed
		(sowed)	weep	wept	wept
sow	sowed	sown	wet	wet	wet
speak	spoke	spoken	will	would	—
spend	spent	spent	win	won	won
spin	spun	spun	wind	wound	wound
	(spat)	(spat)	wring	wrung	wrung
spit	spit	spit	write	wrote	written

oak, *starved* boy, *howling* wolf, cannot be matched by any simple adjectives. A mastery of verbals will shorten time spent in reaching a mature style. Of still more immediate value to the student is the fact that knowing the verbals enables him to unerringly identify the predicate—verbals never form predicates. In the foregoing paragraphs the finite verbs have been described as those limited by person, number, tense, voice, and mood. In the following complete pattern of the verbal *seeing* one may note that verbals have only voice (if transitive) and tense (only present and past); there are nine possible forms:

	Infinitive		Participle or Gerund	
	Present	*Past*	*Present*	*Past*
Active	to see	to have seen	seeing	having seen
Passive	to be seen	to have been seen	being seen	having been seen
				seen (short form)

Verbals in the regular group ending in *-ed,* and not logically in combination with nouns or pronouns in asserted actions, can be identified quite easily. If the word is used to describe a noun or pronoun it is called a participle. In the expression *parched corn,* a glance is sufficient to recognize that though *parched* is a verb form and *corn* a noun no assertion of action is made; *parched* describes *corn.* This, incidentally, is known as the short past participle (see preceding table), which is the most useful of all verbal forms for precise description.

On the other hand, if one uses the expression *parching corn,* then *parching* may be either a simple present participle or it may serve as the subject of a sentence: "*Parching* corn preserves it from weevils." In this sense *parching* is used as the name of an action or process. Engineers and technicians are constantly describing processes (see Chapter 4).

Verbals represent whole sentence ideas; they are a means of subordination and compression. They pack action into the sentence to aid the predicate. A less important clause can be reduced to a single participle. Instead of the construction *the desert is painted,* one might just as forcefully say *the painted desert.* In fact, the phrase form is more effective because it permits the color idea to be submerged and saves the emphasis for the main action word of the predicate: "The painted desert *leans* against the soft blue wall of the northern sky."

Dangling Modifier

In the use of any phrase form containing a verbal one may encounter the troublesome dangling modifier. Generally a dangling modifier occurs because the active form of the verbal is used with the sentence verb in the passive voice. In the passive voice the actual noun modified by the verbal is shifted from its normal position or omitted from the sentence entirely. The word the verbal modifies is then not readily understood, and the sentence may sometimes sound ridiculous: "*Awaking from a sound sleep,* the train was seen approaching." Verbals should be placed near the words modified so that the meaning is unmistakably clear. Further information on verbals will be found in

Chapter 7, where they are discussed as devices for subordinating ideas.

So far in this review of the basic mechanics of expression, the essential elements of the sentence—verb forms, verbals, and punctuation between main clauses—have been covered. The next and final area of review is the paragraph.

The Paragraph

The technical writer's concept of a paragraph should be sharpened and focused to the same degree of mastery as the sentence concept. Indention alone does not make a paragraph. And poorly organized, incoherent, incomplete paragraphs are just as effective in blocking communication as poor sentences.

One may begin by reexamining the familiar term paragraph. Perhaps it can be understood in a new light. One might suppose, for example, that he has been asked to build a fire on a desert picnic. He picks up an armload of mesquite and ironwood sticks and carries them to a suitable place and arranges them just so; then he lights the fire. If he does not arrange those sticks in a certain way, the purpose is not achieved. To be sure, the sticks might eventually burn placed end to end, but they would certainly not serve as a useful cooking fire. Likewise, in the writing of paragraphs, one obtains the most effective transfer of ideas when the supporting detail is purposefully arranged to develop the main topic. The order of arrangement may be one of simple convenience, or it may be an order contrived to produce a special effect. If one begins with the generalization (topic) and supports this by details, he will be using the deductive order; if he begins with particulars and proceeds to the generalization, he will be using the inductive order. The topic will usually lend itself to one particular order of arrangement better than another; a process, for example, would demand a chronological order, whereas description might have spatial order.

One may think of a paragraph, then, as a bundle of related ideas focused about a given topic to create a certain impression. Sometimes it may be only a sentence; at other times it may reach across pages. In both long and short paragraphs, unity can be preserved by keeping the topic in mind and allowing no illogical shifts in point of view, time, or place. In technical writing paragraphs are generally shorter than in other styles of writing. It will be observed, however, that in the early stages of this course, longer paragraphs are assigned. Writing longer paragraphs is helpful in correcting the faulty or incomplete paragraph habit found in most beginning writers. The carefully planned single-topic paragraph also develops the logical processes. If one can master the sentence and the paragraph, he can do any of the longer assignments with distinction.

In coming to the end of this chapter on general concepts, one should not fail to take stock of his resources in basic English as revealed by the discussion. If what has been read sounds completely new, an English handbook review is advised. It is also worthwhile to study the instructor's grading system. The fastest progress is made by the student who does not make the same mistake twice. For this reason one should always make certain he understands the instructor's marks on his papers and what correction should be made.

The most damaging errors to a man's professional standing are given special emphasis to hasten their elimination. These "seven deadly sins" are indicated by Arabic numerals as explained in the next section. A few other marks that the instructor may use are listed following the numbered errors. The relative percentage values of individual exercises will of course depend on the judgment of the instructor. The student will be informed of these values as early in the course as possible.

Grading Symbols

NUMBERED ERRORS

1. Spelling errors will be indicated by the figure 1 wherever words are not spelled in the standard way. This includes misplaced and missing letters in either handwritten or typewritten material, failure to dot *i*'s and cross *t*'s, and the failure to use capital letters to begin obviously proper nouns.
2. Punctuation omitted or in error between main clauses is marked by the figure 2.
3. Illiterate words, marked by the figure 3, must be eliminated to keep from bringing discredit upon the individual and shame upon his alma mater. Example: the form "it's" for the possessive pronoun *its*.
4. The misuse of tense forms or the use of nonstandard verb forms

are indicated by the figure 4. Examples: "I clum" for *I climbed;* "had saw" for *had seen;* "boughten" for *bought.*

5. Sentence structure must be good. A sentence fragment or a muddled sentence, or any construction which leads the instructor to believe that the student does not recognize a complete, unified sentence, will be marked by the figure 5.

6. Paragraph faults—faults such as shifts in topic, time, place, point of view—which spoil the unity of a paragraph, or disarranged ideas which indicate a lack of paragraph sense, are marked by the figure 6.

7. Illegible writing is a hindrance to communication and must be avoided. The letters *a* and *o* must be closed as *a*'s and *o*'s should be; an *f* is made with the bottom loop below the line in a counterclockwise direction; the letters *w, u, n,* and *m* must be recognizable. No one is expected to write with Spencerian beauty, but all of us must write clearly. Words that are not legible will be marked by the figure 7.

ARBITRARY LETTERS AND SYMBOLS

AWK—Awkward. The meaning is understood but the wording is cumbersome. Revision is needed.

Ante—Antecedent for the pronoun is in doubt.

D—Diction. This reference to diction marks the misuse of words— words used out of context or proper association. For example, if one meant to refer to the *hugeness of the ore deposit* and said the *enormity of the ore deposit,* the effect would be startling. *Enormity* means "great wickedness." When in doubt one must use the dictionary and find there the numbered definition which fits the sense in which he wishes to use the word.

G—Grammar. A capital *G* or a small *g,* meaning grammar, refers to something considered nonstandard usage but not included in the numbered errors. The student must first be sure he understands the nature of the marked grammar fault and then correct it.

P—Punctuation. Punctuation between main clauses is marked by the figure 2. All other required punctuation is marked by the capital letter *P. Commas* which are preferred in standard technical practice, but which might be omitted by some good writers, may be inserted by the instructor at no extra penalty.

||—Faulty parallelism. Faulty parallelism shows up in coordinate pairs of words, phrases, or dependent clauses, or in a coordinate series. Some penalty is placed on faulty parallelism because it disrupts the logical assimilation of ideas.

\#—Number. This tick-tack-toe sign simply means that the term marked has the wrong number—whether singular or plural.

⌗—Delete. The familiar pigtail, with an item circled, means that the circled item should be taken out.

∧—An insertion point. Something is needed.

¶—The paragraph sign. Faulty paragraphs will be marked by the number 6. At times, however it is useful for the student to know the point at which material should have been indented. This paragraph sign is then used.

X—An error of fact when used in the paper is marked by a capital X. If an X occurs at the top left side of the page, it indicates no credit for the assignment. The student should then revise or rewrite as necessary to meet the specified assignment. If the student has failed to understand the previous directions, a few minutes with the instructor may be needed.

Hints on Rewriting

The objective in this course is to reach certain minimum goals. If these are not reached the student has failed. But no one profits by a failure, neither the instructor nor the student. It is the instructor's desire that every student should learn enough to pass. One of the best ways of learning is to rewrite until mastery is achieved. The plan suggested in the Preface for rewriting has proved to be a good one. However, regardless of make-up privileges offered by the instructor, any substandard paper should be rewritten. Furthermore, all errors in mechanics should be carefully avoided in the next paper. Any signs, symbols, or comments not understood should be discussed with the instructor. The loss of credit may have been due to a lack of clear thinking or a lack of focus, faults about which no specific comment can be made. It may also have been due to a failure to follow specifications on length, kind of treatment, subject, style, mechanics, or a combination of these things. A good final grade is a result of good day-to-day performance.

Grades of course do not mean success. Some who make A's with the help of a well-meaning editorial accomplice may profit less than those who make C's. Those with a receptive attitude and a continuing interest in improvement are the ones most likely to succeed in this course and to succeed later in handling the communication problems of a professional engineer or scientist.

2

Definition:
What Is It?

The student has been told how to recognize technical writing by its style, its subject matter, and a few other characteristics, such as its use of graphic aids, formulas, numbers, and abbreviations. Just studying these attributes of style and content is not enough to enable a person to do technical writing. Technical writing is a craft and as such must be "learned by doing."

Mastery of a craft begins with practice in the use of the basic tools of the craft. Here the tools are the kinds of informative writing that answer the questions:

1. What is it?
2. How does it look?
3. How does it function?

In learning these ABC's of technical communication the student will encounter some of the techniques used in literary creative writing, because it, too, is a craft. But the comparison had better stop there. And all the preconceived notions of the means of communication in writing should be suspended until they can be reapplied from the technical writer's viewpoint. For unlike literary creative writing, which must conceal its techniques, the well-oiled machinery of technical writing is in plain view; technical writing is most effective when its technique is showing.

On the basis of the writer's purpose, technical writing might be subdivided as definition, description, and narration. But these terms do not mean quite the same thing as they meant when the student encountered them in his freshman English courses. Definition explains and identifies; description explains an idea and creates an image; narration relates, describes, and explains what happens. In practice these basic kinds of writing rarely occur singly. They are presented singly and in three separate chapters in this text for the obvious reason that it is simpler to master one thing at a time.

INFORMAL DEFINITION

One of the earliest indications of intelligence in a human being is his desire to identify strange things, to name them, and to compare them with other similar things already known. This habit of asking about unknown things begins as soon as one is able to speak his language and continues throughout life. (The point at which a person ceases to be curious about things has been called the beginning of old age.) New ideas are learned by identifying them and relating them to what is already known. If this identification is less than a full, exhaustive treatment, it is called informal definition. If it follows a regular form, possesses an orderly arrangement of the differentiating information, and completely distinguishes its subject from all other subjects, it is called formal definition. It will be necessary here to differentiate an informal from a formal kind of definition as practiced in technical writing. Informal definition is presented first because it requires less practice to master.

When the answer to the what-is-it question can be supplied in the form of an appositive or a parenthetical statement, the definition is probably informal. It is certain to be when the information is less than a sentence in length. And it may be informal when the definition is a sentence or more, provided the sentence is not a formal defining sentence like the ones used for formal definitions. Informal definitions are like courteous asides to the reader—never exhaustive, never following a formal pattern. An informal definition, though generally short, may be extended to any length. Most of the offhand explanations to acquaint the reader with the strange or unfamiliar aspects of a subject are extended informal definitions. In literary or nontechnical writing the short humorous essay is a parallel to the informal definition. Some of the short motion picture productions are like informal definitions. Such subjects as boredom, carelessness, and worry have been done with great effect. Robert Benchley defining human frailties of one kind or another will be remembered by older students. Technical teaching films and textbooks are filled with informal definitions.

From the foregoing informal definition of informal definition one may correctly infer that it does not have a prescribed form. It does have specific uses:

1. Informal definition is used to insure the reader's understanding of *common terms with a new meaning.* Many technical words have been borrowed from the vocabulary of everyday speech. In their technical use they may have an entirely different meaning. The animal kingdom has furnished many of our useful technical terms. Words like *donkey, horse, mule, bull, cat, dog, pig, hog, goose, bird, crane, fish, frog, monkey, mole, weasel, ferret, alligator, worm, snake,* and *spider,* and their compounds are scattered throughout the technical vocabulary. Words for familiar things, such as *bucket, cup, hat, apron, cloth, tooth, sock, toe, truck, car, carriage, train, seed, bloom, soup, bench, stool, table,* and *gun,* and their compounds, are useful technical terms in industry. Other familiar terms with less obvious differences between the technical and nontechnical meanings include words like *home* (in navigation), *attitude, bump* (in supersonic testing), *logic* (computer), *noise* (random radiation), *sink* (heat), *hole* (transistor), *donor, dope, shell* (physical chemistry). Common words with technical or unfamiliar meanings can cause all manner of confusion unless informally defined. One can imagine the consternation caused the uninitiated bride of an oil-field worker who said of his day's work: "We set the christmas tree at the Number 1 Barnes; then we pulled down the jackknife and snaked it over with the big cat to a dry hole where we are going to start fishing tomorrow."

2. Informal definition is used when *denotative, technical words stand for well-known ideas.* Scientific words are often preferred in technical writing to express the common idea, especially when there may be more than one meaning of the common term or common idea. For example, when referring to the bones inclosing the brain but not including the lower jaw, one should say *cranium* instead of *head* or *skull.* Of course the extent and nature of the informal definition depends upon the reader level expected. Most of the time a familiar synonym or short phrase complemented by the contextual meaning is sufficient to make the use of unknown words understandable to the reader. Examples of technical words for common ones: *paronomasia* (pun), *oncology* (study of tumors), *thorax* (chest), *vellication* (twitch), *consanguinity* (kinship), *oleaginous* (oily), *pediculous* (lousy), *caliginous* (obscure).

3. Informal definition is used when *strange terms stand for new*

ideas and new things. These terms are a more difficult problem—like solving for two unknowns in the same equation. Examples, comparison with known ideas or things, contrast, and sometimes negation are used to help explain a new concept and the word for it. More probably the new term for the new idea will be given a formal definition.

FORMAL DEFINITION

If the writer suspects that his reader may be unfamiliar with an idea (the referent) and the term which stands for it, he should resort to formal definition. Formal definition is advisable even though the reader may have some notion of the meaning. In this way the writer makes certain that the reader's concept is similar to the one he intends. A complete, organized identification of an idea or thing is called a formal definition because it has a regular, clearly recognizable form.

Reduced to its lowest terms, a formal definition is a defining sentence in which the subject is the species to be defined, the subjective complement is the genus (the smallest group or class to which the subject belongs), and the modifiers are the differentiae that distinguish the subject from other members of its group. The term species, genus, and differentiae are somewhat loosely used in this context. Some might prefer to think of a formal definition as a statement naming the term to be defined as its subject, its smallest class as its subjective complement, and its distinguishing characteristics as modifiers of the complement. But the biological analogy makes a more useful working definition for technical writing: *species* equals *genus* plus the algebraic sum of the *differentiae,* since some of the differentiae may be negative —that is, what the species is not. For example, as part of the negative differentiae for a formal definition, one could say "A definition not having a defining sentence with the essential parts in the order just named is *not* a formal definition."

Though it may be argued to the contrary, formal definition as referred to in this text must contain the recognizable elements just named. Not only the elements themselves but the grammar and syntax of the defining sentence must remain unchanged. For those who prefer a mathematical concept, the defining sentence may be expressed as a formula.

From the foregoing definition it is correctly inferred that a formal definition is always a complete sentence. Formal definitions may be extended to any convenient length by using the defining sentence as the first, or topic, sentence of the paragraph, as shown by the examples at the end of this chapter.

Students in attempting to write formal definitions encounter difficulty in handling the parts of the defining sentence because they attempt to write the defining sentence before they fully understand the term to be defined, or they choose a genus much too large for the species. If the class (genus) is too large, the job of differentiating the term (species) from so many other terms within the same class becomes unwieldy. In defining a watch, for example, one might think first of *device* as a suitable genus. But there are thousands of devices. To call a watch a device would help little in identifying it. The genus could be narrowed to a *time-measuring device,* and the species might be narrowed to a wristwatch. The wristwatch now would only need to be differentiated from the pocket watch, the ornamental watch, the stopwatch, the alarm clock, the striking clock, the electric clock, the punch clock, the night watchman's clock, the sundial, the hourglass, the fire clock, the clepsydra (or water clock), the horologium, and a relative newcomer, the atomic clock. Thus, it will be seen that a time-measuring device is a genus much too large for defining a wristwatch.

On the other hand, the genus named must include at least one other species; otherwise, it is not a genus. A rope clock might be defined as a "fire clock which measures time by the burning rate of rope," differentiating it from the candlenut clock, which measures time by the burning rate of candlenuts, and the candle clock, which measures time by the burning rate of a candle.

Formal definitions require clear thinking, accurate use of terminology, and completeness. Sometimes this completeness may necessitate the writing of an entire paragraph, a chapter, or a book. The length, of course, depends entirely upon the purpose of the writer and the size and scope of the problem represented by the term to be defined. College textbooks are examples of expanded formal definitions. Popular nonfiction books may also be formal definitions.

In learning to write formal definitions it is best to practice the extended formal definition of 150 to 200 words. A paragraph definition is written by continuing the differentiae after the defining sentence has been stated. The defining sentence cannot be expected to carry all of the differentiae in a complicated idea. It must be made to carry a good portion, however; and it does this when the most distinguishing characteristic is placed in the defining sentence. The remaining differentiae are usually arranged in the descending order of importance following the defining sentence. The student can simplify the selection of the differentiae to be placed in the defining sentence by first making a list of all the differentiating statements he can think of. The one which answers the question "What one thing can be said about the species which will set it apart from the other species within its genus?" is the distinguishing characteristic, and it should be placed in the defining sentence. The remaining differentiae arranged in a descending order of importance should then follow to complete the paragraph.

If the differentiae do not come readily to mind, perhaps a comparison, a contrast, or a negative statement will help. Examples may also be used when needed to completely identify and differentiate a subject. When all else fails, the student may resort to negative statements as a way of getting certain ideas clearly before the reader. The derivation of the term itself can also throw important light on the meaning. Even a small amount of description, especially in defining mechanical devices or processes, will help.

In arranging the differentiae in the extended formal paragraph definition, the student should observe all of the rhetorical devices for obtaining coherence and unity within the paragraph. Coherence will be improved by using transition words and by pointing out the causal relations between the statements within the paragraph. If more than one paragraph is needed to fully define the new term, a topical outline should be made before writing begins. The outline should indicate how many of the differentiae should be placed in each paragraph. In the longer formal definition any or all of the devices for extending the definition may be used. This includes explanation and description, and even narration, provided these contribute to the identity and differentiation of the term. In defining a process, for example, it is often necessary to narrate a short portion of the process to show how it differs from a similar process. Description and narration, however, the next two kinds of writing to be discussed, can actually hinder the reader's understanding if the emphasis is drawn away from the purpose of differentiating and identifying the terms being defined.

In writing an extended formal definition, the first step obviously is to write a good defining sentence. The student's own room should provide plenty of items for practice—the bed, the chair, the eraser, fingernail clippers. The student should look at one of these objects and try to think of its smallest subgroup and its one most distinguishing characteristic. Although the name of the species should not be repeated in the genus, it is not always practical to avoid this. When the name of the species is derived from the genus name, there is no reason to evade the repetition: "A crescent wrench is an adjustable wrench which has its movable jaw set at about 60 degrees to the handle." After the defining sentence has been satisfactorily worked out and checked to see that all its parts are there, it may be well to reverse the terms to see if the definition still makes a valid statement: "A wrench with its movable jaw set at about 60 degrees to the handle is a crescent wrench."

The parts of the defining sentence are further illustrated in this definition of a fish: "The *Melanogrammus aeglefinus* (common name, haddock) is an important food fish found on both sides of the Atlantic, allied to, but smaller than, the cod." In this equation-like statement the species equals the genus (food fish) plus the differentiae (found on both sides of the Atlantic, allied to, but smaller than, the cod). The species-equals-genus-plus-differentiae statement can be tested by moving the species across the equals sign, thus: "An important food fish, allied to, but smaller than, the cod, found on both sides of the Atlantic, is the *Melanogrammus aeglefinus* (common name, haddock)." After a satisfactory defining sentence has been constructed, the definition can be expanded until the haddock is completely identified. Description may be effective here if its purpose is to differentiate, thus: "The haddock differs from the cod and other members of the Gadidae family in size, color, and shape and in the arrangement of its fins." Then these features could be briefly described. Further distinctions might include facts about its range and feeding habits, even its commercial value. The definition would be complete when the haddock had been differentiated from all other species of the *Melanogrammus* genus.

STUDENT EXAMPLES

Extended Formal Definition

Explosive Forming

Explosive forming is a forming process for sheet metal which does not require the use of dies. Metal to be formed is incorporated as the bottom of a cylindrical, vertically oriented container, whose side is made of concrete. The container is filled with water, and a rapidly burning compound, such as gunpowder, is suspended in the water; force required to distort the sheet is supplied by the ignition of the gunpowder. The pressure force produced by this action is transmitted to the sheet, via the water, but as an omnidirectional hydrostatic pressure. This hydraulic force produces the distortion of the plate. When the process is required to form more intricate shapes, two alternatives are possible: a female die is employed, whereby the metal is forced into the die, thus assuming its shape, or a shaped charge is used. The forming does not resemble any other stamping or drawing process, which is its main advantage; it bypasses the tearing and scalloping inherent in conventional methods. This is due to the fact that, under such tremendous loads, the metal cold-flows.

The Contour Search Pattern

The contour search pattern is the only satisfactory type of pattern for searching mountainous areas with conventional aircraft. Other patterns, such as the route search, parallel search, and expanding-square search, are flown at constant altitude. Because of this criterion, these patterns would have to be flown at a high enough altitude to clear the highest elevation in mountainous areas. As a result, objects of the search located in the mountain valleys could easily be missed. The contour pattern involves searching from a near horizontal plane from the aircraft, instead of near vertical as is done with the other pattern methods, thus providing a greater chance of sighting an objective. The contour search pattern is started from the topmost terrain, and the aircraft is flown around a mountain at 500-foot levels, "tucked in" close to the mountain side to allow the scanners a shallow scan angle. As one contour circuit is completed, the altitude is normally decreased 500 feet, and a new contour circuit is started. This operation is continued until the entire mountain has been searched.

The Bourdon Tube

The Bourdon tube is a metal tube used in pressure-measuring instruments. It is essentially a tube of elliptical cross section, formed into an arc, with one end anchored and the other end free to move. The anchored end is open and fastened to the instrument case where it is connected to the pressure system by tubing. The closed end is free to move, except that it is attached to a series of links, levers, and gears. When fluid enters the open end, it causes a pressure to be exerted upon the closed end which tends to straighten the tube. As the pressure causes the tube to straighten, the links, levers, and gears transmit the movement to the gage indicator and cause it to move along the graduated scale of the instrument. The tube is constructed of spring-tempered brass, bronze, or beryllium copper and will therefore return to its original shape when the pressure is released. The principle involved can be illustrated by the familiar Halloween novelty, the rolled paper tube which uncoils when one blows into it.

Lacquer

Lacquer is an organic chemical used for surface coating, notable for its fast drying rate. A lacquer consists of two principal types of ingredients: a nonvolatile portion which forms the film and a volatile portion which affects application. The nonvolatile portion contains three ingredients: film-former, plasticizer, and resin. The volatile portion consists of three types of ingredients: active solvents, latent solvents, and diluents. The drying of a lacquer involves only evaporation, due to the presence of a film-former already in polymerized form. Nitrate cellulose is the most important film-former. Varnish, the counterpart of lacquer in organic chemical coating, requires "driers" as catalysts in the film-forming process. A lacquer may be dry to the touch in a few minutes, and it will dry hard in one to six hours at room temperature. Plasticizers are added to the nonvolatile portion of lacquers in order to improve the elasticity and flexibility of the film, while resins are used to improve the adhesion of the film to a surface. Solvents and diluents, although they do not affect the final film properties, are added to modify the evaporization rate and to decrease the viscosity sufficiently to enable spraying of high-content lacquers.

EXERCISES

1. Write five sentences containing informal definitions. Underline the informal definition in each sentence.

2. Write three formal sentence-length definitions. Label the species, the genus, and the differentiae in each.

3. Write an extended formal definition of 150 to 200 words. Develop it as a single paragraph with the defining sentence coming first, followed by additional differentiae. Place the most distinguishing characteristic in the defining sentence. The remaining differentiae should be arranged in descending order of importance.

4. Study and discuss the student examples of extended formal definitions which were given in the preceding section.

3

Description:
How Does It Look?

Chapter 2 was primarily concerned with a kind of writing that identifies and differentiates a given idea or a thing. This chapter shows how the idea can be further explained and visualized by a basic kind of writing called description. Technical description has a dual function: to expand or create a concept and to create a mental image. It defines, explains, or describes as necessary to effect a precise understanding and a clear vision. Technical description does not produce the photographic word picture of literary description. It goes beyond what a thing appears to be in order to reveal what a thing actually is. No line-of-sight obstacle can deflect the powers of technical description. Its viewpoint is omniscient. It can give details which are beyond the vantage point. And finally, like all technical writing, its purpose is to give information, not to create a mood or stir emotions.

KINDS OF DESCRIPTION

Technical description has three recognizably different forms: the catalogue description, the blueprint description, and the general-purpose description.

Catalogue Description

Goods are ordered from thumbnail word sketches giving color, finish, material, size, shape, and price. These word sketches, designed to give the factual information needed in the shortest space possible, are called catalogue descriptions. They may or may not be accompanied by a photograph, a graphic sketch, or an exploded drawing. A

33

list of available subassembly parts identified by code number may also be included, especially when the item is to be procured by mail. The average writer, unless engaged in writing catalogues, will not have many occasions to write the compressed, highly coded, and procurement-slanted description.

Blueprint Description

Though they are not ordinarily thought of as such, blueprints are descriptions. Not only are the lines coded so that each line may be interpreted to form a certain image (boundary lines, dimension lines, contour lines) but dotted lines indicate shapes not seen from the reader's vantage point. Other blueprint signs and symbols represent details which make the image just as vivid and precise to one who reads blueprints as if the picture had been made with a camera. The blueprint includes, besides the physical configuration, all of the information needed to produce the item: material specifications and manufacturing notes that include tolerances, testing procedures, and hints and cautions if special manufacturing techniques are involved. A blueprint completely describing the technical design of a complex machine may exceed a quarter of a million sheets and weigh several tons.

Engineers who produce blueprints and work frequently from them must know how to read and write the verbal statements they contain. In the early years of his training, an engineer takes a course in mechanical drawing, blueprint reading, graphic arts, or some other study which enables him to produce properly coded drawings. He has learned the drawing symbols for coding information. But the verbal symbol may give him difficulty. Yet blueprint legends containing manufacturing and testing instructions and other general information should be just as clear and objective as the drawing itself. There is no room in the legends for ambiguity, no room for unnecessary adjectives and connotative words that could lead the reader into a different concept than that intended. Words which the reader may not understand should be informally defined. Ambiguous or obscure statements, as well as legends, lead only to confusion and unnecessary expense.

General-Purpose Description

It has been shown that the catalogue description furnishes all the necessary information for purchasing and that the blueprint description gives all of the necessary information for manufacturing an item. The third type of technical description, the general-purpose type, gives the reader a general idea of what a thing looks like and indicates its functions. This is the type of description used in reports to management and in reports to customers, to clients, and to the general public. It may be accompanied by photographs and drawings. Like other technical writing, its fundamental purpose is to inform. It does so by explaining ideas and making word pictures.

In learning to write technical descriptions the student may wish to work from a picture, but the written description when completed must be clear to the reader without the picture. Writing the description so that it can be read and understood without the help of a drawing or photograph develops the student's ability to observe detail and spatial relations. With only words to guide the reader, it becomes apparent at once how important it is to keep the object oriented at all times so the image can be developed logically in the reader's mind.

The aim of general-purpose description is to make the reader see and understand as much about an object as he needs to understand in order to form a general idea of the item described. The writer determines from the expected reader level how much technical detail should be included. For the student, unless otherwise indicated, the reader level is that of his own class. The student should adjust his level of writing so that he will be understood readily by three fourths of the class, and, with a little help from a dictionary, by all of the class.

General technical descriptions range from short descriptive one- or two-sentence sketches interspersed in other kinds of writing to the more formal descriptions involving several paragraphs when a complicated device is described. Sometimes it is necessary to make extensive reports which are primarily descriptions of complex processes or mechanical equipment. But any item, no matter how small or how large, can be described in a systematic and logical manner if one understands and applies the writing procedures described in the next section.

WRITING GENERAL DESCRIPTION

Formula

Accurate word images of complex devices cannot be transmitted from writer to reader unless both minds are following the same organizational plan. This implies that an object cannot be effectively described until it has first been carefully observed by the writer and that it cannot be understood by the reader unless it is logically sub-divided and shown to the reader as a complete functional whole. If the organization of the object is clear and the details are vivid, the reader can reconstruct a duplicate image in his own mind as he reads the description.

A great deal of time can be saved in learning to write technical descriptions if the student simply memorizes the steps which have been reduced to letter symbols in the following formula:

$$T = N + (G+O) + (Snd) + F$$

where T = the technical description,
N = the name of the object,
G = the general impression,
O = the orientation of the object to the reader,
S = the subdivisions,
n = the number of subdivisions,
d = the necessary details to be included about each of the subdivisions,
F = the function or use.

This same procedure could be expressed in verbal symbols as fol-lows: The student begins by accurately naming the device or object to be described. Next he compares the object, if possible, with a familiar thing to suggest size and shape. The orientation of the object to the reader comes next. The description starts with a logical subdi-vision of the object. The most basic structure (the frame, the base) is named first, followed by a convenient number of subassemblies. The basic structure is also described first; then each of the subassem-blies, or parts, is described in turn and related to the base or frame. The concluding sentence explains the function or the use of the object.

Reader Level

Before any analysis of descriptive style, one must realize the con-trolling influence of the reader level. If the reader level is low (non-technical), familiar terms are preferred even with some loss of precision. It is better to lose some precision than to baffle or puzzle the reader. The reader is willing to look up a few words per page, maybe three or four, but when too many words are new to him, he begins to lose interest. Certainly the advice given in Chapter 2 on informal definition would apply here: to follow unfamiliar terms with informal definitions. Technical description does not mean the use of the most specialized term that is available to the vocabulary of the writer. In order to insure communication, one must paint the picture and create the concept in the *reader's vocabulary*, not the writer's.

The reader level dictates not only the technical level but also the sort of information accompanying the word picture. In the blueprint description, for example, the finish would be called out on the drawing in standardized, universally understood units (microinches root-mean-square, abbreviated "rms"), but in general description it is more meaningful to say a smooth, polished, rough, or sanded surface. Likewise, there would be no point in naming the constituents of type 4340 steel; it would be quite enough to refer to the alloy as a deep-hardening alloy steel. Neither would it be necessary to name the type and grade of stainless steel, brass, or bronze unless the specific alloy played a vital role in the function or use of the object. The purpose of *general description* will be better served the more vividly the reader pictures the object and the more clearly he understands it.

Word Choice

Given a certain reader level, the choice of informative and image-making words becomes the writer's biggest problem. By analysis it will be found that descriptive effects in technical writing are not obtained in quite the same way as they are in literary description. In technical description, adjectives as a functioning class have been replaced to some extent by more precise nouns and by specific verbs. Adjectives which are quantitative and universally understood are preferred. Emotion-charged adjectives are strictly off limits, and adjectives expressing value judgments are generally shunned.

When an adjective is used in technical description it must be selected with care. The English language is replete with adjectival synonyms, some of which are so close in meaning that they differ only in their associations. It is especially difficult for one whose native language is other than English to pick the precise synonym for the meaning he intends. A word like *blunt*, for example, can be a synonym for *dull;* but if *blunt* were used to refer to a color, it would be an obvious misuse of the term. One might of course guess that the writer's meaning in this instance was a dull color. In technical description, however, there is no place for guessing; the reader must see and understand clearly what the writer intends.

In technical description, adjectives are largely omitted or are replaced by other modifying devices which do not have emotional overtones: the prepositional phrase and the modifying verb forms, the infinitive and the participle. The short past participle, from the standpoint of economy of space and increased power, describes with more effect than most adjectives. Words like *serrated, chafed, chamfered, stippled, riveted, welded, burnished, scuffed, routed, bored, bent, burned, painted, plated, cast, forged, extruded, coiled, spiraled, helixed, folded, centered, split,* and *spun* show action and appearance in the same word.

Fewer modifiers (adjectives) are needed in technical description because, insofar as the reader level permits, exact scientific and technical names are used which do not require much qualification. In contrast with the connotative nouns used in literary description, nouns selected for technical description should denote only a single object. If unfamiliar objects with unfamiliar names are described, the writer should follow the new word with an informal definition; for example, in a general description the radome over the radar equipment might be called simply a hat-shaped plastic cover.

Another reason fewer qualifying adjectives are needed in technical description is that specific, active verbs are selected. The specific verbs just offered as examples of the short past participle give some idea of the effects which may be gained by using the exact verb. When these specific predicates (the specific predicate is the main verb of the clause) are used, some picture making occurs in the verb. For example, in the sentence "The carbide insert is brazed to the tool," the description included in the verb replaces both adjective and adverb modifiers. When one replaces the specific predicate by a more general predicate, as in this sentence: "The carbide insert is *joined* to the tool with *brazing metal*," the general verb *joined* is not only less forceful but it requires three more words as modifiers to say the same thing.

Spatial Relations

How the writer indicates to the reader the relation of the parts of an object to each other and to the whole object determines whether an organized composite image forms in the reader's mind. As the reader follows the description, he attempts to build, construct, or arrange the pattern of the object in his mind. If there are no guide words to indicate spatial relations, the reader sometimes forms distorted and inaccurate pictures. If halfway through the paragraph of description one discovers that the object being described is no larger than a marble, when his mental image of the object was at least a yard wide, all he has read becomes meaningless, and the paragraph must be reread. This is why it is good to begin a description by comparing the object to something familiar to the reader. An idea of its approximate size and shape helps to start the spatial relations on the right scale. Student writers sometimes forget that the reader may never have seen the object and must form his idea entirely from the description. If spatial relations are not clearly indicated, pictures formed by the reader may be lopsided, inverted, or outsized.

Positions and shapes, also, should be noted in universally understood terms: *a vertical plane, a horizontal surface, perpendicular to the horizontal axis, tangent, concentric, rectangular, cubic,* and so on. Dimensions should be given in the English system and rounded to the nearest fraction apparent to the unaided eye. In general, dimensions expressed as comparisons to familiar objects are more effective than numerical fractions for creating a picture. Again, words like *little, very, small, big, up, down, in, out, above, below, back,* and *front* are likely to cause confusion. But terms like *up* and *down* may be used with caution when the object is clearly oriented to the reader.

Logical Subdivisions

A poor choice of words or a failure to show spatial relations can blur the picture, but the writer can really throw his reader into confusion by failing to recognize the logical subdivisions of an object. A technical man must learn to observe what is structural and what is functional in the design of an object. All parts are not of the same level of significance. Like a living organism, a complex assembly has its organization centers and its supporting appendages. The major subdivisions, while described individually, must be clearly related to each other and to the structural frame or body of the mechanism. This can be done by carefully observing the head and tail of the object to be described. A puppy barking at the rattling end of a snake does not understand the organization.

Subordination

General description, it has been shown, selects precise words, shows spatial relations clearly, and makes logical subdivisions. One quality yet remains to be discussed without which clear, trenchant description is impossible: subordination of detail. To develop a compact, graphic style with more ideas per line without sounding either compendious or curt, one must organize the descriptive details into coordinate and subordinate groups. The most significant details are selected as the subjects of main clauses, and the lesser details are worked in as dependent clauses, phrases, or single modifiers (see "Clarity" and "Compression" under "Extrinsic Qualities of Style" in Chapter 7).

One of the surest ways to vitiate a description is by the excessive use of the verb *is*. (This does not mean *is* when used as a helper to form the passive voice of a transitive verb, as in *is framed, is struck,* or *is hammered.*) The verb *is* thwarts subordination by stringing minor details out as main clauses each having a subjective complement. This kind of sentence used with moderation is of value in giving information, but it is nearly worthless in forming a picture. Instead of making a concatenation of minor details with *is* verbs, the minor details should be subordinated as single-word modifiers or prepositional phrases, or as dependent adverb, adjective, and noun clauses. The verb position of the main clause should be reserved for an active specific verb.

Another commonly overused verb, almost as overworked as the verb *is,* is the verb *has. Has* is used effectively as a helping verb to form tenses of other verbs, but standing alone as the predicate, *has* shows only possession. *Is made* and *consists of* are a little better, but one in a paragraph is enough for either of these. And speaking of frequency, once or twice for *is* and once for *has* should be the limit in a paragraph.

In conclusion, general description informs and creates an image; its purpose is not to be confused with the procurement description of a catalogue or the manufacturing description of the blueprint. Some instructions for writing catalogue and blueprint descriptions have been given, but the emphasis in this study will continue to be on the general-purpose description, the kind of description most frequently needed by scientists and engineers.

STUDENT EXAMPLES

Description of Mechanical Device

Homemade Turkey Caller

This turkey caller is a small wooden box containing a slide device which, when moved, creates a "chirp" that resembles the turkey cry. The ³⁄₁₆-in. thick mahogany wood box is 3 in. long and 2 in. square. Only one 2-in. by 3-in. side is open, whih during normal operation is the top. A ¼-in. by 1-in. by 1-in. wedge-shaped block of oak wood is glued in the center of the bottom of the box. A slide device consisting of a ³⁄₁₆-in. dowel extends lengthwise and protrudes 1 in. through holes at either end of the box. Attached to the dowel and directly above the wedge block is a 1-in. square piece of ⅛-in. thick slate. A back-and-forth motion of the dowel rod, with the attached slate rubbing the thin edge of the oak wedge, generates a "chirp" which resembles the turkey call. Cupping the hand over the open top varies the tone and volume. Rubbing small amounts of rosin on the top of the wedge produces a more raspy chirp.

Alligator Clip

The Mueller alligator clip derives its name from its similarity in appearance to the profile of an alligator's head. For the purpose of illustration, a profile view is used, with the "nose" end on the right side. The clip is made of two pieces of lightweight steel oriented directly above each other. The lower piece is two inches long, and the upper piece is slightly shorter. One-eighth inch to the right of center of the lower piece is a small pin that fastens both pieces together. This pin also provides the pivot point for the upper piece. The pin fits through the center of a spring that applies pressure against the inside of each piece, to the left of the pin, to hold the clip in a closed position. The clip is squeezed open by applying thumb pressure to the flat portion of the left end of the upper piece, while resting the lower piece against the forefinger. Each jaw has a serrated edge and a rounded nose that give it its alligator appearance and provide a toothlike gripping surface. The alligator clip is used to make a temporary electrical connection between an electrical terminal and a wire that is permanently attached to the clip.

The Ekco Knife Sharpener

The Ekco knife sharpener resembles a smoking pipe in both form and size. The sharpener consists of two rows of hard steel sharpening disks mounted vertically in an alloy case to which is attached a wooden handle. The case is stamped from alloy into a U-channel form, an inch and one-half long and one-half inch wide. Two rivets are placed in an axlelike manner in holes drilled through both sides of the case. On each rivet there are four disks separated one from the other by washers. The two rows of quarter-size disks overlap; that is to say, a disk of one row fits between two disks of the other row. The disks rotate freely on the rivets. The handle is connected to the case by a short, flat metal strip. The cutting edge of the knife is placed in the groove created by the overlapping disks. It is then drawn parallel to the rivets through the groove. As the knife is drawn, the disks rotate, sharpening the blade by shaving metal from the knife edge.

The Keuffel and Esser Log Log Duplex Slide Rule

The Keuffel and Esser log log duplex slide rule is a mechanical calculator on both sides of which are printed twenty-one graduated logarithmic scales. The slide rule is slightly longer than a foot, about two inches high, and one-quarter inch thick. It consists of three main printed sections: the rigid part of the frame, called the body, having two sections; and a center section, called the slide. The body sections, one of which is longer by about three quarters of an inch, are connected to one another by four L-shaped metal brackets. The brackets are riveted to the longer section and screwed to the shorter to permit any fine adjustments necessary for proper alignment. The rule is constructed of a mahogany base on which are laminated six white plastic strips with the printed scales. A sliding runner showing a hairline indicator straddles the body so that it can move from end to end of the rule to permit a more precise reading of the scales. Calculations are made by manipulating the movable slide between the fitted scales.

EXERCISES

1. Make a list of ten denotative words and ten connotative words. Connotative words are words that may mean different things to different people, depending upon their education and experience.

2. Write a descriptive sentence about each of ten familiar objects.

3. Bring to class a sample paragraph of technical description from a magazine. Be prepared to give the reader level.

4. Write a 150 to 200 word paragraph of general description on a simple mechanical device—any device with at least one moving part.

4

Narration: How Does It Function?

Two of the basic kinds of technical writing, definition and description, have been presented. The third basic kind is called narration because it is chiefly concerned with what happens in time and space. Narration for the technical man relates action and, as necessary, defines, describes, and explains to make certain the reader understands *what* is happening. It explains, for instance, any causally related sequence of actions which produce a desired result. Shop instructions, engineering process descriptions, and general process descriptions are all forms of technical narration.

This chapter is devoted to a study of technical narration (process) as it is employed in science and industry. The procedures for writing the various kinds of narrative description are examined with special emphasis on the ways of obtaining and holding the reader's attention and of insuring his understanding of the time and space relations. Finally, the most useful type of narration practiced by the engineer or technical person, the general process description, is defined and illustrated.

KINDS OF PROCESSES

The term process as used here refers to a definitive, descriptive, expository kind of writing with a time sequence as its dominant characteristic. This kind of writing may be subdivided for the purpose of learning as process instructions, process specifications, and general process descriptions.

Process Instruction

This kind of process is written in shop language, slightly below the academic level of the persons expected to read it. The directions are given in the imperative mood in a chronological order. For a complex series of actions intended to be performed by a worker, the steps are often explained and the expected results spelled out. Cautions or safety measures may come at the end of certain steps within the process. The shop process is sometimes posted beside complex machines, particularly the hazardous ones, to instruct workers in their use.

The familiar process instructions—instructions for performing a process—are found on or in all do-it-yourself kits. Relighting instructions for a hot-water heater or the break-in instructions for a new automobile are typical of this kind of writing. It should be noted that describing and explaining are done in the indicative and subjunctive moods. The directions to act, however, are always in the imperative mood; this is the mood used for giving commands or making entreaties. The imperative for all practical purposes can be mastered by learning just *one* form: "*Open* the valve." The second person singular, present tense, is the clue to the imperative mood, in which *you* is the understood subject. (For a further discussion of the moods of verbs, see Chapter 1.)

Process instructions are directions for performing operations in sequence. They do not give information needed for reproducing the process. This is the engineer's process description or specification which will now be described.

Process Specification

When all the information for setting up a process is given, including drawings for erecting equipment, the kind of materials used in the equipment, even the ratio of chemicals in various solutions, it is called an engineering process specification. The process specification may also include shop performance data, erection instructions, and various other bits of technical information. Industrial organizations often number their process specifications serially (process technical bulletins, process standards, and the like) and issue them from the engineering department.

General Process Descriptions

Since the process instruction is rather straightforward and quite well understood by the average engineer and since the engineering process specification is largely controlled by stereotyped format, there will be no further discussion of these two types of process narration. The third type of technical narration, the general process, will be presented in detail because it requires considerable practice to write effectively. General process description provides information about a process or relates *what happens.* It does *not* give directions for performing operations or specifications for setting up equipment, as do the two types of writing previously discussed.

The general process description is of two kinds: *a)* the giving of information about a process, written in the passive voice and *b)* the telling of what happens (re-creation of the process), written in the active voice. Giving information about a process involves no new techniques and needs no special emphasis. In this kind of process description, the steps in the process are explained in chronological order, with the details slanted toward an *understanding* of what the process involves rather than toward the actual happenings or the specific action involved in the process. Statements are made *about* what happens; they do not *show* the process to the reader. Chronological order of the information gives unity to the paragraphs. The presentation seeks to hold the reader's interest to the extent that he wishes to have answers to the questions which already exist in his mind from a previous knowledge of the process.

All of the techniques for obtaining sharp focus, precision, and conciseness discussed previously in relation to technical description apply also to the general process description. One may use active or passive voice, present or past tense, indicative or subjunctive mood, as the occasion demands. The recognizable characteristic of this kind of expository writing and its unifying device is the *time sequence.* Without this time sequence the writing could just as easily be classed as definition or technical description. Like the other two types of processes described earlier, the process instruction and the process specification, it does involve a unit of time during which a series of causally related actions occur to produce a planned effect; hence, it is narrative within the meaning of the term used in technical writing. In writing this type of general process description one has only to practice the techniques described earlier for technical description and general expository writing. Chronological order is dominant, and the reader's interest is held by his natural desire to have the questions which have been raised about the process answered.

The most useful type of general process description is that which *shows* the reader what happens. This type comes nearer the literary meaning of narration, a kind in which the reader is made an observer or an actual participant in the process. It is recognized by a strong *action line*, the use of the present tense, the indicative mood, and the active voice (refer again to Chapter 1 on voice, mood, tense, modal auxiliaries, person and number; if there is any doubt remaining on the use of these terms, one should check an English handbook).

When a writer tells what happens in a process by re-creating it in the active voice, the reader's interest is focused on the *doer* of the action. When the doer is made the subject of the verb, the reader is drawn into the scene. He begins to watch for the reaction or result of the doer's actions. The writer takes advantage of the natural pull of the story to obtain a greater degree of understanding of highly specialized information. This is possible because of the increased attention of the reader as the action sequence unfolds; it is much easier to learn new things and to remember what happens when one has actually witnessed them. Learning the craft of this basic kind of writing requires practice and careful attention to the techniques to be described next.

The second type of general process description, the general process which re-creates or *shows* what happens, also presents a series of related actions, but it can be distinguished from the first type by its dominant action sequence. As in the first type, information when needed is given in the indicative or subjunctive mood (modal auxiliaries may also be used), but the narrative sequence, called here the *action line*, must be written only in the indicative mood, active voice; there should be no modal auxiliaries (words like *can, could, should,* and *may*) and *no* imperative forms. At any point where the equipment or the basic principles need describing or explaining, the action line simply pauses while the necessary information is given in the passive voice, using modal auxiliaries or the subjunctive mood if desired. Then the writer picks up the action line, returning to the active voice, present tense, indicative mood (this means no modals, no subjunctive forms) and continues the action.

The first type of general process description is used when the reader is known to have previous knowledge of the process and a strong desire to learn more about it. But the general process description with the strong action line can be used even when the reader may be presumed to have no knowledge or even no particular interest. It possesses the advantage of having a better vehicle for carrying the information and of holding the reader's interest—the strong action line which pulls the reader into the process as a bystander or witness. In other words, the general process which makes use of the narrative technique is actually a more versatile tool for conveying information about processes than the first type described. The general reader prefers to be *shown* what happens rather than simply told *about* what happens.

WRITING THE GENERAL PROCESS DESCRIPTION

As a preliminary step in deciding whether to give information about a process in the passive voice or to recreate the process in the active voice, the writer should answer these questions:

1. What does the reader already know about this process?
2. Is there an underlying principle of operation which the reader must understand?
3. What is the scope; that is, how much space and time will be covered in the process?
4. Are there any natural breaks or time plateaus which could serve as natural subdivisions of an outline for the development of the process?
5. Is the reader's interest already aroused in the subject?

The procedure for writing the narrative process is about the same regardless of the answers to these questions; but the choice of words, the viewpoint, and the mood and voice of the verbs vary to suit the reader level and the purpose of the writer. The instructions on writing which follow apply equally well to both types of the narrative process. Some special instructions for developing the action-line process are given at the close of the chapter preceding the exercises.

The general technical process begins by naming and defining the process if it needs defining. It then spans the process to give the reader an idea of what is to come. Further, it may explain material, equipment, and theory before the sequence of action is begun. In the general process, however, details are never given in such a manner that the reader could set up the equipment, and the actions are never so specific that the reader could perform the process. One might think of the necessary equipment as being "shadowed in" (as is sometimes done to show certain flow paths in commercial advertising involving equipment processes) and the reader as a bystander.

When the stage is set, the action begins—either information about action or the action itself. To insure the reader's understanding, one must carefully note the passing of time through the shifting scenes. This can be done by using transition words (time markers) and by describing action in a logical arrangement so that as one action is performed the next action follows as a cause or an effect of the preceding action. The passing of time can be shown by a single adverb or by a prepositional phrase placed before or after an idea in the usual adverbial position. Sometimes it is necessary to remind the reader of what has happened and to indicate what is yet to come. This is done by a transition sentence. If the process has natural time intervals, these may be pointed out as they are reached.

Since action is the keynote of the process, action words should have special attention (action here refers to meaning, not voice). By a careful selection of specific verbs as predicates and a generous use of other verb forms as modifiers, the action can be set at any desired pace without affecting the length of the main clauses (see discussion on verbals in Chapter 1).

Verbal forms added to the specific asserting action of the verb impart a great deal of movement to the sentence without loading it or giving an effect of breathless crowding of detail. By a judicious selection of verbal forms the writer can make the process either skim along at a frightening pace or screech to a grinding halt. Or, having stopped the action for the time being, he can explain how a broken thread automatically stops the flying shuttle to prevent further damage to the part already woven (this sentence contains six verbals). Once the student has mastered the verbal forms he need never be at a loss to relate a process, either the information type or the action-line type.

In this text the general process with the dominant action line has been selected for class practice because it offers the greater challenge as a design problem. Both types of general process are written in the third person and follow the chronological sequence. The recognizable difference lies in the presence in the second type of a dominant action sequence related in the indicative mood and active voice. Once begun, the action line moves steadily forward. If the process branches, one must simply tell the reader this, take one branch of the process through the next step, and then return for the other. The concluding sentence simply finishes the process, or it may summarize the process.

The difficulty, if any, experienced in writing the general process with the dominant action line is in controlling the predicate verbs; these must be in the third person, active voice, indicative mood. A shift to the imperative mood changes the type from general process to process instruction—that is, directions to perform. A shift to the subjunctive mood, or to the intermediate moods created by modal auxiliaries, is a departure from the factual indicative mood used to relate a series of actions. It should be pointed out that the imperative mood is never used in the general process, but it is permissible to use either active or passive voice, subjunctive or indicative mood, when supplying the necessary information for the reader as the general process moves through its action sequence.

The reader should be given only as much information as he needs to understand the process step by step as it is related. This is true for either of the two types of general process. If the equipment is described in too much detail, it may sound more like a process specification; and one slip in the use of the imperative mood (giving commands or making entreaties in the second person) changes the general process description to instructions for doing.

Uses of the General Process Description

Three types of process description using the chronological sequence as a unifying device have been defined in this chapter: process instructions, engineering process specifications, and the general information process, which was further subdivided into two types, comprising *a*) the general process which informs by *telling* what happens, and *b*) the general process which informs by *showing* what happens. Before the student attempts the assignment on the dominant action line type of general process, some further discussion and examples will be helpful.

Both types of general process are widely used forms of the narrative process description. They may vary in length from a single sentence or paragraph to book-length articles. The span of time and the complexity of the action determine the number of paragraphs needed to relate the process. If part of a longer process is to be described, it might begin something like this:

In the Anderson Essolex process of extracting oil from cottonseed, a trace of solvent remains in the oil after the first distillation, which must be removed by stripping. The distilled solvent is pumped to the stripping column, where it is heated to the boiling temperature. Live steam is then bubbled through the oil to wash out the traces of solvent. The oil, containing solvent-saturated water droplets, is then returned to the stripping column, where it is again recycled until all traces of solvent have been removed from the oil.

From this opening sentence the reader knows how the stripping operation to be described fits into the whole process, and the absence of a strong action line indicates this is to be information *about* a process.

Another example of narrating a unit of time from the large process is a paragraph on the crushing stage of plaster making:

Before the gypsum ore can be made into plaster by the Raymond hammer-mill process, it must first be crushed to a three-quarter-inch maximum particle size so that it can be fed uniformly into the calcining mills. This is done in two crusher operations. The ore in random-sized chunks as it comes from the mines is dumped from the gondola cars into funnel-shaped chutes located beneath the railway switch. The ore falls through the chutes upon a four-foot-wide rubber conveyor belt, which hauls it up a 30-degree incline and drops it into the throat of the jaw-type crusher. Massive iron teeth, faced with hard metal, crunch the ore to fist-sized bits as it falls between the slowly chewing jaws of the crusher onto a two-foot-wide rubber belt below. The faster moving two-foot belt sends the ore up another incline to the charging chute of the rotary crusher. When the ore clatters through the rotating, hammer-mill crusher, vibrating screens at the outlet catch oversized particles and return them to the charging belt for another crushing cycle. The fines, three-quarter-inch and under, fall into an elevator pit. There a chain elevator, bucket type, lifts the finely crushed ore a vertical distance of 46 feet and drops it into a temporary storage bin from which it is moved by screw conveyor about forty yards to the raw materials storage bin in the calcining plant.

The action line is easily recognized in this second example. The predicates of the main clauses in the action line are in the indicative mood, present tense, active voice. The predicate action is made more vivid by the use of specific verbs. Additional supporting action is obtained through the use of verbals—that is, other verb forms not functioning as predicates.

Another example, this one a process short enough to be related completely in one paragraph:

Concrete strength is related to its pouring consistency, which is measured by its slump, or the amount the wet concrete will sink down after being momentarily retained in a special cone-shaped form. Since the consistency of a given mix is an index of its ultimate strength, the slump test is a standard means of controlling the quality. In making the test, the inspector takes the slump cone, a sturdy galvanized sheet-metal vessel shaped something like a camper's six-quart coffeepot without a lid or bottom, a foot rule, and a two-foot section of three-eighths-inch steel rod to the job site where the concrete is being poured. After writing the necessary identifying information in his data book, he begins the test procedure. First he sets the truncated cone, big end down, on a smooth surface and fills it in three layers, tamping it 25 strokes with the rod for each layer. On the last layer, after he has tamped the specified number of strokes, he adds enough mix to slightly overflow the cone end and with the rod strikes it off level. Then he carefully lifts the cone by its two handles. The slope on the cone permits it to be removed with ease, allowing the unrestrained cone of concrete to sink until its consistency brings it to rest at some point below the height of the slump vessel. The tester next sets the empty cone on the level beside the poured concrete, lays the tamping rod across the top of the slump vessel, and then measures with the ruler the difference in inches between the horizontal tamping rod supported on the cone and the top of the sagged concrete. Since the cone is one foot high, the distance measured is the slump in inches per foot.

It will be noted that this last example is an *operator-dominated* process. The previous example of the ore-crushing stage in the gypsum plaster-making process was an *equipment-dominated* process. Both examples make use of the strong action line. To have used modal auxiliaries like *could, should, would, may,* and *ought* would have weakened the effect of the actions. This does not mean that modal auxiliaries are not useful engineering tools; they are. When not enough is known to make a forthright statement, qualifying and evasive verb helpers can save the engineer's neck. But they are not useful here. In either of the preceding examples these modals would have hindered rather than helped. It will also be noted in the examples that, when the reader needed additional information about the equipment or the principles involved in the process, the passive voice or the modal auxiliaries were used as needed. As soon as the question was answered, however, the action sequence in the process went on.

Unique histories and first-person narratives of procedures used in experiments are not within the scope of this text.

Dominant Action Line in Technical Papers

To fully appreciate the heightened interest gained by using the general process with the dominant action line, one has only to attend any of the technical society conferences. Some papers are extremely dull because the writer has not made use of the techniques for displaying his information by means of the narrative process description. His audience may be familiar with his subject, may even be interested beforehand, but he fails to hold their attention because he does not *show* what happens. He puts all his information in the passive voice. He fails to make use of the added intellectual suspense derived from creating a sequence of related actions with the subjects acting upon direct objects.

A careful reading of some of the articles in popular technical magazines will reveal this technique. In some articles it becomes a perfected art: the reader's interest is caught and held by almost overwhelming curiosity or desire to know what happens next. The illustration which follows shows how effective the active voice becomes in creating a scene of action.

> Reduced to the human equation, this means that the men who cut the cane rise early, long before daylight, drink a cup of black coffee, usually about two o'clock in the morning, take their horses, and ride to the field. Cane cutting is not by any means the simple process that it would appear to be. The cutter grasps a stalk of cane in his left hand about five or six feet above the ground. Then with a slash or two of his machete he strips loose the dry leaves—*paja* they are called. Then he swings his machete and cuts off the cane stalk just above the ground. He next swings the stalk to the left and brings it back sharply to the right against the blade of his knife. The weight of the stalk and the swing against the sharp blade cut it in half. He lops off the green top which is tossed into a separate pile, away from where he throws the cane. These tops or *cogollo* are later bundled up and used for cattle and horse feed. The cut stems of cane, the *trozas*, are picked up by women and boys, helped by the cutters when the task which they set out to accomplish that day is finished. They are gathered and piled into the cane cart, on top of chains laid across the bottom of the wagon.[1]

This chapter concludes the three basic kinds of writing which the technical man must master: definition—what it is; description—how it

---

[1] From *A Naturalist in Cuba*, pp. 265-66, by Thomas Barbour, copyright 1945 by Thomas Barbour, by permission of Atlantic-Little, Brown and Company.

looks; and narration—how it functions. In the next chapter some useful techniques for the presentation of information will be described.

STUDENT EXAMPLES

Description of a Process (indicative mood, passive voice)

Potting

Potting is a high-density packaging process. This process is intended to provide a moisture-resistant, high-heat-distortion protective coating. The production of highly compact electrical components in the field of micro-miniaturization, its present application, has proved quite successful. Components such as resistors, capacitors, diodes, rectifiers, and transistors are assembled in rubber holding fixtures. A suitable epoxy resin is carefully prepared. Together they are placed in an oven at 50 degrees centigrade for two hours to preheat the assembly and to allow any trapped air to escape from the compound. They are removed from the oven, and the compound is poured directly into the mold. It is allowed to air cure for two hours before the mold is removed. At this point, internal bus wiring called out in the schematic is connected and soldered. The components are instrument checked for short circuits before preparing the second pour. The unit is then placed in a second mold and moved to the oven, where it is preheated under the same conditions as before. This second pour is required to cover the exposed solder joints. After the unit has been allowed to cure properly, it is then ready to be installed in the next highest assembly as a completed subassembly.

Description of a Process (indicative mood, active voice)

Digital Flow Blending

A bidirectional counter can perform flow-rate control and fuel blending for the petroleum industry. This system consists of two automatically controlled feeder lines feeding a blend line. Because both feeder lines operate on the same principle, only the operation of one line will be followed. Fuel flows from a storage tank to a manual shutoff valve and then through a pump to a turbine flowmeter. The flowmeter produces pulses in direct proportion to the flow rate and transmits an amplified electrical signal to a preset counter. The preset counter then develops an add signal for the bidirectional counter which, at the same time, receives a constant-output (subtract) signal from a flow-rate-set oscillator. There is an output correction signal from the bidirectional counter only when the add and subtract signals differ in frequency. A signal difference causes an inverse voltage change at the output of a servo amplifier and a corresponding change in an electropneumatic control valve on the feeder line. The total output from the blend line is therefore established by the flow-rate-set oscillator.

Analog-to-Digital Conversion

This paper discusses analog-to-digital conversion as a part of the process of preparing analog data for microwave transmission. To begin the process, the sensing instrument, such as a thermometer in a satellite, provides an analog output voltage which represents the value of the function being measured. This output voltage is then fed to a comparator where it is compared to a periodic reference signal. The voltage level of the reference varies linearly with time. At the start of the reference, the voltage is equivalent to the lowest expected value of the function. The reference terminates, after a time, at a voltage which represents the maximum expected value of the function. The output of the comparator is a positive square wave which begins at the start of the reference and ends when the reference becomes equal to the function voltage. The time width of the square wave is, therefore, proportional to the function value. The square wave, in turn, controls the number of count pulses which are allowed to enter a digital counter. The counter produces a digital code for further processing. Summarizing, analog-to-digital conversion consists of changing a voltage signal to a time signal and using the time signal to determine the resulting count in a digital counter.

Description of a Process (*indicative mood, active voice, and using the action-line technique*)

How to Crank an Aircraft Engine

When an aircraft engine is cranked, it should be done in an orderly manner so that each step will become a habit and nothing will be omitted. To begin, the pilot seats himself at the controls, fastens his safety belt, and locks the brakes. He then turns on the gas and pushes the primer a couple of times. The primer forces a small amount of fuel directly into the cylinders. After making sure the magnetic switch is off by touching it with his fingers as well as looking at it, the pilot pulls the throttle into the closed position and opens it again slightly. At this point he looks up at the "prop" man and yells, "off and closed," which means the switch is off and the throttle is closed. The "prop" man repeats, "off and closed," and pulls the propeller through the compression stroke a few times. Then he yells, "contact." The pilot repeats, "contact," and turns on the magneto switch. When the "prop" man again pulls the propeller through the compression stroke, the engine starts.

EXERCISES

1. Write a one-page example of process instructions—that is, directions for performing a related series of actions to accomplish a desired result.

2. Write a process technical bulletin or process specification of 200 to 300 words. Use a real-life situation and company models if possible.

3. Find in a technical magazine, and bring to class for discussion, a general process which illustrates the first type studied. This is *not* the process having the active voice sequence of action.

4. Write an operator- or equipment-dominated general process employing the dominant action line. Limit the assignment to a unified paragraph of 150 to 200 words. If a longer process is used, limit the scope to a subdivision of the longer process, one short enough to be handled well in the time span of a single paragraph. The student should note that in this exercise no imperative verb forms are permitted.

5
Techniques of Presentation

At this point in his study, the mechanics of expression having been pretty well mastered and the three fundamental kinds of writing understood, the student is ready to study the next level of the writing craft: technique, a way of using the basic tools. Technique, as one dictionary says, is "The method or the details of procedure essential to expertness of execution in any art, science, etc.; hence, manner of performance with reference to such expertness." According to this definition, the methods essential to the presentation of information discussed in this chapter are techniques. These include formal and informal analysis, considered here as *classification* and *interpretation*, respectively, and argument, which is subdivided into *convincing* and *persuading*. Written and oral exercises demonstrating these techniques are given at the end of the chapter.

FORMAL ANALYSIS

As it is generally conceived, formal analysis is laboratory analysis, either physical or chemical. In technical writing the meaning is extended to include the technique of dividing ideas into meaningful categories for the sake of understanding what is known or for deducing what is unknown. As the student will recall, formal definition in Chapter 2 involved classification, but it was used for the purpose of identifying and understanding ideas. Formal analysis, or classification as it is to be studied in the present chapter, is an orderly means of displaying already identified information so that it may be better understood.

In the formal definition an object is identified in its entirety by naming it, classifying it, and then differentiating it from other objects within its class. This classification concept learned in formal definition may now be transferred to the study of the technique of analysis, particularly formal analysis where subjects are included or not included in a category simply by arbitrarily changing the basis for the classification according to a given purpose.

Basis of Classification

Formal analysis implies an exhaustive treatment once a certain *basis for classification* has been decided. The basis for classification controls the subdivision. One of the limitations of formal analysis lies in the fact that, once the basis has been stated (and it must be stated at the outset), no item within this basis may be ignored and no item may be discussed which is outside the basis of the classification. Formal analysis is not as frequently used as informal analysis (interpretation), to be discussed later in this chapter, but it is nevertheless a valuable tool—one which permits the scientist or the engineer to break down mountains of detailed subject matter into informational units suitable to his purpose. Useful knowledge can be imparted on varieties or groups of objects with great economy of space. If one wishes to discuss certain characteristics which a large number of objects have in common or have as differences, he can use this technique and avoid the monotonous repetition of discussing each item individually. Formal analysis is thus a useful technique only where the materials to be discussed lend themselves to meaningful subdivision.

The first important consideration in using the classification technique is to find a useful basis by which a group of objects can be profitably subdivided. This will be determined by the purpose of the writer. The basis having been determined, the next step is to name the subclasses within the group controlled by the basis. The basis should be a logical one and useful to the reader. A chemist, for example, would probably not be interested in the brushing characteristics of paint or the drying characteristics, or perhaps even the wearing life of the paint, but a painter would, and certainly a homeowner would. A man, for example, has just finished building a walnut chest. This special object is to be an adornment in his den. The walnut grain must be visible beneath a permanent hard glossy finish. At the paint store where he normally trades, he explains his needs to the salesman. The paint salesman does not confront the customer with the chemical composition, the brushing characteristics, the drying rates, and the probable wearing qualities of every kind of paint in his store. No, indeed. Reason tells him that, so far as this customer is concerned, all the information he needs about all the kinds of paint in his store can be presented in a few sentences, because the subject has been limited and the basis of classification determined by the specific request of the customer.

The genus of transparency suggested by the desire to preserve the walnut grain has eliminated all pigmented paints, enamels, and, in fact, all water, oil, latex, and other kinds of opaque finishes. It further eliminates all transparent finishes not intended for use on hardwood. The experienced salesman, knowing his stock, immediately understands that the only classification of all the paints in his store which will be of value to the customer is the transparent hardwood finishes. He would also know that the most likely basis of classification—since the customer was obviously not a professional—was according to the ease of application. The customer has already mentioned hardness and durability. The salesman, bound by a three-point basis—easy application, hard finish, long life—has only three kinds of transparent hardwood finishes in stock which meet this combination requirement: the natural resins from the Orient, the synthetic resins, and the drying oils. The salesman then points out these transparent finishes which meet the basis for ease of application, hardness, and durability, and names and differentiates each of the species in terms the customer can understand. If the customer then wants information on drying time, the finishes will be reclassified on that basis into quick, medium, and slow; this will occasion some regrouping, with the oils taking the longest to dry. A still further classification may be needed to give the customer his deciding information: toxicity. He has small children who might use their teeth on the chest corners. There would be an immediate reshuffling of all transparent, easy to apply, hard film, durable finishes along the new lines of the toxicity basis; and one of the slow-drying oils requiring several applications with plenty of rubbing in between to obtain the desired luster might be selected simply because it was nonpoisonous.

Any large class of materials, items, objects, can thus be classified and discussed according to some useful basis. The basis used by the salesman would not have been meaningful to a chemist interested in analyzing the finishes. A jobber would have been interested in still a different breakdown; all the finishes, for instance, might have been classified according to their turnover rate or the profit margin or the time cycle required to procure them.

When the formal analysis, or classification, technique is used to present information, the order of the essential parts changes somewhat from definition which also involves classifying. The scientist classifies insects, animals, clouds, plants, and so on for the purpose of identifying them. He starts with the species, then moves to the genus, then to the differentiae. The *technique used for presenting information* begins with the genus, instead of the species as in definition. Then the basis for classification is given. Sometimes it is helpful to name another basis or two by which the objects could be classified before proceeding with the basis used. When the basis is clearly defined, the subclasses according to that basis are named and differentiated from each other. The subclasses may be described as each is named, or all may be named and then individually described.

Though this technique is used frequently, it seldom extends through an entire report. In learning the technique, a 150-word paragraph is an ideal length for practice. The shorter the sample can be to insure that the student understands the technique, the better. Using the order of arrangement just given—group, basis of classification, species, and differentiation—the student can write a successful single-paragraph or multiple-paragraph analysis by observing these precautions:

1. The basis must be clear to both the writer and the reader. To insure that the basis is clear to the reader, it must be defined by the writer in terms which have significance for the reader; that is, the basis must be one which can be defined in universally understood units. If this is not done, it will be impossible to distinguish the subdivisions from each other.

2. There must be no remainder; once the basis has been determined, all of the items which fall within this classification must be named and differentiated. In other words, once the basis has been set up, the analysis must proceed to the end; and if some classes cannot be specifically identified, the unknown subclasses must be recognized and labeled as unknown.

3. In formal analysis all subclasses must be described according to the same basis. To name one subclass according to one basis and another according to some other basis is to render this technique completely useless, even confusing.

4. *Partition* is sometimes confused with the analysis technique. In breaking down the subdivisions one eventually comes to the point where any further subdivision would break a single class or item into its various constituents or parts. This is referred to as partition. Partition might be illustrated thus: In the classification of hammers according to materials used, one might have lead hammers, fiber hammers, and steel hammers; but any further subdivision would be partition. Partition is useful in describing the subclasses, but it is not considered a technique in the sense that formal analysis is a technique.

To review the highlights of the discussion of formal analysis: one should remember to state the basis early; to make the subdivisions mutually exclusive, that is, to avoid overlapping of the subdivisions; and to make certain the group or class possesses at least two logical subclasses by the basis used.

INFORMAL ANALYSIS

In the previous section, it was shown that a kind of writing (definition) used by scientists to identify a species becomes, with a few changes, a useful technique (classification) for presenting information about large groups of items of any kind. Informal analysis, discussed in this section, is a further adaptation of the classification technique. Instead of beginning with a group of items, it begins with a complicated problem. The solution is reached by establishing a basis (standard of judgment) and then systematically selecting from all of the possible solutions (alternatives) the one which best satisfies the basis.

The exercise of judgment by the writer is the most important difference between formal and informal analysis. In the formal-analysis technique the definition of the basis controls the classification; opinion and judgment are not involved. But in the interpretation or informal analysis technique facts are assigned to categories according to the judgment of the writer. This difference is analogous to the difference between science and art. The scientist classifies facts; the artist rearranges and interprets them. Short formal analyses such as test reports can be included in the informal analysis, but the process is not reversible. The presence of opinion, value judgment, or interpretation in the formal analysis reclassifies it to informal analysis.

Uses of the Informal Analysis Technique

Problems which involve a choice between two or more acceptable solutions may be solved by a reasoning process described here as the informal analysis technique. One-answer problems—those having no alternatives and those solvable by mathematical calculations—belong to the formal category. The results of mathematical calculations may be used as evidence in making the informal analysis, but the inference itself is never reached by mathematical calculation. For example, if one wishes to learn the weight of an airplane, the airplane is simply rolled onto a platform scale or is hooked to a dynamometer and weighed. The weight found in universally understood units is acceptable to all technical people. This is a mathematical solution. Only one answer is possible; no judgments, no interpretations are permitted.

On the other hand, if the problem is to find a cheaper way of weighing the airplane, this will be grounds for interpretation, because the solution must be reached by deduction and inference. The major standard will probably be cost, and there may be several minor standards, including production delay. With some imagination this example can be extended to a life-sized problem: The airplanes are presently being sent from final assembly to the compass rose for weighing at a cost of $75 each at the rate of one per day. Investigation shows that if the airplanes were weighed in the empty bay at the end of the final assembly line, they could be weighed for $15 each, thus effecting a $60 savings per plane. Further investigation, including a design and construction cost study, shows that it would cost $30,000 for relocation of the weighing facility, $20,000 for construction, materials and labor, and $10,000 for a new platform-type scale made necessary because the dynamometer weighing mechanism at the compass rose cannot be installed inside the building, where there is insufficient ceiling clearance. This alternative means of weighing the airplane would take only 60 days to complete, and the changeover could be made with no production delays. Still further investigation, however, reveals that only 500 more planes remain in the contract. At the scheduled production rate of one a day, only 440 planes would remain to be built by the time the new weighing location was ready for use. At $60 per plane the relocated scales would make possible a savings of only $26,400 (440×$60) against an expenditure of $30,000. That fact removes this first alternative from further consideration.

But during the investigation two other alternatives have been discovered, both of which are cheaper than the present manner of weighing, and hence eligible for consideration. A plant engineering study shows that the building trusses can be remodeled so that the ceiling clearance is sufficient to accommodate the dynamometer weighing equipment at the compass rose. The entire move, including the remodeling job, can be made for $18,000.

The other alternative, suggested by the production foreman, is a temporary shelter to be erected outside the final assembly building with sufficient headroom to accommodate the compass rose weighing equipment. The total materials and labor for this alternative will not exceed $12,000, and the job can be completed in 30 days, leaving a total of 470 planes to be weighed. It happens that during the remaining six months of the contract (April to September) the weather is expected to be mild. The planes can be towed outside and weighed for $20 each, only $5 more than the original estimate for the final assembly line position. With 470 planes remaining in the contract at a saving of $55 per plane, a saving of $13,850 above the $12,000 expenditure can be realized. The work order obviously will be issued to relocate the weighing operation in a temporary shelter outside the final assembly building.

Another example, perhaps more plausible, might be that of a plumber who has decided he needs an additional delivery truck for his plumbing firm. Being a small operator, he establishes $2000 as his maximum expenditure for the truck. The truck must have space to haul his necessary supplies and equipment, about a thousand pounds, and, in addition, at least five joints of pipe. This will necessitate the truck's having a pipe rack. The carrying capacity, the pipe rack, and the maximum cost would thus constitute his major standard. The truck should also have good tires, low mileage, and a 90-day warranty against repairs. These might be considered the minor standards.

The plumber surveys the area; this is the research and testing phase. In all the area he can find only three trucks which meet his standard for maximum price, and which meet in varying degrees the standard for good tires and low mileage. All are half-ton pickup trucks. A Ford and a Dodge have 30-day warranties; a Chevrolet has a 90-day warranty; for this illustration these three trucks are designated A, B, and C. Truck A can be bought for $1000; it has an indicated 30,000 miles and an almost new set of tires. It has no pipe rack. Truck B can be bought for $1650. It looks clean. The original owner, who is contacted by the plumber, testifies that the speedometer reading of 17,000 is the actual mileage. The tires are good but nearly treadless. It has no pipe rack. Truck C can be bought for $1095. It, too, has no pipe rack, but it has a new set of tires. The speedometer has been turned back to zero, but the dealer who reconditioned the vehicle gives a 90-day warranty against repairs.

Thus, all of the trucks are below $2000, but none has a pipe rack, which is a part of the major standard. At this point the plumber can investigate further, or he can decide to purchase a pipe rack separately, a decision which would keep all three trucks within his standard if the cost of the pipe rack is not above $350. From the yellow pages (more research) he learns that two welding shops build the type of pipe rack he needs, one at a cost of $175, the other at a cost of $180. Reevaluating each of the choices, A, B, and C, in turn against $1825, his new standard ($2,000 less $175 for the pipe rack), he decides on truck C. He reasons that because of the three-month warranty, truck C has been completely overhauled, a consideration worth at least $200 to him. He knows he can have the tires recapped for less than $50. Thus he has made a decision for action based on the standards set and the evidence he was able to obtain about the possible choices.

The monumental decisions of government and business which are shaping the industrial and political history of the nation are made in much the same manner as the plumber's decision to purchase the truck. The biggest decisions require more standards of judgment, more research, more sophisticated reports, but the analytical process is the same. When the major and minor standards have been determined and expressed in universally understood terms, they become the controlling factors in the solution of the problem. The minor standards become minor factors, comparable to fringe benefits thrown in for negotiating purposes. However, weighty matters must sometimes be decided on the minor factors when the major factors are nearly equal—that is, when two or more alternatives meet the major standards in almost the same way.

Before a manufacturer decides to put out a new line of products, to relocate a plant, to raise his prices, to give up billboard advertising, to hire a second vice-president, or to merge with his competitor, every major and minor factor is weighed in a delicate balance. One electronics manufacturer, for instance, surveyed many sites prior to locating its computer division in Arizona. Some months after the initial establishment of the company's computer division on the campus of Arizona State University and before the permanent plant was constructed, the author was prompted to ask the division head why the company had finally decided to locate in Arizona. He frankly admitted that his company had considered more than three hundred possible sites. Using a previously determined set of standards, the field had been narrowed to three locations which were nearly equal: one in another state and two in Arizona. He said the major factors for future growth and the availability of a technical labor supply were considered very nearly equal in the three locations. The final decision was the result of a minor factor: the enthusiastic attitude of the University dean and his engineering faculty. This decision, resulting from months of fact finding and careful analysis according to exacting standards has paid off handsomely if one is to judge by the fact that this manufacturer's computer division has doubled its operations here every year since 1956, when the first contingent was brought to the University campus.

Relocation of an existing industrial plant or the locating of a new one undoubtedly involves many major and minor factors. Major factors may include such things as future growth potential, availability of labor, climate, water, and power. Other things of a less critical nature might be considered as minor factors, such as good roads, proximity to large cities where adequate housing can be obtained, and, in some instances, the availability of year-round recreational facilities. Other less definable minor factors might include good local government, corporation law, taxes, good schools for employees' children, and nearby institutions of higher learning where employees may continue their advanced training. The weather might be a major or a minor factor, depending on the kind of plant. The average relative humidity could be a factor in locating a spinning mill, for example, which requires a high humidity in the spinning rooms. An electronics firm might require an excessively dry atmosphere to prevent deterioration of products during manufacture and storage.

Generally, if a great deal of prestige or high dollar value is involved, requiring informal analysis reports, these reports are assigned to experienced engineers and scientists who have proved their keen analytical prowess and good judgment by a long apprenticeship. With some training, however, the period of apprenticeship in writing such reports is considerably shortened. This will be evident to the student after he has learned to write the recommendation report discussed in Chapter 8.

Procedure for Writing the Informal Analysis

In producing the make-believe but real-life sample of the informal analysis technique required in the exercise at the end of this chapter, it will be well for the student to remember that the problem must be one which is complicated by factors not readily understood or solvable by mathematical means. Both the problem (need) and the standards (major and minor) must be clearly stated in universally understood units. Then a statement of the extent of the research must indicate that every reasonable effort has been made to turn up all of the possible choices. Before the student's effort can be classed as interpretation, he must have left to him at least two choices which satisfy the major standards. Any choices which do not do so should be eliminated at the outset. Only those which could satisfy the standard are to be described.

One easy pitfall is to compare the choices with each other—the Ford and the Chevrolet, for instance, in the example of the plumber's truck. This is the unscientific way to make decisions. The question should be, how well does the Ford or Chevrolet meet the established standard. When this is known, the decision is reached by comparing the way the Ford meets the standard with the way the Chevrolet meets the standard. Decisions made by prejudice, snap judgment, or irrelevant whims not related to the problem are personal indulgences one should allow his wife; but when the company's money is to be spent, it does not matter whether it is a Ford or Chevrolet, red or blue. It is the one which best meets the standards of the transportation problem to be solved.

Another pitfall is the dilemma. The informal analysis technique has not been demonstrated unless a decision is reached. A report which leaves the employer with an either-or decision is pretty nearly worthless. In order to obtain a definite answer, management may allot additional funds for further research and testing; or, if conditions warrant, management may replace the investigator. In the class assignment which follows at the close of the chapter, the student should imagine himself faced with an industrial problem or assignment. In an imaginary situation, where unlimited data can be fabricated, the dilemma should not occur. This probably will be the last time in his entire career that the engineer will be permitted to fabricate data, and he should make the most of his opportunity.

ARGUMENT

One can hardly say that formal analysis involves argument. The facts are either true or false; if false, they are corrected when a new discovery is made. There is, however, no argumentative basis, since opinion is not admissible in formal analysis. The technique of informal analysis does have argumentative *overtones.* It involves conclusions based upon the writer's appraisal of the evidence; but, since its primary purpose is to inform rather than to change opinion, it is still not classed as argument.

In this section the writer's purpose rotates another 90 degrees from informal analysis to a presentation of the facts with the intent of changing opinion. The dictionary defines argument as discourse intended to convince or to persuade. Information and evidence are still involved, but the manner of presentation changes to take full advantage of the well-known principles of logic used by debaters. If the technical man makes his appeal to reason, whether deductive or inductive, he is attempting to *convince.* If he appeals to the feelings, he is attempting to *persuade.* Both these types of the technique of argument will be discussed; persuasion, however, must be used with care, for its subjective nature is not in keeping with technical style. Persuasion should be recognized, though, for at times it masquerades as reason. Technical arguments when analyzed often reveal cleverly disguised appeals to the emotions.

In the student's earlier courses in English, argument may have been classified as a kind of writing, along with exposition, narration, and description. In technical writing it is regarded as a technique of presenting information. In the technique of formal analysis, the subject matter was divided into its logical subdivisions so that it might be better understood. In the informal analysis technique the facts were rearranged according to the judgment of the writer. In argument, the third technique, significant cause-effect relationships are pointed out among the facts for the purpose of changing a reader's opinion. Effective argument induces or impels the reader to accept the writer's judgment on the cause-effect relationship of the facts. Discourse which produces a high degree of correlation between the writer and the reader's ideas is called convincing argument.

Because it is necessary for persons in positions of technical responsibility to be able to think straight, the subject of logic should be required as a part of the engineer's training in communication. Some engineers are already familiar with symbolic logic through the study of Boolean algebra. Perhaps that course could be extended to cover verbal reasoning processes. Communication, a core course, has proved a valuable thought straightener for engineers. Perhaps those who have been able to do the other core courses by more than the skin of the teeth might profit by courses in ethics, logic, and philosophy. But whether he acquires his knowledge of the principles of logic by experience, general reading, or common sense, the technical man must learn to think straight. The study of the argumentative technique presented here should be complemented by a review of the processes related to clear thinking in a standard logic text or in an English handbook.

Deductive Reasoning

Practical people tend to shy away from anything associated with logic, probably because they remember the deductive Aristotelian syllogisms of high school days which they mouthed and joked about, but which they failed to understand as having any great value. The high school student little dreams of the debt modern inductive science owes to the discoveries that have been made by purely deductive reasoning. These same high school people have become half-educated practical scientists and engineers who do not realize that the inductive method of modern science complements the deductive ratiocination of the philosopher. Ratiocination, a nonmathematical system of reasoning, was the forerunner of modern science. Long before men learned to observe and gain knowledge from experiment, they were able to discover things by pure reasoning. John Stuart Mill says:

> When Newton, in this manner, discovered the laws of the solar system, he created, for all posterity, the true idea of science. He gave the most perfect example we are ever likely to have, of that union of reasoning and observation, which by means of facts that can be directly observed, ascends to laws which govern multitudes of other facts—laws which not only explain and account for what we see, but give us assurance beforehand of much that we do not see, much

that we never could have found out by observation, though, having been found out, it is always verified by the result.[1]

Here is a classic example of a great discovery made through the reasoning processes and, of course, later verified by observation. The Aristotelian formula for discovering knowledge should not be discarded. It should be learned and used to check fallacies in the conclusions reached by inductive reasoning. The two reasoning processes complement each other: Aristotle's method can show the student his bad generalizations; inductive logic can prevent his making bad deductions.

In deductive argument a generalization is made and then supported by particulars. In the inductive process, as will be shown, the particulars come first, concluded by a generalization. When one considers the tremendous scope of the engineer's communication activities and the amount of time he spends attempting to persuade or convince his reader (or listener) of the truth or falsity of some idea, it is only "logical" that he receive some training in argumentative discourse. From his training in mathematics the engineer has already learned how to present an effective line of inductive reasoning. He has had little experience, however, in discovering the fallacies in his own deductions and those of others. He will therefore profit by a review of some of the argumentative techniques. The deductive reasoning discussed here is best suited for the reader or audience which is not likely to have strong opposing convictions. The inductive process is used when the writer or speaker anticipates lack of interest in, or even opposition to, his ideas.

Inductive Reasoning

If the writer thinks he may encounter disagreement or that his reader may actively oppose his argument, he should reason by the inductive process—never by deduction unless he is prepared to dodge the rotten tomatoes and eggs of prejudices that are sure to be figuratively, and sometimes literally, hurled. The inductive process gives the writer a chance to arrange his materials so that what is known and accepted by the reader is presented first. The writer thus gains entry to the reader's mental throne of judgment for a fair hearing. The hus-

[1] John Stuart Mill, *Dissertations and Discussions: Political, Philosophical, and Historical*, Vol. IV (Boston: William V. Spencer, 1867), p. 420.

band, after a late night out with the boys, is practicing the inductive method when he tosses his hat in first. If the hat comes flying back, he knows there is too much opposition to move directly toward his goal. He must either prolong his absence to make the heart grow fonder, or he must slip in the back way.

The engineer employs the inductive form of argument if, for instance, he is called upon to write a report about a new process which he knows in advance is objectionable to his immediate superiors or to persons who will be approving the budget for the project. He begins by acknowledging the good points of the existing process and the objectionable features of the new process he is presenting. There is no opposition to these admissions, and so the psychological tendency is to try to be fair in response to the demonstrated fairness of the writer. Because the reader wishes to be fair, the evidence in support of the proposed new process is received with a minimum of opposition. When the reader is not preoccupied with a defense of his own ideas, he is much more inclined to follow the evidence and to accept the inferences the writer makes.

If, therefore, one anticipates a favorable or at least unhostile response, the deductive method—generalization supported by evidence —is a short, convenient method of presenting an argument. On the other hand, if it is known that the person or persons who will read the argument are disinterested or actually in opposition, the only recourse is to use the inductive method. With this method a change of opinion is literally induced by the evidence so that the inference (the conclusion), when it is finally reached, seems logical.

A convenient and enjoyable way to test one's ability to "think logically" is to prepare a three-minute speech, half of which presents one viewpoint on a given subject, with the other half presenting the opposing viewpoint. The two viewpoints are often referred to as "the pro and the con" of a controversial subject. The pitfall in this assignment, which traps one out of four, is the failure to reduce the subject to unity. The technical man must learn to recognize the shift in subject used to draw attention away from the unfavorable aspects of the subject he is presenting. For example, the disadvantages of an existing process are presented, followed by the advantages of the proposed process. This is *two subjects*. To be logically fair, the advantages and disadvantages of each process should be given. A man charged with the responsibility of making important decisions must discern the fallacy of shifting subjects.

Generally speaking, when an engineer is given an equation in symbolic terms, he can proceed in a straight-line analysis. But he is not always able to catch a *verbal* shift in terms, even of his own shifting. Reducing a subject to unity will reveal whether one's own argument is faulty, and the same process can be used to see whether an opponent's argument is fair or "loaded." A second subject is most likely to sneak into the argument when the disadvantages are given. One might, for instance, be impressed with transistor amplifiers. He could present his two viewpoints as the advantages and disadvantages of transistor amplifiers but not this: the advantages of transistors and the disadvantages of vacuum tubes. Or, to take another example, the student parking problem on the campus could be presented from the student viewpoint and the administration viewpoint. But off-campus parking is not admitted, since that is another subject.

In the simplified oral argument the viewpoint favored, whether affirmative or negative, should be presented last, because the last viewpoint presented has the psychological advantage of greater emphasis. Since this is technical argument and not public debate, the evidence for both viewpoints must be presented objectively and completely. Moreover, it must be factually accurate and concrete enough to appeal directly to the reasoning faculties rather than the feelings. Unsupported generalities, personal references, exaggeration, flamboyant or sentimental statements are out of place in technical argument. Informal argument which involves the feelings has a very limited use in technical communication. Such emotionally involved reasoning is generally referred to as persuasion, briefly discussed in the next section.

Persuasion

If the evidence at hand is not sufficiently convincing, the writer may urge his reader into agreement by arousing his emotions. This is done by associating the idea with another subject known to be desirable—the beautiful girl in the cigarette advertisement, for instance. Persuasion is an attempt to induce one to act or accept an opinion before the formal reasoning processes are completed. This form of argument can be useful for attaining short-term goals of argument; but if persuasion is not eventually transformed into conviction by logical evidence, it can just as easily be reversed by the next wind that blows. Samuel Butler must have had something like this in mind when he said, "He that complies against his will / Is of his own opinion still" (quoted from Bartlett's *Familiar Quotations*).

Being mostly concerned with factual, objective presentations, the engineer seldom has need for an emotional appeal. There are times, however, when emotional tactics, if restrained and in good taste, may be employed—in a sales brochure, a popular lecture, or popular magazine article. For best results in technical persuasion, only the overtones of the emotional appeal should be evident. Persuasion tactics like the excursions into pure fancy and untruths characteristic of some national advertising is beyond the pale of engineering thought and action.

In this chapter the techniques of formal analysis, informal analysis, and argument have been discussed. The exercises suggested at the end of this chapter should produce enough samples of these techniques to demonstrate the student's ability to use them.

STUDENT EXAMPLES

Formal Analysis

Classification of Electrical Machines

Electrical machines may be classified by motion, capacity, physical size, and distinguishing electrical characteristics. For the purpose of this classification, the various types of electrical machines will be classified according to their distinguishing electrical characteristics. The word machine will cover both motors and generators, because the exact function is determined only by the direction of power flow within the machine. The first division is between a-c and d-c machines. Only the subdvision of d-c machines will be further classified. The three main subdivisions of d-c machines are shunt, series, and compound wound. The shunt machine has the field windings in parallel with the armature. This machine has very high starting torque and starting current requirements. In its operating range, the speed or voltage output decreases only a few percent as the load increases. The series machine has the field winding in series with the armature. A series machine has very low starting torque and current requirements. It is essentially a high-speed machine which exhibits a high-percentage decrease in speed or voltage output as the load increases. The compound-wound machine has both series and shunt fields. The characteristics of the compound-wound machine may fall anywhere between the series and shunt machine characteristics. These three basic classifications of d-c machines cover all types of d-c machines in use today.

Rocks Formed in the Earth's Crust

Rocks formed in the earth's crust may be classified according to the manner in which they were formed. On this basis, rocks are grouped into three major classes: igneous, sedimentary, and metamorphic rocks. Although rock formation in each of the classes is the result of natural phenomena, the manner of rock formation in any one class is quite distinct from that in the other two. Igneous rocks are those rocks which were formed by the cooling and solidification of liquid rock material either in or on the earth's crust. Sedimentary rocks were formed by the compaction and cementation of rock fragments transported and deposited by wind, rain, or other natural agent. In this class, the rock fragments retain their original characteristics. Metamorphic rocks, on the other hand, were formed when the characteristics of igneous or sedimentary rocks were caused to undergo drastic change when subjected to high temperatures and pressures for extended periods of time.

Aircraft

Aircraft may be classified in many ways, such as by use (passenger, cargo, bomber, etc.), by the using agency (government, commercial, private), or by carrying capacity. But for the purpose of studying aerodynamic behavior, the most useful classification is by maximum operating speed. The speed is conveniently measured by comparison with the speed of sound, because aerodynamic behavior and the speed of sound both vary with the density and temperature of the air. This results in four main categories of aircraft: subsonic, transonic, supersonic, and hypersonic. The subsonic range includes all aircraft that operate exclusively at less than the speed of sound. Aircraft that operate on the fringes of the speed of sound, Mach 0.9 to 1.1, are in the transonic class. This class is produced by the transition from a preceding pressure wave to no preceding pressure wave. The third category, the supersonic aircraft, operates at speeds above the transonic range but below Mach five. The hypersonic classification is reserved for aircraft that exceed Mach five, or five times the speed of sound.

Informal Analysis

Elimination of High Production Costs

Conveyor belts carrying cross-shaft forgings from the preliminary coining press to the final coining press have been wearing out rapidly, thereby increasing production costs. Costs must be reduced below the break-even level immediately; however, possible solutions must not cost over $100. Standards department personnel have observed that the press operator first processes a large number of parts, ejecting them onto the conveyor, which carries them to the second work station, where they come in contact with a gate. Moving to the second station, the operator then processes parts which have stacked up against the gate on top of the still moving endless belt. Two possible solutions have been suggested: 1) A better grade of endless belt could be purchased for $65 which would be more capable of withstanding the present job conditions. 2) A reduction gear could be installed on the conveyor to slow the belt speed to approximately one foot per minute; in addition, a limit switch could be installed on the gate to shut off the conveyor motor when the conveyor becomes filled. The cost of both of these items, including installation, would be $55. The second solution is the better one since, in addition to the fact that it would cost less, it would also remove the cause of excessive belt wear.

Analysis of Magnetic Recording Tape

Much time is consumed in repairing tape recorders and splicing magnetic recording tape which has broken during use. To minimize this maintenance time it is necessary to choose a tape which will cause the least wear on the record heads of the machine and which has lasting durability. Tapes A and B have been chosen from preliminary tests of all available brands because of their superior quality of frequency fidelity. After 500 hours of testing under normal operating conditions it was found that tape A, due to its built-in lubricant, causes 10 percent less record head wear than tape B. During this test tape A broke 20 times, while tape B broke only 16 times. After a storage period under normal conditions the 500-hour test was run again. This time no difference in record head wear was detectable, but while tape A broke 23 times, tape B broke 41 times, showing definite signs of brittleness. These tests show that during the early life of tapes A and B they are essentially of the same quality, but after a long period of usage tape A is less abrasive on the record head and is more durable than tape B.

Selection of Spark Plugs for Car Fleet Use

It has become necessary for a company operating a large fleet of cars to select a different brand of spark plug for future use in its cars. To qualify, the plugs must cost less than 80 cents each, last a minimum of 15,000 miles, and require servicing not more than two times during the first 15,000 miles. Past experience and cost have limited the choices to brand A, brand B, and brand C. The company decided to do its own testing, with 50 cars using brand A spark plugs, 50 using brand B, and 50 using brand C. A plug's life was considered ended when it had deteriorated sufficiently to cause abnormal engine performance or increased fuel consumption. The plugs were serviced when one or more of a set caused abnormal engine performance or increased fuel consumption. The following data was collected after each of the cars had been in normal use for 20,000 miles.

Brand	Cost	Average Life (miles)	Times Serviced (first 15,000 miles)
A	$0.80	20,000	3
B	0.76	16,000	2
C	0.75	12,000	2

The data shows that brand A met the cost and mileage requirements but needed servicing more than twice. Brand C failed to last 15,000 miles. Brand B met all the requirements and should be selected for future use.

EXERCISES

1. Write a 150- to 200-word paragraph using the formal analysis technique (classification) to present information. Other possible bases for classification may be mentioned, but only one basis is permitted for the classification paragraph itself. After the class (or group) and the basis are given, the subclasses are named and differentiated, according to the basis selected.

2. Write a 150- to 200-word paragraph of informal analysis (interpretation). Use at least one standard of judgment, including major and

minor factors, and at least two alternatives. A conclusion must be reached. No dilemmas.

3. Make a three-minute class speech presenting two viewpoints on any controversial subject. The subject should be introduced and defined as necessary, and the scope and plan of the speech indicated, during the first half minute. The viewpoint not held by the speaker should be presented first. After about one minute on the first viewpoint, a clear transition should be made to the one held by the speaker. The last half minute should be used to summarize the evidence of both viewpoints and to reach a decision. The speaker's preference must be clearly indicated. Not sticking to a single subject should be grounds for failure in this assignment.

4. Clip short examples of the formal, informal, and argumentative techniques from magazines or newspapers and paste them on an 8½ by 11 inch sheet. This sheet may be handed to the instructor for checking.

6
Structural Devices
for Extended Discourse

In previous chapters attention has been given to the basic kinds of writing and to some useful techniques of presentation. Three more special devices—introduction, transition, and conclusion—are now to be studied before the longer report is attempted. These special devices are discussed separately but are combined for practice in a single five-paragraph exercise at the close of the chapter. Other devices, such as abstract, table of contents, and the like, are discussed in Chapter 9.

In these days when everyone must be in a hurry, there is a temptation to jump into the swim of things even before the direction of the current is known. Instructors, too, are sometimes guilty of rushing the learning process by throwing students into deep water before they learn to swim. This is fine for separating the ones who can swim from the ones who go to the bottom. But with a little instruction and shallow water practice, most people learn to swim just as they learn to walk or to read—gradually, the simplest things first. The junior- or senior-level student may show readiness for technical report writing, but he will need a few simple instructions, some practice, more instruction, then more practice. Without this first-things-first approach, many otherwise capable students might become too discouraged to try.

The learning process for the craft of writing may be illustrated by the case of the small boy who asks to be allowed to saw a board with his father's saw. In all probability the father (being a wise father) will give his son a few simple instructions in holding the board and in holding the saw. He may add a few precautions such as "Take it slow," "Don't push too hard," and "Keep your thumb out of the way," and then stand back and watch his son saw the board in two. The boy learns quickly because he is capable of understanding and applying the few simple instructions given. The learning of this skill might have been delayed a good many years if the father, when asked, had sucked in his breath and said, "No, sonny, you are too little to use a saw"; or pointing to his carpenter's square had said, "You see those figures, boy? You have to learn what they mean before you start using the saw." This father might have then proceeded with a discourse on how the figures are used to obtain the vertical cutoff angle of rafters with a given roof pitch; and, for good measure, he might have thrown in a few hints on sharpening and setting the saw teeth.

Something of the first approach is being used in this text. It has been found that a good many engineering seniors are not far beyond the board-sawing level in communication skill. It could be that in their first attempts to express themselves they were discouraged by the complicated figures on the English grammar square. At any rate, it has been found that the higher level skills employed in writing the longer reports can be more rapidly learned by students who have mastered the elementary problems first: the sentence, the paragraph, the fundamental kinds of writing, a few useful techniques, some special rules on the framework or supporting structure of extended discourse, and, finally, the full-length report.

It is the framework of discourse which must now be understood so that its design and extent will be adequate for bearing the full weight of the report. The introduction begins the discourse; the transitions (like columns) support and distribute the weight until the conclusion, the end, is reached. A formal presentation of ideas requires an introduction to give the subject meaning, purpose, scope, and plan. As the report unfolds, transitions guide the reader by indicating changes of time, place, topic, viewpoint, and so on, and by marking the progress and cross-reference topics so that at all times the reader understands exactly where he is, where he has been, and how far he has yet to go in the communication. When the end is reached, the reader needs to be reminded that the promises made in the introduction have been fulfilled and, if the communication has been a problem type, what conclusions have been reached.

INTRODUCTIONS

All rational discourse begins with an introduction. Very short communications may be achieved through nothing more than attention-getting words, such as *hey, listen,* or other words which hold the attention of the reader or listener for the short statement which follows. A paragraph may need a phrase or even an entire sentence to introduce it. When it is desired to write more than a few paragraphs, some kind of formal introduction is required.

Subject

A formal introduction begins by naming and, if necessary, defining the *subject.* Unfamiliar subjects may require formal sentence or paragraph definitions. This depends to some extent on the kind of subject and the length of the paper. The reader needs to know the writer's meaning—that is, the meaning the subject has in the present context. Following the definition, formal or informal, the writer may present an explanation to give the reader some idea of the significance or the relative importance of the subject.

Purpose

Definition and explanation prepare the way for the second essential element of the introduction, *purpose.* A statement of the purpose helps the writer as much as the reader, for it reminds him of what he wishes to accomplish in the paper and who the intended reader is. The writer's purpose also fixes the technical level, dictates the kind of detail to be included, and suggests a probable plan of development. A statement of purpose also helps the reader to see the viewpoint the writer has assumed so that he will not be surprised or frustrated by failing to find certain aspects of the subject treated.

Scope

The reader now knows the "what" and the "why." Next he needs to know the scope and plan, the extent of the subject, and the manner in which it will be subdivided and presented. A declaration of the *scope* to be covered in a paper is again helpful to both writer and reader. The writer must determine to what extent the general topic will be discussed before he can decide where to start and when to stop. The reader benefits by knowing in advance the extent of coverage so that he can decide whether his own needs will be served by reading the paper. Thus the scope complements the purpose in confining the coverage to what is useful for the given purpose.

Technical people are sometimes at a loss to know to what extent a subject should be covered. This must be decided, however, prior to the writing and declared in the introduction, using the general purpose previously stated as a guide in setting up the scope. Limiting the scope has no relation to brevity. The paper may be quite long and still be opened with a narrow scope—a thin cross-sectional slice, a deep probe as one would plug a watermelon to sample it for ripeness, a general discussion of the large topic in distant perspective, a representative sample of the subject, a minute detail magnified to ten times natural size. Whatever the scope, it must clearly indicate to the reader how the subject matter to be presented is related to the whole body of knowledge or to the general subject; and once a certain scope is defined it must not change within the paper—it cannot change as long as the purpose holds fast.

Plan

The last of the four essentials which must be present or implied in the introduction is the *plan*. In short papers the plan can be stated quite simply; in fact, it can be woven into the statement of the scope. If the scope includes, for example, a discussion of only two topics, a listing of these two topics in order will constitute both scope and plan. The reader expects that the topics will be discussed in the order named. For long, complex reports, however, it is a useful technique to list all the main topics in the order in which they will occur. In papers having a table of contents one should use the same phrasing in referencing subtitles in the introduction as that used in the table of contents.

Other Information

In addition to the essential elements just named, the introduction may be expanded to give any information helpful to the reader's understanding of the paper. Such things as background, unusual circumstances under which the information was gathered, and special formulas or special terms which need explanation may also be included here. If a lengthy explanation is needed—and in technical papers this is often so—it is better to devote the first main section of the paper to basic theory, or to other extended introductory information, so that the introduction can be limited to less than 10 percent of the entire paper.

Technical communication certainly does not take place until the reader knows what the subject is, what is to be accomplished by the paper, what is the limit of the subject area to be covered, and what is the order of the major subtopics to be discussed. To begin the main body of a formal report without an adequate introduction is irrational and about as socially unacceptable as making advances toward a well-behaved young lady without proper introduction. For those who are unconcerned about introductions, the state provides free room, board, and medical treatment in confined quarters. These people are said to be irrational. The normal, sane way to make oneself understood is to begin at the beginning and to tell the reader what is to follow.

TRANSITIONS

In the preceding section on introductions the student was told how to start. In this section he is told how to keep moving. In the next section he will be told how to stop.

The difference between an interesting, clearly understandable paper and a dull, confusing one may not be the material at all. It is probably because the one paper has good transitions and the other has poor. Transitions lead the reader from thought to thought very much as does a well-marked roadway. Single-word and single-phrase transitions point either backward or forward, but whole sentence transitions may point forward and backward and backward and forward. And the entire paragraph devoted to transition may make dozens of backward and forward references. The variety and extent of the transition devices used depend to some extent upon the reader's familiarity with the subject being discussed. When the reader has been over the road before, fewer guideposts are needed. In speaking, one must double or triple the number of transition devices used in writing. (See Chapter 11 for transitions in public speaking.)

Single-Word Transition

Single-word transitions show time, place, cause, manner, degree, consequence, direction, and other relations. As single words they are placed within the sentence at any point where they are idiomatically acceptable. They are needed at all intersections and byroads of thought to keep the reader headed in the right direction. Transition words keep the reader oriented to the subject and moving smoothly over the area mapped out in the introduction. They also show causal relations and consequences. Some frequently used single-word transitions are these: *as, before, after, next, soon, under, beneath, over, above, inside, outside, near, far, moreover, consequently, however, besides, this, that, both, some, any, first, last, latter,* and *former.*

A short related group of words used to guide the reader is called a *phrase transition.* For example, *on the other hand, as previously explained, concerning this, regarding that,* and *and so on* are all transition phrases, even the last one. The words *even* and *last* in the preceding sentence are transition words. The phrase *preceding sentence* in the sentence just completed is a transition phrase. And the word *just* is a single-word transition in the sentence before this one. The word *before* and the phrase *this one* are likewise transitions.

Single-Sentence Transition

Single words and phrases are not sufficient to tie together all of the complicated parts of a long paper. Whole sentences or even paragraphs must occasionally be written to support an extended discourse. A single-sentence transition has a two-directional reference, backward and forward; that is, it ties two loose ends together. A sentence transition may also relate one paragraph topic to the previous paragraph topic, or it may anticipate a topic yet to come.

Paragraph Transition

When a decided turn in thought occurs, as between major subdivisions of a long report, one or more paragraphs may be needed to make a smooth transition. The paragraph transition offers unlimited opportunities for structural shoring and columnar supporting of the main topic. Some sentences in the paragraph transition may be devoted to backward reference, some to forward reference. Some sentences may be used to repeat *key terms* or to reiterate general principles which the writer feels the reader must keep in mind. The transition paragraph is complete when the functional objective of the paragraph is reached: guiding the reader from one major topic to the next. The short paragraph at the beginning of the discussion on transitions is an example of a transition paragraph.

In writing the transition paragraph, one may wish to recapitulate what has been said, to mark well the point in the whole paper where the reader now is, and then to point toward the final objective. This common courtesy to the reader heightens his interest and reassures him that the writer knows where he is going and that he has not forgotten the reader. A technical paper without transition is like a sight-seeing tour in a strange land with a non-English speaking guide. One might as well have stayed at home or caught the next bus.

CONCLUSIONS

A paper with a good introduction and good transitions can still fall far short of its deserved effectiveness by failing to take advantage of the structural support of a conclusion. Conclusions tie up the main ideas of the paper in a neat package and give them to the reader in a brief, compact form. They are often placed first in industrial reports so that management may have a recapitulation of the research done and the decisions reached without reading the entire report.

Summaries

The form and content of the conclusion will depend on the kind of paper. Some reports have become so formalized that conclusions have been entirely eliminated or have been shifted to the beginning of the report as just mentioned. Formal test reports, inventories, technical procedures, process instructions, and the like do not need conclusions. But reports that go places and say things need to say again what they have said and where they have been. If the nature of the report has been to present several categories of particulars on a given subject, then a *summary* of the main categories showing their relation to one another is all that is needed for a conclusion. Summaries of this kind are familiar structural devices at the end of textbook chapters. A conclusion, in summary form, by hitting the high points, gives the reader a panoramic and unmistakable view of the whole subject. One last repetition of the writer's main thoughts helps to fix them in the memory.

Decisions

Another form of conclusion is written for reports which promise to evaluate, to discover, to prove, to decide, and so on. This form of conclusion is recognized by its definite *decision* or decisions. The decision type of conclusion summarizes the evidence presented, negative as well as positive. Then it makes its decisions, or it may summarize the decisions, if any, reached in each of the major subdivisions of the paper. When all the evidence and subconclusions have been summarized, the final conclusion is reached.

Determining Type and Placement of Conclusions

It should be observed here that the word *conclusion* is a larger term than *summary* or *decision*. The structural device is referred to as the conclusion, but conclusions are of two types: the summary and the decision. Reports that are merely instructive use a summary. Reports that are written to show the results of investigations must use the decision type of conclusion. In the decision form the writer summarizes the evidence and reaches as many decisions as the evidence will support. The decisions when reached may be stated in sentence or paragraph form, in an informal manner, or they may be stated formally and itemized by Arabic numerals. One important caution is that no new evidence can be presented in the decision type of conclusion. But in certain types of investigative reports the decision may be followed by recommendations (see Chapter 8).

Opinion is somewhat divided on what to call conclusions and where to place them in reports. Some companies have "summaries" placed only at the beginning; others follow the same policy but call them "conclusions." And there are several in-between combinations, including at least one company which requires the "conclusion" to be placed at both the beginning and the end of longer reports. The only useful advice on the placing or titling of conclusions is to write a conclusion which best serves the purpose, whether a summary or a decision conclusion as defined in this text. It is an easy matter then to check the practice of the employer on what to call it and where to place it in the report.

As a matter of fact, summaries placed at the beginning of technical papers reporting sophisticated research have often been mistakenly called abstracts. So wide is this practice that a species of pseudo-abstract is now widely written which is nothing more than a summary. Such summaries may be easier for the author to write than abstracts, but they are harder for the librarian to index. The reader, too, when he searches the volume of abstracts, is often baffled by a summary which contains numerous references to a paper he does not have. A practical distinction between the summary-abstract and the true abstract is made in Chapter 9.

WRITING PRACTICE FOR STRUCTURAL DEVICES

This chapter on the major structural devices of extended discourse —introductions, transitions, conclusions—is concluded with a teaching aid, to be used at the instructor's option, which may prove to be a learning shortcut. The student is asked to write a five-paragraph exercise—no relation to the Army's five-paragraph field report—on a single subject from two viewpoints, with a strict limitation on the length of the paragraphs. (The subject previously used for the three-minute speech may be extended and adapted for this exercise.) The introductory paragraph, 50 to 100 words, will state the subject, purpose, scope, and plan. In this short assignment these may not be expressly stated, but they must be clearly implied. Next, the opposing viewpoint, the one not held by the writer, is presented. This is developed as a unified paragraph of 125 to 175 words. It is followed by a transition paragraph of 50 to 100 words in which the writer looks backward, summarizing the evidence of the first paragraph, and looks forward, indicating what will be discussed in the succeeding paragraph. The second main paragraph of 125 to 175 words, giving the other viewpoint, follows the transition paragraph. The conclusion is a decision type paragraph of 50 to 100 words which sums up the evidence in the two viewpoints and reaches a decision.

It is fairly safe to assume that the student who turns out these laboratory sample paragraphs according to the specification understands the structural devices they represent and that he can produce them in real-life situations. This exercise will also show whether the student can follow directions, and it will test his ability to limit his discourse to a single subject rather than to introduce two subjects (see Chapter 5 on "Argument"). Further, it tests his ability to recognize significant evidence and to present fairly a viewpoint he opposes, something an engineer must be able to do. It demonstrates the level of skill the student has attained in the mechanics of expression and in the advanced skill of unity and coherence in the paragraph. All this is revealed in a five-paragraph exercise of 350 to 550 words.

STUDENT EXAMPLES

Five-Paragraph Report

Concrete Highways

This paper will discuss the construction of concrete highways. The topic will be considered from the point of view of a group concerned with the financing, maintenance, and safety of public roads. Following a discussion of the disadvantages and advantages of concrete highways, a conclusion will be made based on the information presented in this paper.

The initial cost of constructing a concrete highway is very large when compared with the construction cost of highways built with other surfacing materials. Oftentimes the state or federal government finds it more convenient to finance several low-cost roads over a long period of time rather than shoulder the large initial cost of a more permanent concrete highway. The permanence of concrete highways is not always a desirable characteristic. It would be unsound to pay a premium for a road surface that will last fifty years when it is anticipated that the road will have to be realigned in a few years. Concrete highways are expensive to alter. This factor sometimes makes it necessary to postpone important safety improvements such as a minor realignment.

Having considered the bad points of concrete highways, one must now examine the advantages of this type of highway construction. Since most highways in this country are not made of concrete, a serious study may reveal that factors other than safety, durability, and cost are involved.

Concrete is one of the most durable of all paving materials used in the construction of modern highways. Many twenty-year-old concrete highways are still serviceable. Because of its durability, the maintenance expense for concrete highways is much less than the cost required to maintain other types of roads. Concrete highways provide excellent braking friction; at the same time, they allow a smooth ride. The light color of the concrete reflects light at night, improving highway illumination and reducing the required number of light fixtures. With modern machines concrete highways can be constructed in much less time that it took a few years ago. Easily placed forms also decrease the construction time. In addition, this type of highway is smoother, safer, and more attractive than other types of roads.

The initial high expense of concrete paving is offset by its long life and low maintenance cost. Highway departments could save more money by anticipating the traffic of tomorrow and building lasting concrete highways to carry it. Except in a few cases where the highway is going to be used for only a short period of time, concrete is the most practical highway surfacing material.

Fallout Shelters

The continuing deterioration of diplomatic relations between Russia and the United States is forcing the American public to make a new decision. They must decide whether to build family fallout shelters. The issue has divided Americans into two camps—those opposed and those in favor of fallout shelters. To determine which camp to join requires that one examine both sides of the issue. The arguments presented by those opposed to fallout shelters must be weighed against those favoring the shelter.

The proponents of the fallout shelter avow that a nuclear attack upon the United States is a definite possibility. They insist that Russia will, without hesitation, resort to nuclear attack to achieve her objectives when she is no longer able to gain them by threat and coercion; she may even resort to such action rather than lose face before her allies. Those favoring fallout shelters contend that these shelters are absolutely necessary if this nation and its people are to survive any nuclear attack. They maintain that investment in a fallout shelter must be viewed as a form of life insurance, the cost of which will be offset by the increase in the survival rate. The proponents of the issue declare that in this era of nuclear missiles we must anticipate and be prepared for a surprise nuclear attack or suffer the consequences. They emphasize that the need for fallout shelters will increase as the world's nuclear stockpile increases.

It is apparent from the philosophy advanced by the proponents of the fallout shelters that they believe Russia can and will use nuclear warfare to achieve her goal. Those opposed to building fallout shelters deny that such is the case. They base their argument on the belief that Russia can achieve her objective without risking the national suicide which might result from a nuclear exchange.

The opponents of fallout shelters declare that Russia will not subject this nation to nuclear attack. For this reason they believe the construction of fallout shelters to be an unnecessary waste of materials, time, and money. They allege that Russia will continue in the future, as she has in the past, to achieve her objectives without having to resort to war. Those against the construction of fallout shelters insist that Russia realizes that, should she use nuclear weapons, she would certainly bring the entire United States nuclear retaliatory force against her. Many of the opponents believe that even if this nation were subjected to a nuclear attack, the fallout shelters would be virtually useless. They allege that, because of the destruction wrought by such an attack, fallout shelters would merely prolong death by a few days. Many of the opponents have developed the attitude of the fatalist.

Those against building fallout shelters contend that Russia can achieve her objectives by threat and coercion without nuclear attack. They declare that fallout shelters would only delay the inevitable. Conversely, those in favor of fallout shelters emphasize the fact that Russia's actions as a nation are unpredictable. Recognizing the fact that this country could be subjected to nuclear attack, they advocate fallout shelters as a means of insuring a higher survival rate. Analyzing both arguments, it is apparent that one must build fallout shelters. Any investment in these shelters will pay rich dividends in the event of nuclear attack.

EXERCISES

1. Study the introductions in three of your textbooks. Do they serve their purpose well; or, after having studied them and the book they introduce, would you change the introduction in any way? Are the elements of subject, purpose, scope, and plan recognizable?

2. Copy or bring to class a paragraph from a well-written magazine article and underline all of the single-word transitions, indicating by an arrow whether they refer to something which has passed or to something which is yet to come.

3. Find a transition paragraph in any of your texts. Pencil directional arrows under the transitions which look back and under those which look forward, including single words, phrases, and complete sentences. Do you notice fewer transitions in "hard" reading?

4. Write an imaginary concluding paragraph, summary type, on the "History of ——————."

5. Write a five-paragraph exercise, as previously explained, on any controversial subject. Evidence may be either fabricated or obtained by research, at the instructor's option. The viewpoint held by the writer should be placed last, to take advantage of this emphatic position. The evidence should be so convincingly demonstrated that the reader is impelled to agree with the decision reached.

6. Analyze a 4000 to 5000 word journal article for introduction, transitions, and conclusion. Write a critique giving examples of the good and bad practices observed.

7

Developing a
Technical Style

By this time most students will have observed that it takes more than standard form and technique to say a thing effectively. The new dimension is style.

This point in one's study can be compared to the first stage in the process of learning to sew. A young housewife cutting out her first dress has no thought of style; she is too busy following the pattern lines, matching *x*'s, checking warp and woof. When the thing is stitched up, she is elated to discover that it looks like a dress. Later, when she knows how to sew, she may spend hours pondering over piece goods, pattern books, and fashion magazines, carefully selecting the material, the pattern, and the style. She is not concerned anymore with mechanics; she is striving for *effect*. Likewise the student who has learned to follow directions and to write the basic patterns must now strive to develop a clear, concise, and objective style.

For many students style has remained an enigma, almost understood at times but never quite getting through. This is because the word style can be used to mean so many things, to so many people. The late Walter S. Campbell (pseudonym, Stanley Vestal), a noted author and teacher of professional writing at the University of Oklahoma, thought of style as "organized, classified speech." Writing at the height of the technological push that ended World War II, he said:

> This problem thus boils down almost entirely to a question of style —a style adequate to convey the scientist's matter clearly and effectively to readers who are not experts, but who are, after all, intelligent, and who have some education, or merely have gained through living a power of thought that enables them to go some way to meet the writer on scientific subjects. A man does not have to be a chef to understand a cookbook.

It is noteworthy that, so far, no genius has ever written anything worth understanding which nobody else could understand. The greatest authors in the past have been the most popular. There is no good reason why this should not be true of scientific writers. Science is organized, classified knowledge; style is organized, classified speech; surely they can be fitted together. This is the problem which the scientist must solve. To me, it seems his major problem.[1]

A good definition of style is not likely to be found whole and entire, for each is colored to some extent by the writer—even the one this writer is about to make. But if some additions and subtractions are allowed, the meaning of style can be derived from two famous quotations[2] and from the dictionary. One man said, "The style is the man himself"; and another, "Style is the dress of thoughts." Which is right? Both. One aspect of style is personal, intangible; the other is impersonal, mechanical.

One dictionary includes among its meanings for style this definition: "manner or mode of expression in language; way of putting thoughts into words." This sense combines the meanings of style just quoted and the one which will be used in this chapter. The manner or mode of expression includes all of the *intrinsic* qualities of style, and the precise manner in which technical communication is done in words includes all of the extrinsic qualities. One is "the man himself"; the other is "the dress of thoughts."

INTRINSIC QUALITIES OF STYLE

According to the dictionary definition, style can be analyzed by splitting it straight down the middle like a ripe watermelon. One half is called *in*trinsic; the other half, *ex*trinsic. The intrinsic half can be split into five pieces—objectivity, restraint, reliability, honesty, and interest. The extrinsic half can be split into two pieces—clarity and compression. The individual qualities of style, those reflecting the intellectual character of the writer and his manner of speaking, are called *in*trinsic. *Ex*trinsic qualities of style are impersonal. They include mechanical and structural devices for putting ideas into words. These will be discussed later after the five intrinsic qualities have been presented.

[1] Walter S. Campbell (*pseud.*, Stanley Vestal), *Writing Non-Fiction*, (Boston, Mass.: The Writer, Incorporated, 1944), p. 181. Quoted by permission of the publishers.
[2] John Bartlett, *Familiar Quotations* (Boston, Mass.: Little, Brown and Company, 1948).

Objectivity

The formal language of science and technology has always been objective. This is indicated by the use of the third person, or in certain situations, by the impersonal "we," a first-person plural. Exceptions are made for renowned scientists, who may use the first person to add their personal authority to a statement. By the beginning writer, however, and generally by the experienced engineer or scientist, the impersonal, objective third person should be used in technical writing. When the informal or familiar pronouns turn up in such an obviously formal setting, it is like seeing a man in a sport shirt at a formal dance. It represents ignorance of the style or defiance of it, neither of which is socially acceptable.

The third-person pronoun creates the atmosphere of objectivity by taking the reader's attention away from the writer so that it can be better focused on what is being said. When the author stays in the background, reader objections to what is being said are less apt to be carried over to the author. The impersonal "we," meaning the corporation or the laboratory or some other organization, is almost as impersonal as the third person. This form is used in reporting joint efforts, or it may be used to refer to a segment of a company, a laboratory, or the like. The *second person* (you) is not used in formal writing except in giving process directions, as discussed in Chapter 4.

Objectivity not only involves the use of the third person; the whole context must be impersonal, not controlled by personalities and the emotions. Insinuations, hints, snide remarks, and personal judgments are out of place in scientific discourse.

Restraint

An obviously extravagant statement in formal discourse is not just poor style; it is a revelation of the unscientific attitude of the writer. Exaggerations or unrestrained pronouncements do not suit the formal context. A proper restraint also curtails the use of adjectives and adverbs. In their place descriptive nouns and verbs are used. Attempts to arouse the emotions (excessively, that is) are taboo. Adjectives involving value judgments—that is, those which have no universally understood standard of meaning—are to be avoided or used with caution: *prodigious, gigantic, beautiful, lovely, charming, delicious, dainty, cold, hot, weak, strong, good, bad,* and so on.

Reliability

Error has never been favored at any level of human relations, not even among thieves. And it has never been without its penalty. Every decade of technological advancement pushes the penalty for error higher and higher. At the high price the nation is now paying for "reliability" (for removing the inherent error), there is little patience left for the man who is careless with the facts. The shortest way to the door for an engineer or other technical worker is to be a constant error maker. Errors in fact, errors in judgment, errors in observation, errors in copying, errors in calculation, errors of whatever nature are out of place in technical work. The habitual goofer sooner or later finds his way to the pay window for his last check.

Reliability is a reflection of the man himself. He must guard this quality jealously, since so much expense and needless labor can result from careless handling of factual material—mistakes in materials, mistakes in processes, mistakes in assembly, unreported damages which cannot be seen. And if carelessness is practiced at work, it will be reflected in communication. Reports must be checked and double-checked for accuracy. Hearsay is as much out of place in a formal report as it is in court. Technical reports must have blueprint accuracy. When another man's material is quoted, it must be checked word for word and all the punctuation included. An exact reference should be made to its source. Source reference and misquoting are discussed in Chapter 9.

Honesty

For the man or woman intent on a professional career, nothing, not even error, damns so permanently as intellectual dishonesty. Intellectual honesty is an absolute in technical style. Any shading or any degree of intellectual dishonesty deprives the professional man of the respect and trust of his colleagues. Society may have forgiveness for intellectual dishonesty, but the professional world does not. A professional man may be forgiven immorality or disorderly conduct, but intellectual honesty is the one virtue he must cling to at all costs, even at the cost of his job. Intellectual dishonesty does not present itself in bold attire before one's eyes; it sneaks up in innocent-looking shortcuts to save one's time. They will never be seen. And so more and more shortcuts follow. The engineer is never tempted to be intellectually dishonest in big things until he has been habitually dishonest in little things. The first time, for example, it might be setting an assumed value for a test specimen which slipped in the pull test machine; or the slight, ever so slight, doping of evidence to make a prediction come true; or a more insidious temptation, especially for young engineers, to allow people to give him credit for something he has borrowed but failed to acknowledge. When the engineer's character has been well contaminated by intellectual dishonesty in little things, the big temptation comes, and one day a choice is made that leads to disgrace and loss of professional standing.

One of the most notorious examples of professional fraud brought to light in recent years was that of the Piltdown man. If one consults a dictionary or an encyclopedia published before 1953, he will find a detailed account of the discovery of Piltdown man, a description of the skull and facial structure, and perhaps even a picture of Piltdown man. This specimen, along with other artifacts from the Piltdown excavation site, had been housed in the British Museum and accepted by the scientific world as one of the missing links in the evolution of man. And it might have gone on being considered so if it had not been for the carbon 14 radiation dating method. When tests were run on the remains of the Piltdown man, it was discovered that the skeleton was only about fifty years old. Further examination showed that the jawbone and teeth and other parts of the skull had been expertly reshaped and then etched with acid to obtain the aged appearance. No disgrace was suffered in his own person by the perpetrator of this hoax on the scientific world, for time and death had long since laid him in his grave a famous man.

Interest

Technical writing may be objective, restrained, reliable, and intellectually honest, and still be dreadfully dull. Interest, the remaining intrinsic quality of technical style, is needed to give pleasure to the reader. Some interest, to be sure, is always present in factual reporting, particularly to the specialist who is willing to dig in any rock pile where he thinks there might be an ounce of useful information. But with very little more effort the technical man could make what he writes interesting enough to be widely read.

Interest can be created and held by the simple expedient of keeping an unanswered question before the reader at all times. The big questions, of course, are raised by the introduction. These are answered by finding the answers to many little questions. The technique of maintaining interest lies in the way the little questions are answered. Just before an answer is given, another little question is raised. And just before this one is answered, still another question is raised. This goes on until the last topic is reached when there are no more questions to raise. With this technique there is less chance for the reader's interest to lag. When this technique for holding attention is applied with restraint and good taste, it adds the fifth intrinsic quality of technical style—interest—to the report.

EXTRINSIC QUALITIES OF STYLE

The personal, or intrinsic, qualities of style just explained are not easily recognized or exhibited by beginners, especially the quality of suspense or interest. The extrinsic qualities, however—those which concern structure, or the way thoughts are put into words—can be recognized and definitely labeled in student writing. These basic structural characteristics of technical style, which include clarity and compression, are required of all technical people who aspire to reach professional status.

Clarity

Technical knowledge is transmitted only in the blue spectrum of the white light of truth and certainty. When the reader fails to comprehend the exact shade of meaning intended by the writer, communication breaks down just as surely as it does when an electronic signal has become unrecognizable by too much interference. Muddled thinking, ungrammatical structure, and the nonidiomatic use of words and phrases not only distort the meaning intended but sometimes completely invert the writer's idea so that the exact opposite of what was intended is understood by the reader.

One of the common obstructions to the understanding of technical reports is the predilection of young scientists and engineers for using the esoteric terms of their specialized fields. This may be due to the same human weakness that causes a young MD to grow a mustache to make himself look older, or it may be due to the inability of the writer to translate his new vocabulary into his own language. Whether it be intellectual vanity or the inability to translate, the excessive use of highly specialized terms can cause a garbled communication. Some professional groups have deliberately developed a special meaning for familiar words and invented new words to keep the reader from understanding. Some of this may be an extension of the childhood game of using pig Latin to keep the younger brother or sister from knowing what is being said. On the other hand, the excessive use of technical terms may be a deliberate attempt to give the patient the feeling that his money is being well spent.

Everyone knows that an expanded technology must swell the language with thousands of new words and that in describing new discoveries new words must be used. But in many instances the language is unnecessarily proliferated; existing words could have been used just as well. In some sciences the effort to communicate with the outside world has almost reached the vanishing point. The good Anglo-Saxon language has been forgotten; and if communication does occur across technical disciplines, it comes about, not through language, but through the more internationally understood mathematical symbols. The tendency to multiply technical words is an occupational disease, present in varying degrees of severity in all branches of specialized learning.

It may help the young engineer or scientist to know the clinical and subclinical symptoms of this disease so that he may change his habits early enough to escape technophantiasis of the vocabulary, as the disease might be called; though not a fatal disease, it greatly restricts the usefulness of its victims. The symptoms exhibited in the early stages are of three general types: terms are used playfully to impress the reader with the writer's knowledge; specialized terms are used because the writer has not yet learned his newly found technical language well enough to translate it; there is a deliberate attempt to prevent any but the initiated from understanding the subject matter. These symptoms, occurring singly or in combination, might be referred to as technantics. Mild symptoms are expected in a recent graduate of a technical school, but resistance usually develops with age and growing knowledge. If technantic symptoms persist after the first few years, it may indicate that the technical graduate has become a confirmed technanticist. In spite of the purifying stream of humanity which washes by their classroom doors, the incidence is high among education, psychology, and engineering science professors. Technophantiasis-nepenthe, the crippling stage of this occupational disease, is recognizable by the fact that the scientist, the engineer, the teacher has ceased to care whether he is understood or not by the average intelligent person.

An intelligent reader does not object to a few words per page which he does not understand; he will understand these from the context or by using a reference work if one is at hand. But if more than this number occur on a single page, and especially if the terms occur in long, unbroken trains, the writer is deliberately and contemptuously confusing the reader. Even when the writer's purpose is to communicate only with people of his own special circle, he runs the risk of being misunderstood when he uses more than two esoteric terms in the same sentence. The playful use of technical words to impress the reader, the ignorant use of technical terms because the writer does not know how to translate them, or the deliberate use of technical terms to keep any but the initiated from understanding is poor style in technical writing.

Clearness is affected in a host of other ways besides the unnecessary use of technical words above the reader's level. Because the technical man cannot afford to be misunderstood, he must consciously strive to eliminate every communication barrier he is able to recognize. The structural characteristics of good style learned in expository English composition may now be dusted off and reapplied to technical communication.

A full discussion of the many hindrances to clarity is beyond the scope of this text. The list that follows will remind the student of those malpractices most damaging to clearness in technical writing. Any of these malpractices which are not readily understood should be reviewed in the nearest English handbook, and this should be no farther away than arm's reach.

Hindrances to Clearness

Ambiguity	Misspelled words
Dangling modifiers	Muddled thinking
Excessive predication	Parallel structure
Excessive subordination	Shifts in subject, tense, mood,
Illiteracies	voice
Illogical conjunctions	Violations of idiomatic usage
Illogical transition words	Wrong punctuation or lack of
Jargon	needed punctuation
Lack of or indefiniteness of	
antecedents	

In this section it has been shown that the clarity of ideas is greatly affected by the choice of words. On the other hand, the attempt to be precise, that is, clear, may lead a technical man into prolix jungles of qualifiers, exceptions, and "if's" and "and's." This tendency is offset by the structural quality of compression, the other segment of the extrinsic half of the style melon cut at the opening of this chapter.

Compression

Ideas must not only be unmistakably clear in technical writing; they must be presented in a denser matrix than in informal or creative writing. The great density of ideas is brought about by a quality of style referred to here as compression. When the language is compressed to the point that all unnecessary or extraneous material has been eliminated, it is concise. According to one dictionary definition, concise "implies the stating of much in few words, by removing all superfluous elaborations." Technical writing as produced by its more skillful authors is succinct and terse, rather than laconic or pithy. Ideas must not only be unmistakably clear; they must be presented in close formation. This does not mean cutting the sentences or reducing the total word count; it means that the idea density is raised by removing superfluous elaborations. Elaborations are forced out when compression techniques are applied.

Six useful means of compressing the language—packing more into the shipping cartons without increasing the cubature—are here described.

1. *Subordinating.* To subordinate means to lower in rank or significance by position or grammatical construction. Emotionally and mentally mature technical people often sound childish in written communication because they express almost every idea, including minor details, in simple main clauses. No effort is made to show subordination in the grammatical construction of sentences. To obtain the compression characteristic of a mature style, one should try to give the ideas a grammatical rank comparable to their significance. The most significant ideas are generally made the essential elements of the main clause. Slightly inferior ideas may be placed in dependent clauses; and an idea of still lesser rank might take the form of a completely abbreviated clause, the verbal phrase. Further subordination is indicated by placing an idea in a prepositional phrase,

used either as adjective or adverb. Single-word adjectives and adverbs offer about the lowest level of subordination. A meaningful adjective or adverb can often be substituted for a long phrase or an entire clause. And finally, ideas may be subordinated by word building, especially by the use of compound nouns and adjectives.

2. *Abbreviating.* Technical style admits the free use of all standard abbreviations and of nonstandard abbreviations when they are fully explained and serve a useful purpose. Nothing should be abbreviated, however, which can cause the reader to become confused.

3. *Cutting meaningless words.* Words which do not add any new idea or do not serve any useful purpose should be examined carefully for possible omission. One good method of testing the usefulness of a word or group of words is to read the construction without the word or words to see if any significant meaning is lost. If nothing essential is lost by omitting the word or phrase, it should be struck from the sentence.

4. *Eliminating unnecessary words, or tautology.* The kind of repetition grammatically referred to as tautology is more than a repetitious word. In technical style especially, tautology is extended to mean the repetition or inclusion of what is perfectly obvious.

5. *Eliminating useless sentences.* Not only should unnecessary words be stricken, but an entire sentence may need to be excised. When sentences do not add enough to the general idea to justify the space they occupy, they should be left out, and any useful ideas in them should be salvaged and incorporated as subordinate elements in other sentences. Every sentence, every paragraph, must say something.

6. *Substituting denotative nouns for connotative nouns and specific verbs for general ones.* The noun with a restricted or single meaning is preferred in technical style to the general words which connote many things. Specific action verbs carry much more force than the overworked general ones. However, in the process of substituting more specific nouns and verbs to gain compression, the writer must not forget the problem of reader comprehension. The reader level and the purpose of the writer are the deciding factors in making the choice between precise denotative nouns and more general ones familiar to the reader.

The writer may have to add a few extra words of informal definition as a courtesy to the reader when it is absolutely necessary to use highly specialized words outside the reader's vocabulary (see Chapter 2 for informal definition).

Compression in technical style is obtained by grammatical subordination, by choosing the level of sentence element to match the desired level of importance of the idea, by cutting out unnecessary or repetitious words, by compounding words, and by substituting single specific or denotative words for ideas expressed in longer form. Brevity is not a characteristic of technical style at which the writer aims; rather it comes about as a by-product of conciseness and the other compression practices. Conciseness is the goal; it may result in more or fewer words. Brevity of itself may be an indication of mental laziness on the writer's part in trying to find the concise way of saying a thing. Brevity that results in the omission of essential words without regard for precise meaning may confuse the reader. Conciseness, the desired objective, is achieved by "removing all superfluous elaborations."

Good technical style is as clear and functional as it can be made. It is compact, not because the writer has eliminated any necessary thing, but because the writer has removed what is not needed. The idea density is high because the writer has logically subordinated the minor to the major ideas. Minor ideas are given minor roles in grammatical subordination.

EXERCISES

1. Obtain a 200 to 300 word passage of a formal report published in a current technical journal. Copy it, giving credit in a footnote reference (see form in Chapter 9). Paraphrase the passage. Turn in the paraphrase and the original copy to the instructor.

2. Again paraphrase the formal passage of Exercise 1, but this time limit main-clause verbs to the indicative mood, active voice, *first* person.

3. Copy a 200 to 300 word passage from a technical article in the *Reader's Digest*—any subject, any issue. Give credit in a footnote reference. Rewrite the passage in formal technical style, using active or passive voice, indicative or subjunctive mood (or modal auxiliaries) as desired, but use only the *third person* for main-clause verbs. Submit the original copy and the rewritten passage to the instructor.

4. Read three technical articles in any issue of the *Reader's Digest*. Note the style qualities, both intrinsic and extrinsic, and the reader level. Next, prepare a topical outline of the most technical (specialized) bit of information you have picked up this year from any source. The topical outline should be suitable for a 200 to 300 word article in the style of the *Reader's Digest* articles. Footnote references should be made to give credit for the technical material and the *Reader's Digest* models. Using only the topical outline and a dictionary, write a *Reader's Digest* style article in class; time limit 50 minutes. (Hint for solving exercise 4: Begin by attracting attention; then show the reader how he is affected by the information about to follow. Translate the technical information into easily understood language. Make your style compressed, but not clipped; interesting, but not sensational. Close with an indication of the attitude that the reader should now have: what he should do, think, feel, see, know, believe.)

8
The Short Report

Report writing has become an indispensable part of modern civilization. Every activity from hog raising to space flight produces its various and myriad reports. Without them industrial life would cease, and discoveries, if made, would die with the men who made them. Most industrial and scientific reports are routine and objective in nature; they require simple directions for writing. However, certain other short reports which also deal with facts have a subjective quality that requires experience and a flexible and varied form that demands some prior training. In this chapter, therefore, short reports are classified and discussed, and an opportunity is presented for the young engineer to become familiar with at least one kind of report that will greatly affect his usefulness to his employer.

A cataloguing of short reports with specific instructions for writing for each type would be useful to the professional technical writer, especially if the forms studied were the same ones used by his employer. But this degree of specialization lies beyond the objectives of a practical course in technical communication. Besides the difficulty of naming the kinds of reports, there is the even greater difficulty of agreement on the format and type of material handled under a given report name. For example, a short report known in one company as an engineering report may be called, in another, an inspection report. A research report may also be termed an investigation report, or simply a laboratory report or a memorandum report. Reports generated by staff-related departments in one industry may have the force of directives; whereas, the same kind of reports in another industry would be considered only as information. The obviously practical thing for the student, then, is to gain a general understanding of the underlying principles of report writing. The format and nomenclature can later be adjusted to suit the employer.

For general instruction, therefore, the most useful basis of classification is the nature of the material in the report. Short reports on this basis may be studied as factual reports and opinion reports. Factual reports are those chiefly concerned with transmitting information. Opinion reports make use of information from factual reports, but they rearrange the data to reflect the writer's interpretation of the significance and meaning of the data.

FACTUAL REPORTS

Factual reports are written to transmit or record needed information. Students of this text have already had sufficient practice to do these reports with a minimum of instruction, particularly when the employer specifies the format or furnishes printed forms. For example, in a chemical or physical test report the engineer simply follows directions, interprets the specifications, and makes the calculations needed for the formal report. Advance instructions would not be of much use. It is assumed that a mature technical person will have enough common sense to ask questions, at the time the report is assigned, about any details not clearly understood. Other reports may be in either category. A progress report would be classed as a factual report if no explanations were included and as an opinion report if unusual delays had to be evaluated and predictions made for returning to schedule.

OPINION REPORTS

After the young engineer or scientist has demonstrated his ability to generate and transmit facts without error according to prescribed form and for the purpose intended, he may be asked to give an opinion based on the facts. This may come within the first year of employment, or it may never come if there is evidence of careless handling of the facts in the preparation of the formal reports assigned to him. Opinion reports are generally assigned to older, more experienced men because they involve more than knowledge. They require judgment, and judgment comes through experience. When the employer's profits are at stake and a choice in direction must be made, the best judgment is sometimes inadequate. Complex problems requiring careful analysis of all major and minor factors before an opinion is reached are, therefore, seldom assigned to a new man. But maturity in judgment can be hastened by classroom training. Writing opinion reports in the controlled classroom environment artificially ages and seasons the student's judgment in the same way as the aging furnace toughens an aluminum alloy. In the aging furnace at cake-baking temperature as much toughening occurs in a few hours—precipitation of hardening ingredients in the crystal lattice structure of the aluminum matrix—as would occur in a thousand years at room temperature. Likewise a simulated on-the-job problem, analyzed and interpreted in a systematic way, can cut years from the trial-and-error learning process.

Typical of opinion reports, and perhaps the most useful to management, is the *recommendation report*. This type of report, also called by other names, involves both formal analysis (factual report) and informal analysis (interpretation). Formal-analysis reports furnish the evidence to support the writer's informal analysis. When problems arise which have more than one answer, some competent person or group of persons is assigned to study the facts and to write a report which reaches a conclusion and recommends the best course of action. Though the recommendation report deals with the facts, it is not solely a transmission of information. It is an evaluation, a search for meaning and significance of the facts. It involves a systematic investigation with logical deductions and conclusions that, if accepted by the reader, will lead to action. Problems with plant facilities, materials, processes, methods, management, labor, and customer relations are often solved by the recommendation report. The report writer's reputation and his employer's money may depend on the soundness of judgment shown. The first recommendation report assignment on the new job is a vote of confidence by the employer. It comes when the supervisor is convinced that the new man has intellectual honesty, an analytical mind, thorough knowledge of the facts, and ability to communicate. If he successfully completes this important analysis, he will have reached a high point in service that will surely lead to recognition and advancement.

Because the *recommendation report form* varies with the employer, the best advice is to observe the general layout and style of the reports in the department file. If the employer has an established form, it must be religiously adhered to. In the classroom assignment about to be described the student should regard the instructor's directions and the example as the working specifications of his employer.

On the job, the problems come ready made, and the evidence is obtained by research and testing. But in the classroom, the student will have to create his problem and his evidence by using his own imagination. Given a certain real or make-believe problem, the first step is to plan a procedure for solving the problem. It may be difficult to predict all of the steps needed to develop a convincing body of data and to describe at once a brief procedure for gathering the data. The report writer should first determine who will read his report, and having determined the reader, he will then be able to outline a convincing procedure for obtaining the evidence. A thorough reading of the pertinent specifications and of previous reports on the same or similar problems will also help in deciding what new evidence will be needed.

A better report will result if the student complicates the imaginary situation enough to require the sifting and weighing of considerable evidence before he forms his conclusions. But if the problem selected turns out to be too complex to be covered within the assigned word limits, it should be narrowed or simplified. The important thing to remember is that this report is to be written as if it were an actual report under actual working conditions. If a clear-cut decision is not justifiable from the evidence at hand, one should conduct further tests and produce data, as necessary, to remove all reasonable doubt. One or more valid conclusions must be reached, followed by the recommendations for action or inaction, as the case may be.

In gathering and presenting the evidence, the investigator must show that the variables are truly isolated, that his results are consistent and reproducible, and that inferences, wherever made, are based on clearly demonstrable cause-effect relationships—no unwarranted generalizations. The size of the test sample is itself a test of the engineer's judgment. How many pieces, for instance, should be checked to justify scrapping a 100,000 lot? That depends. If they were all made on the same stamp, mold, or die, one piece might do it. But the piece examined might have been made near the end of the lot, and 95,000 made earlier might be good; a representative sample will reveal the extent of the problem. On the other hand, the whole lot might have to be checked, depending upon its critical or noncritical use. A problem as important as locating a new plant might require consideration of a hundred sites. A new vaccine might take thousands of controlled tests. Safety, cost, public interest, and public relations are factors which determine the size of the sample and the extent of the report.

Complex problems involving the outlay of millions of dollars are not likely to be assigned until the new man has proved his ability to exercise good judgment in little things. Short reports that do not involve a lot of money are the ones likely to be assigned to the new man. One may suppose, for example, that he is working for an aircraft company and has been asked to check the performance of a new product to determine whether it meets acceptance standards. This happens to be an aircraft breathing-oxygen regulator. The new employee's first move, of course, is to check the purchase order and the drawing specifications. The numbers and names of any specifications pertaining to the product must be carefully copied from the drawing. The technical librarian or secretary can help locate the needed documents. Next, the department report file and correspondence file should be checked for the history of the problem; some companies require that this information, if any, be referenced first in the report. Then the investigator should devise his tentative procedure for making the performance check.

The specifications of this hypothetical regulator call for a simulated function test to resemble as nearly as possible the installation and function of the instrument on the airplane. Since his laboratory has no mock-up available, the investigator requisitions the necessary production lines and fittings from stock for the simulated test assembly. According to the function test specifications, the regulator must operate satisfactorily at -65 F. Without adequate cryogenic facilities, he decides to produce a low-temperature environment with makeshift materials. He brings the test panel to a stable -65 F temperature with dry ice and proceeds to give the regulator the specified function test.

The investigator carefully records his test data. On the third cycle under pressure of -65 F the demand valve of the regulator ceases to function. The equipment is obviously below acceptable quality standards; the report shows the function failure and recommends that the vendor's equipment be returned.

In this report the function test procedure was carefully followed, the data recorded, the report written according to instructions. The *introduction* states the subject, purpose, scope, and plan; the *procedure* summarizes what has been done to obtain the evidence; the *discussion of results* rationalizes all of the contingencies which arose and all of the unusual problems encountered in the interpretation of the evidence; the *conclusion* is clear and precisely written; the *recommendations* follow logically as the only possible course of action. The report is then passed to the supervisor for approval.

Before the supervisor endorses the action with his authoritative signature, he carefully checks the procedure. He notices, from his broader experience, that no mention is made of venting the room air from the lines before the function cycle was begun. He asks whether clean lines were used. While the investigator is assuring his superior that sealed, clean lines were obtained and that all fittings were checked for evidence of organic contamination, the older man, by process of elimination, has guessed the possible cause of failure. He explains that it is entirely possible that some moisture from the residual air in the lines and equipment could have condensed as frost on the valve seats and caused the function failure. The supervisor requests a rerun, adding the important venting of the system to the procedure before the function cycling is begun.

The test is repeated with a new regulator exactly as before but with the venting added. With dry, aircraft breathing oxygen replacing the room air in the system, the regulator functions perfectly. Since this is the only change in the previous test, it may be safely assumed that the cause of failure was an icing of the valve mechanism. The beginner has learned a good lesson in the importance of checking for all possible variables before making the final decision, and his company has been saved the embarrassment of rejecting perfectly good equipment.

The steps, in chronological order, for doing the recommendation report assignment are summarized below:

1) The problem is written as the *title of the report*.

2) The background, purpose, scope, and any other pertinent facts are presented in the *introduction*. Since this report demands a *certain* situation, the student must not suppose a conditional, "If a man needed so and so." The report must be written from the viewpoint of one already on the job facing a specific problem.

3) The reader must be told by the *procedure* how the evidence was obtained—a summary of the important steps taken.

4) When the necessary research has been completed, the results must be processed and discussed in a form readily *understood* by the reader. Charts, graphs, tables, or other graphic aids may help emphasize significant facts. The reader must know *why* certain data is, or is not, significant. The choice of a format for the presentation of evidence depends again on the kind of reader expected. If opposition is anticipated, the inductive arrangement of evidence is the best. For this assignment, the student may imagine the report is written to be

read by his supervisor (the instructor), or he may consider himself a consulting engineer and direct his report to a client or customer.

5) *Conclusions* should be based on the evidence at hand. They can be enumerated as separate items or stated in paragraph form.

6) The recommendations for action may also be stated as numbered items, or they may be stated less formally in paragraph form. For example, as enumerated items the recommendations could be stated in the following way:

It is recommended

1. That such and such be done, and

2. That such and such be given emergency status, etc.

The recommendations must point out the best course of action in the light of the conclusions reached. The writer should assume that this report will affect the profits of his company and his own future—and possibly the lives of others.

The value of the recommendation report depends, thus, upon the soundness of the writer's judgment. It requires a great deal more skill in organizing and writing than the factual report because it must *appeal* to a particular reader not only in its choice of words but also in its logical display of convincing evidence. In these respects the recommendation report resembles other widely recognized forms of opinion reports: business forecasts, quality control or inspection reports, appraisals, proposals, inquests, and all kinds of consulting reports.

On the other hand, the great bulk of operating reports generated in manufacturing, selling, and purchasing of goods and services are routine factual reports written chiefly to convey information. These are significant and necessary to the employer, but they can be written by almost anyone in possession of the facts. They require expert knowledge and a sharp eye for accuracy, but they present no challenge in composition; hence, the emphasis in the foregoing chapter has been placed on the writing of opinion reports.

STUDENT EXAMPLE

Recommendation Report

INDEPENDENT RESEARCH COMPANY

Tire Division

Conduct Tire Tread Wear Tests for the Crandall Transportation Company

Introduction

On September 30, 1959, a letter was received from Mr. P. B. Elston of the Crandall Transportation Company, Middlecity, Iowa, requesting tread wear tests on tires manufactured by the Wilson, Kingston, Dodson, and Browning tire companies.

The Crandall Company, which operates a passenger-car service in every major city, desires to purchase only one brand of tire. It was requested that tests be conducted under controlled conditions on premium and first-line tires and that recommendations be submitted.

Procedure

Thirty-two sets of tires were tested—two sets of premium and two sets of first-line tires for each tire size: 6.70–15 and 7.10–15. The tires were tested on eight cars; four cars used 6.70–15 tires, and four cars used 7.10–15 tires. These cars were identical with those owned by the Crandall Company.

Prior to the start of the test, the tires were inflated to pressures recommended by the Tire and Rim Association: 26 psi for 6.70–15 tires and 24 psi for 7.10–15 tires. Tread depths were measured using a dial indicator; an average tread depth was computed for each type of tire.

The cars were loaded so as to place 1160 pounds on each tire. The weight on the tires was about 4 percent more than the maximum load recommended by the Tire and Rim Association (Crandall cars with passengers and luggage often operate on overloaded tires).

The test was performed on an oval track. Each tire was subjected to a total of 4000 miles of road wear. This consisted of a daily schedule of two 400-mile runs at a constant speed of 60 mph. The tires were rotated every 1000 miles.

At the completion of the test, the tires were removed, and the tread depths were again measured with a dial indicator. Final tread depths measurements were subtracted from original tread measurements, and the average wear data of both tire sizes were calculated in terms of miles per one-thousandth inch of wear.

Discussion of Results

The overall results were as follows:

Make	Premium Tires	First-Line Tires
Dodson	81.4	80.0
Wilson	80.9	79.4
Browning	80.6	79.1
Kingston	80.3	78.1

Since the test was performed on an oval track and at a constant speed of 60 mph, better tread mileage was obtained than would have been possible in city traffic operation. Because of the continual "stop-and-go" situations encountered in city traffic, tread mileage would have been reduced by approximately 24 percent.

Conclusions

The results show there is only a slight difference between the tread mileage of premium tires and the tread mileage of first-line tires. For example, the Dodson premiums (highest rating) averaged 81.4 miles for each one-thousandth inch of tread wear, while the Kingston first-line tire (lowest rating) averaged 78.1 miles. Within each particular make of tire, the difference in tread mileage between premium and first-line tires was not more than 2 percent.

Recommendations

Based on tread mileage only, first-line tires are almost equal to premium tires. From the results obtained, the Dodson first-line tire would be the logical choice. The saving on each tire ($5.00) compensates for any extra tread mileage offered by the premium tire.

Before any decision is made, it would be advisable to conduct additional tests to determine the safety features of each different make of tire. Safety factor plus tread mileage would offer a more complete guide for tire selection.

EXERCISES

1. Obtain a list of reports from an employer (your own, if employed) and arrange them into two categories: those which transmit information (factual reports) and those which interpret the information transmitted (opinion reports).

2. Write a laboratory report giving information without opinion or interpretation. Set the report up as a formal analysis to obtain some type of specific information. Work with materials and problems you are now encountering or expect to encounter after graduation, for example, civil, mechanical, chemical, electronic, electrical, aeronautical, or agricultural engineering problems.

3. Write a 400 to 500 word formal analysis, with no comments or inferences, of the assets of an imaginary or real employer.

4. Write a 400 to 500 word informal analysis of a problem which has been handed to you by your employer. Explain the problem, set up the standard or standards for its solution, dig up the possible alternatives, examine them, and, then, on the basis of the standards established for solving the problem, make your conclusions and recommend a course of action. (See Chapter 5 for the techniques of formal and informal analysis.) Unless otherwise instructed, use the form of the example shown for the recommendation report.

5. Write a 400 to 500 word opinion report giving the cause of failure in a material, an engine, a wrecked airplane, a process, a bridge, a paint job—anything of interest to you. Assume the reader is familiar in a general way with the subject and that he is skeptical of your ability to account for all of the variables and to reach a valid conclusion. The conclusions may be numbered or written in paragraph form. Give no recommendations.

9
The Research Paper

This discussion on the technical research paper is presented as if the chapter itself were a research paper. This is to permit the student to have his style manual, as it were, conveniently before him while he studies the subject. The chapter begins with the sample title page and closes with the appendixes, as indicated by the table of contents for the research paper. The student research paper following this chapter will serve as a further resource on style. The form, content, and mechanics of expression have been checked and altered in a few places, but the opinions and conclusions reached are the student's own.

Report on

THE TECHNICAL RESEARCH PAPER

(Title of paper)

Technical Communication

Arizona State University

Tempe, Arizona

(Course title and place)

by

John A. Doe

Senior Civil Engineering Student

(Student's name, class, and curriculum)

May 6, 1964

(Scheduled completion date)

TABLE OF CONTENTS

LIST OF FIGURES

ABSTRACT

Before an engineering student takes a job in the technical world, he should learn to do systematic research. A good step in this direction can be taken by writing a research paper using the indexed periodical literature of the library as the chief source of information. The student begins the library research paper by selecting and outlining a suitable subject. Using the main topics of the outline as a guide, he searches through all available technical information sources to find a representative sample of opinion on his subject. The notes taken during the search form the body of the report. Organizing the material to support a thesis gives the student experience in weighing and sifting facts from opinions; writing of the research paper in accordance with a specific format develops the student's powers of observation and comprehension. A four- to five-thousand-word technical research paper thus serves as a means of teaching library research methods and of extending the student's knowledge in his chosen field of specialization.

I. Introduction

One of the critical bottlenecks in modern man's efforts to control his environment is communication. The scientist and the engineer are held in check by the slow and feeble exchange of technical knowledge. Today, in spite of the billions[1] being spent in research, scientists move toward the nation's technological objectives at worm-gear speed for want of a fast, sure vehicle of communication. Our technical people cannot communicate effectively.

Reports from our more sophisticated research projects, generally written by teams of technicians who unfortunately do not understand the basic science and mathematics they must write about, are lying in unread heaps in laboratories all over the country—unread because they are difficult reading for everybody.

This situation cannot be changed overnight. The present army of engineers and research scientists are too busy to stop now for much formal instruction in communication. But if the engineers and the scientists of the future now in universities can be taught to read and write standard reports before they graduate, the communication bottleneck of tomorrow will undoubtedly be relieved. Another alternative, of course, is for the universities to continue to graduate men with good training in mathematics and science but with little or no training in communication. To compensate then for the communication deficiency in their engineers, companies could recruit and train an equal number of engineering specialists to do the reading and writing for the engineers. This, of course, would be professional featherbedding, a very costly means of reducing the communications bottleneck. A more practical and a speedier relief is to train the young scientist to communicate in standard technical language before he steps into that first job.

While it is recognized that some editorial work is useful in bringing the writing of a group of scientists and engineers into a standard format, there is no justification for the wasteful practice of completely rewriting engineers' and scientists' reports to the extent that it is being done today. It is not as though the engineer or scientist had never been exposed to the study of English. He has just failed to take his language study seriously; probably his science and mathematics instructors are somewhat to blame for this. If the present generation had made communication skill as important as science and mathematics, the exchange of technical

---

[1] "Scientific Support Estimated $9.1 Billion," Science News Letter, 79 (February 25, 1961), p. 121. (This is U.S. government-sponsored research and does not include another five to six billion dollars annually spent by private organizations.)

information would be far simpler than it is. Perhaps some reemphasis of English is in order all down the line.[2]

The research paper[3] described here is intended to give the technically trained man sufficient working knowledge to enable him to produce readable reports, or at least reports which do not require rewriting before they can be circulated within a company. This procedure is not intended as a substitute for a technical society's style manual for published articles, but it does provide training in assembling, organizing, and writing the library research paper at a much higher level than the usual undergraduate course in technical writing.

In the sense used here a research report requires the analysis of a technical problem by means of published information. This, of course, eliminates at the outset any subject not sufficiently complicated to be called a problem and any subject about which there is not enough published information to afford ample sifting and evaluation. The subject must have significance, too, especially to the investigator. It should be of sufficient length and at a high enough technical level to show that the writer has knowledge of all the major and minor factors involved, the analytical ability to resolve them, and the communicative skill to tell others what he has found out.

The detailed format—footnotes, table of contents, abstract, list of illustrations, introduction, body, conclusion, bibliography—of research reports may vary a great deal among employers. The important thing to remember is that all reports originated by any given organization must follow that organization's technical style and format. And the new man who can adapt readily to the editorial requirements of his department has already begun to create a favorable impression of his ability. In anticipation of the future job, the form presented in the following pages should be considered as though it were the one specified by the employer, and it should be followed just as religiously to the last detail.

The instructor, too, will judge the student's performance from industry's point of view. The quality must be as high as possible for the time allowed. It is well to remember that shortcuts on the first time through can spoil both the quality and the rate of production. If one meets the production schedule as assigned and

---

[2] Standardized tests in mechanics of expression given to 400 Arizona State University engineering students at the senior level have shown that 20 percent are below ninth grade level in mechanics of expression, though considerably higher in total English, including reading and comprehenison.

[3] For the laboratory research report and various other projects which can be substituted for this assignment, additional instructions will be found in Chapters 10 and 12.

follows the instructions carefully, from the planning stage to the final assembly, the end product will be on schedule, and it will be of acceptable quality.

The topics are arranged in their natural order: the selection of a subject, the working plan or outline, the university library as a research center, the breaking of the library code for indexing and filing information, the use and form of bibliography cards and note cards, the detailed procedure for analyzing the accumulated information and getting it into a rough draft, and, finally, the form, content, and mechanics of expression for the finished paper.

II. Selection of a Subject

The initial phase of every production job is to work out an operations sequence. Operations are planned from first to last, in the order that they can be done most economically and efficiently. The library research paper is a production job, a major one for most students. It, too, begins with planning. The first operation is the selection of a subject.

Factors Affecting Selection of Subjects

Student Interest. Unlike the assigned research problems of industry, the technical research paper subject is selected by the student. Otherwise he would miss the opportunity of extending his knowledge in his special field. One of the advantages of a communications course in the senior year is that the student has had enough basic science and mathematics to read the technical magazines (including a few journals).

The selection of a subject in which the student has had little previous training or interest is almost certain to bring frustration, resulting in a switch to a new subject after precious time has been lost—maybe enough to cause failure. The best subjects are generally related to what the student has already shown an interest in. If no subject taken in the three years of undergraduate courses has aroused the student's desire to know more than was presented in the textbook, it is probable, indeed quite likely, that he is in the wrong curriculum.

Other Factors. In addition to the student interest factor, the student should be able to answer these questions affirmatively: Is this a problem type of subject? Is there enough published information available for analysis?

A one-source review type of subject is entirely out of the question. Likewise out is a straight history or process type of subject. The subject must lend itself to questions which cannot be answered until the evidence from a number of sources with varying viewpoints has been analyzed.

Availability of published material is determined by a preliminary check in the card catalogue and the indexes to observe the volume of published articles. At least eight or ten well-written technical articles should be available. These, supplemented by other materials from books and pamphlets, would serve quite well. It is possible that there is an entire book on the subject. But if there are two or more books on the same subject, the subject is most likely too broad. If nothing or nearly nothing is found in technical periodical indexes, the subject is too narrow, and it should be enlarged or abandoned.

Student-Instructor Conference

After the student has made a temporary selection of his subject, he should arrange for a conference with the instructor before proceeding with his research. Sometimes the instructor may have personal reasons for failing to approve a subject, especially one on which two or more persons are already working. The use by more than one person of the same material in the library could cause time-consuming delays. The instructor, moreover, may feel that the student's technical knowledge is too meager to tackle a problem, or he may have suggestions which might turn the selection to better advantage for the student.

The instructor will generally approve any technical subject of the problem type which is interesting and timely and which has sufficient scope for a paper of 4000 to 5000 words.

Before the search actually begins, however, some time spent in familiarization with the way information is catalogued and stored in the local library is of vital importance to the student's success. The discussion that follows, plus some initiative shown by the student, should be sufficient to open the storehouse of information for this and all succeeding research projects.

III. Technical Information Sources

A student without library orientation can wander helplessly through the reading rooms and stacks of a large university library and gain almost no information. The library is useful only to those who know how its materials are coded and stacked. It may be assumed that a working knowledge of the university library is a fait accompli for the average upperclassman. Still, on the off chance that some engineering students have bypassed this valuable learning tool, the story must begin as though the technical student had just entered the library for the first time. Beginning with the card catalogue, the discussion moves to other key sources: to the shelf list, the bibliography sources, the periodical indexes, the current technical periodical repository, and the specialized reference collections.

Card Catalogue

The card catalogue in all probability is the most used single research tool in the library. It contains typed and printed cards with enough information to give an indication of the nature of the volume and where it has been shelved. Some of the information on the card may have little value for this discussion, but certain other bits of information on the card will have value, and they should be carefully studied.

All volumes in the library are indexed in the card catalogue under at least three headings: author, title, and subject or topic. Not knowing a specific title or author, one should check the catalogue first, using the guide words of the general subject. If the general subject fails to turn up any titles, another general subject very closely related should be checked. If no titles can be discovered in this manner relating to the subject, the student should seek a librarian's assistance.

From the librarian he will be able to obtain the Dewey decimal code number for the general subject. With this basic number he can proceed to another card file called the shelflist and browse through the entire library without moving out of his tracks. The shelflist resembles the card catalogue, which is usually located nearby, in that it contains 3 by 5 printed cards similar to those found in the card catalogue—but with this important difference: only one card for each volume is filed, and these are arranged in numerical order under the Dewey decimal code number system.

Once the student has the basic Dewey decimal number for a particular subject, he can determine immediately from the shelflist whether the library has classified any of its volumes by this number, because there is a card (but only one) in the shelflist to represent every indexed volume in the library. Furthermore, since the Dewey system is decimalized to form subcategories of all branches of knowledge, a check through nearby cards, by simply moving backward or forward from the position of the card showing the subject number, will reveal all the closely related subjects. To illustrate the use of the shelflist, one might suppose a student is searching for material on the common subject of caves.[4] From one of the titles on caves found in the card catalogue (or from the librarian) the student has obtained the Dewey number for caves—551.44. At the shelflist, arranged by number only, he finds an index of cards representing each and every volume in the library. This should be a great help to engineers who are at home with figures.

---

[4] It is entirely possible that a recent work on caves could be missed because the latest book on caves might be filed under the new Library of Congress heading, Speleology, which replaced Caves in 1959. The basic Dewey number, however, did not change.

Without taking another step, the student can locate any volume in the library which has been coded and filed with the basic Dewey number for caves.

Titles found by means of the card catalogue or the shelflist can be placed on bibliography cards and located in the stacks by copying the two sets of numbers usually located on the left-hand side of the card found in the card catalogue. These printed cards supplied as a service to libraries by the Library of Congress show the Dewey classification number and the shelf code is added by the local librarian. At this point it is necessary to admonish the student on the importance of carefully copying all the call number. The date and other information near the basic Dewey and shelf numbers, such as <u>rare, reference, large, and special collection,</u> which may affect the location of the book, should also be copied. Large books, for example, are usually stacked separately along the wall near the books having similar call numbers. Special collections and rare books are not generally in the open stack area. Here the services of a library assistant may be needed. Reference books are usually shelved in a separate room. Double checking of the numbers, even to the distinction of large and small letters in the call number, will be rewarded by a saving of steps for both the student and the librarian.

The preparation of bibliography cards from the card catalogue, however, is no assurance that the student will be able to find his way around the library. For the first few cards the information from the card catalogue should be checked against the actual title page of the work on the shelf to insure that the student understands the librarian's way of locating books.

For the technical research paper, the card catalogue and the shelflist are only the starting points for the search. It is the periodical indexes discussed next which yield the most useful information—that about the published magazine article.

Periodical Indexes

Technical magazines and journals, because of the varied viewpoints of the writers and the current nature of the material, are the best source of technical information. The articles are selected from several thousand periodicals and are listed in the indexes by subject or author, or both. The location of these indexes will vary from library to library, but they can generally be found near the reference librarian's desk or in an adjoining reading room. The largest and best known of these indexes, the <u>Readers' Guide to Periodical Literature,</u> indexes by author and subject the more popular nontechnical magazines. A few well-written nontechnical articles, with the technical terms translated into everyday language, will give the specialist a new vocabulary—new in the sense that for the first time he has learned familiar words for his technical jargon—and this will aid mightily in giving the student a better understanding of underlying principles and increasing his powers of expression for his final paper. Also, when technical material is translated and condensed, as it is in The Reader's Digest, for example, a great deal of technical fluff is removed, which actually increases understanding for the technical man whose comprehension of the printed word may be a few years below his mathematics and science rating.

The Readers' Guide is issued bimonthly from September through May and monthly during June, July, and August. It is accumulated annually and biannually. The monthly paperback issues should be searched first, working backward in time to the older accumulations, some of which are for three-, four-, or five-year periods. The Readers' Guide began in 1900, earlier than it will be necessary to explore most scientific problems. (For historical reference one might go to the predecessor of modern periodical indexes, called Poole's Index, which began in 1802 and was discontinued in 1906.)

It will be noted in the Readers' Guide and the other indexes that periodical names and dates of issue are greatly abbreviated and that many of the standard practices for capital letters and punctuation are not followed. The flyleaf supplies the complete names of the magazines indexed. Once the article is located from the index and the information about it—author, title, magazine, date of issue, and inclusive pages—has been carefully copied, the student may return to the reference desk or some other designated place to learn from an alphabetical listing of magazine names where the bound volumes of the desired periodical are stacked. The reference librarian will assist, if necessary, at this point to retrieve the bound volume containing the article in question. The bound volumes of the most frequently read magazines are located in reading rooms or in the stacks, as space permits.

Other periodical indexes arranged in the order of probable importance to this assignment are: Applied Science and Technology Index, previously called Industrial Arts Index; Engineering Index; and Agricultural Index. It is the Applied Science and Technology Index which contains the main stream of technical publications in America, as may be seen by reading the list of about 200 magazines inside the front cover. This index is primarily by subject. Once the article is located by its subject, the author, title, magazine, and issue date can be traced to its location in the library.

When all pertinent indexes have been checked, the selection of the articles to be read should be made as representative as possible by rough calculations. The group of articles finally read should cover the time span of the problem in the approximate ratio of the total number of articles published from year to year. (See the instructions for taking a representative sample of bibliography in the next section.) The technical research paper does not attempt to provide an exhaustive bibliography. The reading done is required to include no more than a good sample of what the best authorities have written on the subject.

Special Research Aids for Technical Subjects

In addition to the periodical indexes the student should be familiar with various other research tools. In every library specialized scientific encyclopedias, guides, handbooks, dictionaries of all kinds stand waiting unused on the reference shelves. The following reference sources from the library of Arizona State University are typical of the great variety of research aids available. They are arranged alphabetically by author or corporate author, if available, or by the first word of the title if no author is given. The numbers may vary slightly in other libraries, but the Dewey decimal number should be the same wherever the Dewey system is used.

American Chemical Society—Division of Chemical Literature.
Searching the Chemical Literature. (a guide)
Ref. serv. desk.—Ref/540.016/Am35s/1950

American Institute of Physics—Publication Board.
Style Manual, for Guidance in the Preparation of Papers for Journals Published by the American Institute of Physics. (a style guide)
Ref. serv. desk.—Ref/620.09/Am34s/1959

American Society of Mechanical Engineers.
Seventy-seven Year Index: Technical Papers, 1880-1956.
Gen. Ref. Room/Index island—
Large Ref/621.062/Am35Va/1957

Association of College and Reference Libraries, Pure and Applied Science Section.
A Recommended List of Basic Periodicals in Engineering and the Engineering Sciences. (a guide)
Ref. serv. desk.—Ref/620.5016/As78r/1953

Ballentyne, D. W. G., and L. E. Q. Walker.
A Dictionary of Named Effects and Laws in Chemistry, Physics, and Mathematics.
Ref. serv. desk.—Ref/503/B212d/1958

Besserer, C. W.
  Missile Engineering Handbook.
  Ref. serv. desk.—Ref/623.74/B464m/1958

Chemical Abstracts.
  S & T reading room—Ref/540.5/C42/1907-

Cooke, Nelson, and John Markus.
  Electronics Dictionary.
  Ref. serv. desk.—Ref/621.3803/C775e/1945

Crane, E. J., and others.
  A Guide to the Literature of Chemistry.
  Ref. serv. desk.—Ref/540.016/C85g/1957

Dalton, Blanche H.
  Sources of Engineering Information. (a guide)
  Ref. serv. desk.—Ref/620.0016/D171s/1948
  (This is an exceptionally well-planned and exhaustive index of sources for research in engineering. It is regrettable that a newer work of this same type is not available.)

DeVries, Louis.
  French-English Science Dictionary for Students in Agricultural, Biological
    and Physical Sciences, with a Supplement of Terms in Aeronautics,
    Electronics, Radar, Radio, Television.
  Ref. serv. desk.—Ref/503/D499f/1951

DeVries, Louis.
  German-English Science Dictionary for Students in Chemistry, Physics,
    Biology, Agriculture, and Related Sciences.
  Ref. serv. desk.—Ref/503/D499g/1959

Electronic Engineering Master Index; A Subject Index to Electronic Engineering
    Periodicals. . . .
  Gen. Ref. Room/Index island—
  Ref/621.38016/E125/1935-1946

Engineering Index.
  Gen. Ref. Room/Index island—Ref/620.0016/En33

Herkimer, Herbert.
  Engineers' Illustrated Thesaurus. (a dictionary)
  Ref. serv. desk.—Ref/620.2/H425e/1952

Hix, C. F., and R. P. Alley.
Physical Laws and Effects. (a handbook)
Ref. serv. desk.—Ref/530.1/H642p/1958

Horner, J. G., compiler
Dictionary of Terms Used in the Theory and Practice of Mechanical Engineer-
ing.
Ref. serv. desk.—Ref/621.03/H784d/1952

Industrial Arts Index.
(Beginning in 1958 was divided into two parts:
1. Business Periodicals Index
2. Applied Science and Technology Index)
Gen. Ref. Room—Ref/600.16/In2

Leidecker, Kurt F., ed.
German-English Technical Dictionary. . . . 2 vols.
Ref. serv. desk.—Ref/629.1303/L532g/1950-51

McCawley, Alfred, compiler
Professional Engineering Registration Laws. (an index)
Ref. serv. desk.—Ref/620.69/M129p/1954

McNeese, Donald C.
Engineering and Technical Handbook.
Ref. serv. desk.—Ref/620.2/M233e/1957

Mellon, M. G.
Chemical Publications, Their Nature and Use. (a guide)
Ref. serv. desk.—Ref/540.016/M489c/1958

Murphey, Robert W.
How and Where to Look It Up.
Ref. serv. desk.—Ref/016/M95h/1958

Nayler, J. L.
Dictionary of Aeronautical Engineering.
Ref. serv. desk.—Ref/629.1303/N234d/1959

Nuclear Science Abstracts.
S & T Reading Room—Ref/539.1705/Un32n/1948—

Parke, Nathan G.
Guide to the Literature of Mathematics and Physics, Including Related Works
on Engineering Science.
Ref. serv. desk.—Ref/510.016/P221g/1958

Pearl, Richard M.
 Guide to Geologic Literature.
 Ref. serv. desk.—Ref/550.016/P316g/1951
Robb, Louis.
 Engineers' Dictionary; Spanish-English and English-Spanish.
 Ref. serv. desk.—Ref/620.3/R532e/1944
Sarbacher, Robert.
 Encyclopedic Dictionary of Electronics and Nuclear Engineering.
 Ref. serv. desk.—Ref/621.4803/Sa71e/1959
Science Abstracts.
 S & T Reading Room—Ref/530.5/Sci27/1898—
Trelease, S. F.
 How to Write Scientific and Technical Papers. (a guide, style manual)
 Ref. stack, level 6—Ref/620.09/T719p/1958
Whitford, Robert H.
 Physics Literature; A Reference Manual. (a guide)
 Ref. serv. desk.—Ref/530.016/W589p/1954
Who's Who in Engineering.
 Gen. Ref. Room/biography island—
 Ref/620.58/W62/1959
Zimmerman, O. T., and Irvin Lavine.
 Scientific and Technical Abbreviations, Signs and Symbols.
 (a dictionary)
 Ref. serv. desk.—Ref/501.48/Z65s/1948

Current Technical Periodicals

 Every library subscribes to a great many periodicals, sometimes thousands. More than 2000 periodicals, 500 of which deal with technical or specialized information, are regularly received in the library of Arizona State. When these arrive during the year, they are displayed alphabetically by name in the current periodical room. At the end of the year, the year's issues (usually numbered as a volume) are sent to the bindery, with the result that magazines sometimes sorely needed are away at the bindery. Since there is not sufficient time in most instances to wait for the magazine to return from the bindery, one must simply substitute other materials or procure the magazines from other sources.

Every student doing a research paper must visit the current periodical room and check to see whether any articles can be found which have not had time to appear in the periodical indexes. The current issues of each magazine or journal which might be likely to publish articles related to the given subject should be checked out and examined individually. This may seem time-consuming, but it actually can be done very rapidly by simply scanning the table of contents in each issue. When all of the current magazines have been checked that from the student's knowledge might contain articles on the subject, the librarian in charge may be able to suggest others. A new magazine may have just begun publication, with the first issue not yet listed in any other spot in the library.

Government Documents

Another source which must be included with other indexes in rounding out the search for technical papers is the catalogue to U.S. Government Publications. It is housed with related government document sources in the bibliography area. The United States Government Printing Office has become the publisher of the most varied collection on earth. Current technical papers are usually available on almost any subject vital to the nation's economy, health, national defense, and so on.

For a more exhaustive bibliography it would be necessary to learn a great deal more about research methods than is needed here. A few facts on bibliographical sources are given in the paragraphs that follow.

Bibliographical Aids

For more extended technical research papers, including this assignment, the student should be familiar with the exhaustive book indexes and other materials in the specialized field of bibliography. When other materials are not readily available, it is possible that these sources could even be utilized in the shorter reports.

The most useful bibliography tool for books in English is the Cumulative Book Index. It lists author and publisher for the books in English which are in print at the time the index is issued.

A book which cannot be located in the card catalogue or the Cumulative Book Index can be found in the bound volumes of the Library of Congress catalogue, if the author is known, for in the LC catalogue the books are indexed by author and not title or subject. The LC catalogue, reissued periodically, contains all of the volumes copyrighted in the United States for the period covered which have been given accession numbers and filed in the archives of the Library of Congress.

If a book can be located in either the Cumulative Book Index or the LC catalogue which appears to be of value to the research project, one can obtain it through the interlibrary loan service. Information about loans from other libraries can be obtained from the research librarians.[5]

Also located in the bibliography room are the bound volumes of book reviews. The Book Review Digest may be used to obtain expert evaluations of a book found in any book index. It is published monthly and accumulated semiannually, annually, and at five-year intervals. It indexes American books by subject and title, and it also indexes and digests the reviews of these books which have appeared in some 70 periodicals. With this information any desired review can be obtained by looking up the periodical containing it at the reference desk or, if in the current year, in the current periodical room. If both favorable and unfavorable reviews are read, a better judgment of the value of the book can be made and a fairer decision reached as to whether it would be worthwhile to obtain it by interlibrary loan.

Throughout this search, one should not fail to ask for the services of the librarians. It goes without saying that librarians as a rule are busy people, and for the work they do and the abuse they receive from students, they are often underpaid. A bit of common sense in following the posted directions for the use of the library's facilities and a lot of common courtesy in moving about through the various areas of the library will make the search more enjoyable. It could shorten the time.

Research materials do not have to be confined to the University library. Information of value wherever it can be obtained—private libraries, newspapers, trade literature, professional societies, employers—may be used. A resourceful student can obtain authoritative information by writing to manufacturers, to laboratories, or to individuals known to be working in the field of interest.

The most fruitful search can be unrewarding and result in an unsatisfactory paper unless a few time-tested procedures are followed in making accurate reference and in taking good notes of the reading done. The practicality of the methods of gathering the material for a research paper described in the next section will not be appreciated as much at the first reading as it will after the paper has been completed.

IV. Research Procedure

The student who approaches this assignment with the idea that it is just an-

---

[5] The interlibrary loan service can also procure microfilm or photocopies of almost any article published, at a nominal charge plus postage.

other freshman term paper assigned in a senior-level course is likely to be pain-fully surprised. This is not just an expository writing exercise which can be done on a Saturday with the aid of five or six good books on the general subject. This is a preprofessional operation to demonstrate the student's skill in the use of keen-edged research tools in dissecting and analyzing a technical subject. This assignment gives the student poise and confidence in handling the more complex communication problems which are awaiting the professionally trained technical man on that first job.

In the directions which follow nothing should be ignored, even though for the present it may seem to be beyond the needs of the assigned paper. The directions on form are to be followed just as carefully and as conscientiously as though that big moment had already arrived and the end product was to be used to measure the worth of the new man on the job.

The procedure begins with a discussion of first operations—planning, familiar-ization with card record forms, and note-taking. Then it moves into some general admonitions on note-taking. It is completed by instructions for assembling the note cards into a usable order for the rough draft.

Preliminary Steps

At the outset one must draw up a work plan and learn to make bibliography and note cards.

It is quite understandable that a detailed outline might not be possible before the research has been done. Even if it were, it would probably change after a few days or weeks of research. A work plan (a simplified topical outline) does not demand thorough knowledge of a subject. It should begin with an introduction as the first item (Roman numeral I), under which some topics indicating purpose and point of view (at least the tentative point of view) should be listed. For most subjects definition may be needed. Perhaps a statement of the extent or scope of the research as it is envisioned at that time should be noted under the introduc-tion heading. The second major subdivision (Roman numeral II) in the plan could easily become a topic involving background material and a discussion of the important developments. In some highly specialized subjects it may be necessary to devote more major subdivisions of the paper to a discussion of the theory behind the problem. By the third or fourth subdivision (Roman numeral III or IV) the prob-lem must be detailed and laid before the reader in some logical order. A fifth subdivision, if necessary, can be used to round out the presentation and make the analysis. The fifth or sixth subdivision should become the conclusion. Thus a work plan can be evolved without great knowledge of a subject. (When the research is

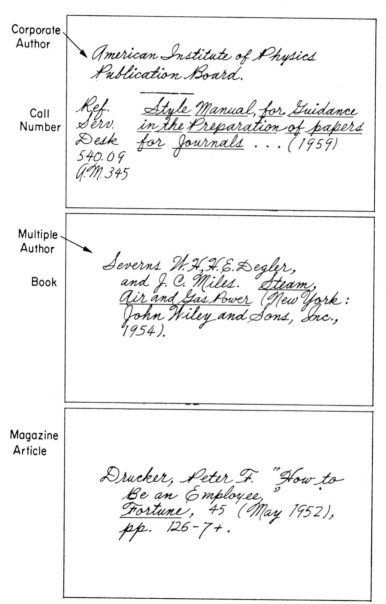

Corporate Author

American Institute of Physics Publication Board.

Call Number

Ref. *Style Manual, for Guidance*
Serv. *in the Preparation of papers*
Desk *for Journals . . . (1959)*
540.09
A.M.345

Multiple Author

Book

Severns W.H., H.E. Degler, and J.C. Miles. Steam, Air and Gas Power (New York: John Wiley and Sons, Inc., 1954).

Magazine Article

Drucker, Peter F. "How to Be an Employee," Fortune, 45 (May 1952), pp. 126-7+.

Fig. 1. Bibliography cards, 3″ x 5″.

completed this outline is replaced by a detailed topical outline for the writing of the rough draft.)

Making the handwritten bibliography card, the student's record of sources, is the initial operation in research. Every source must be listed separately on 3 by 5 inch cards. Cards are used because they can be carried handily and arranged easily in alphabetical order for the final copying of the bibliography. The form shown in Fig. 1 should be followed unless otherwise directed by the instructor. In fact, as a safeguard for obtaining what the instructor wants, it is advisable to make a few sample bibliography cards from different kinds of reference material and to check them with the instructor before a full bibliography is attempted.

Instructors' preferences in bibliography forms are known to vary a great deal. The sample form shown is acceptable for a wide variety of uses, perhaps may even be considered standard, but the student will be wise to note that, though many varieties of bibliography items may be encountered, the only "correct" form is the one his editorial department designates. Common sense will have to serve where sources are encountered which are not like the examples.

In a more ambitious project such as a thesis, an exhaustive bibliography made on 3 by 5 inch cards usually precedes the research work. The bibliography for this technical research paper, however, since it is only a representative bibliography, can be partially prepared at the beginning and completed as the reading progresses. The minimum number of articles to be read will depend somewhat on the scope of the problem. Ten or a dozen representative articles from different authors published at different times in several different magazines or journals would be the goal. A representative sample of the literature is taken across the time span when materials have been published, with the ratio of articles read following as nearly as practicable the total number of indexed articles in any one year. For example, if in 1956 the indexed articles (when the given subject was first reported) are represented by X, in 1957 by 2X, in 1958 by 4X, in 1959 by 8X, in 1960 by 3X, in 1961 by 2X, and in 1962 by X, it is obvious that a representative sample of the literature cannot be taken from any one year; in fact, the most desirable sample will be a ratio of articles selected from the best authors by years, in proportion to the whole numbers just given.

It is sometimes difficult to keep from reading more than is needed. Will power must be mustered here to read only for the task at hand, else the job is never finished. A researcher with a definite objective must discipline himself to read by a work plan and to cover the ground at a gallop. Note cards, 5 by 8 inches in size, should be carried at all times so that, when something is uncovered that

II A

Direct Quotation

Peter F. Drucker, "How to Be An Employee," *Fortune*, 45 (May 1952), pp. 126 - 7+

"The first question we might ask is: what can you learn in college that will help you in being an employee? . . . Do they also teach anything of value to the future employee? The answer is: Yes— they teach the one thing that is perhaps most valuable for the future employee to know. But very few students bother to learn it.

"This one basic skill is the ability to organize and express ideas in writing and in speaking."   p. 126

II A

Paraphrase

Drucker - 2

Drucker says that in the very large corporations the ability to express oneself is more important than any other skill.

p. 126

Fig. 2. Note cards, 5" x 8".

seems likely to serve the purpose at hand, it can be copied or paraphrased conveniently (see Fig. 2). Learning to take notes, useful dependable ones, is a required part of the technical man's training.

Systematic note-taking is a required part of this course project. A researcher working alone may be able to afford the luxury of cutting scraps of pages from his own books and magazines, scribbling his ideas on a pocket handkerchief, or keeping valuable data under his hat band. But this is not true for large projects. Every item of information recorded must follow a certain format and routine, and more than likely it must be in a form which can be coded and made readily accessible by means of electronic data-processing machines. The important thing to remember is that a form will always be required. The one prescribed here is probably the best for the circumstances. It has proved a timesaver for others. The returns in the quality of the assigned report and the time saved may or may not match the time it takes to follow the procedure. But on the longer research projects, stretching over several months and involving many people, a standard note-taking procedure is indispensable.

Here again sample note cards recording various kinds of material should be made first and checked for form with the instructor. The instructor will later wish to see all of the note cards made.

One should observe that the note card illustrations shown have bibliography information near the top upper right which resembles the bibliography item. Book publishers have been omitted, though, and the author's name is not reversed for alphabetical indexing. These and a few other changes are made so that this information can be transferred readymade to the first footnote reference.

One may wonder why the bibliography information is on the note card at all. Why not use a code which would tie the note card to a bibliography card? One of the most time-consuming (and heart-breaking) drudgeries in the writing of a research paper is to discover at the last moment that the code has somehow slipped out of phase with the bibliography cards and that it is necessary to return to the library and check the location of a reference. All intermediate codes which multiply the chances of error are discarded here for the greater assurance of an accurate reference. In approximately two minutes the full footnote reference can be added to the top of the note card; shortened forms of the footnote can be added on successive cards made from the same source.

Inclusive page numbers on magazine articles at the top of the note card serve as a further check on the accuracy of the page numbers given at the end of the note. Sometimes in a hurriedly written page number an error occurs which can be corrected by noting the inclusive pages of the article at the top of the note card.

Multiple Use of Note Cards

Note cards may be used for copying a direct quote, for copying facts, or for copying graphs, tables, drawings, and other forms of information. They can also be used for writing transitions, making summaries and paraphrases, and jotting down original ideas which arise during the research.

Once the project is under way the student should never be found without a supply of bibliography cards and note cards in his possession. Every important idea which comes to him should be written down on a note card. Coding the upper left-hand side of the card to match a major subdivision of the work plan will speed up the sorting process when the search is finished.

For those who may have made a sizable bibliography before starting, it will still be necessary to be on the lookout for new sources as the research progresses. Materials often turn up in unexpected places which have to be recorded on scratch paper. When this occurs they should be transferred to cards later.

Systematic Reading

One of the biggest timesavers is to read according to the work plan. Then, as the way toward the objective becomes clearer, the researcher should keep bringing his work plan into sharper focus by revision and addition. When one phase or major subdivision of the plan has been well documented, the next phase should be started, but without failing at any time to make notes for any part of the plan for which appropriate material is discovered. In this way the job is eventually completed. If it should turn out that some subtopic of the outline cannot be completed because of a lack of available information, the student should then revise his plan by substituting another subtopic which fits the logical development or change the viewpoint of a major subtopic as necessary so that the finished product is not lopsided. A paper lacks unity which promises more than it can deliver.

Another thing to remember is that the rope one tangles with careless note-taking may hang him at the end. A man taking combat engineering training is told to make his lashings good enough to risk his life on. Research notes should be made accurate enough to risk a reputation on. In note-taking, all the words of an author must be accurately indicated within quotation marks, even down to punctuation, spelling, and paragraphing. There is no place in technical research for sloppy reproduction of another man's words. The use of quotations and quotation marks will be discussed in section V, Writing the Paper.

Double-checking borrowed materials at the time note cards are made can save hours of verification later. Not only quotations but facts, figures, drawings, and so on should be put on the note card in such a manner that one may confidently return the materials to the stacks, knowing that the information he has is absolutely right and that he can reference it precisely without again checking the source. As a safety measure here, it is best to place a page number directly after each and every note taken. The point where quoted matter ends one page and begins the next should also be indicated. It may turn out that only the second part of the quotation is needed. A reference to the used portion of the quotation as having come from both pages will then be incorrect.

Where several note cards are made from the same source, the bibliography information at the top of succeeding cards should be shortened with a card number added for the student's reference. For example, the third card for an article by J. B. Brown on "Optical Masers" could be coded Brown-Maser-3. But shortened forms are not to be used on the first card from a given source. With the full form, all of the information needed for a complete footnote will be available for transfer from the note card when the rough draft is made.

A big temptation for most people in note-taking is to crowd too much on a single card, making it illegible. This is one of the reasons 5 by 8 cards are required for this project. Another temptation is to try to put more than one note on a card, or worse, to use the reverse side. The note-card purpose is largely defeated when this occurs. Note cards with more than one item or with writing on the reverse side cannot be shuffled and rearranged; hence, the problem of using the note card for the rough draft is greatly magnified.

As a final observation on undesirable shortcuts, one must not fail to distinguish clearly, during note-taking, what is his and what has been borrowed. One insurance against plagiarism is to make certain that all borrowed material, whether direct quotation, paraphrase, fact, or graphic aid, has a source indicated at the top of the card and that it is followed by a page number so that it can be accurately referenced. Material on note cards without footnote information at the upper right-hand side, without page numbers following the note, and without direct quotation marks around it will be the student's own work. Many of the note cards written during the search can be the creative ideas of the student. It would be foolish to let some of these bright ideas (and sometimes they really are) slip out of the mind in the belief that they can be recalled later. It is quite likely they cannot be recalled in the rush of writing the paper.

Assembling Research Material

Now that the time allotted for research has been spent and the rough draft day has arrived, how can one organize the mass of notes into an interesting scientific analysis of the problem he started out to explore? That depends on the value of the notes taken and to some extent on the analytical faculties.

If the cards have been coded according to the major subdivisions of the work outline, the mechanical sorting into piles of cards belonging to each major topic is no chore. If the reading was at random and no attempt was made to classify and earmark the material when it was read, it may take hours to reread the cards and to try to decide in what major subdivisions the material belongs. When the cards are sorted, the student may be disappointed to find a number of cards which just do not belong anywhere. One should not try to force these into the outline; they can spoil the symmetry and unity of the paper. The goal is, of course, to stay close enough to the plan during the research that this pile of notes may be kept to the minimum. But one should not throw this material away—not yet anyhow. Some of it may do later as footnotes, or it may become part of an appendix.

When each subdivision of cards has been made, it is a good plan to read through the notes thoughtfully, searching for the most logical order and, at the same time, adding a transition sentence here and there to the card so that the relationship between one and another is more apparent. If ideas and new insights come with this perspective review of the evidence, the student should make notes of these also. He should continue this process until the transitions are rather definitely indicated and the major and minor topics are firmly sketched in. If any conclusions come to mind they should be written on additional cards. Phraseology and sentence structure should not concern one at this time. A second time through the stacks of cards may bring the whole subject into still sharper focus. By now an outline has become pretty clearly established in the mind—it should be on paper too—for the writing of the full-length rough draft.

V. Writing the Paper

Once the information is fairly well in hand, the writing of the paper can become a creative and fascinating part of the job. In any project worthy of the name research paper, there are two distinct writing phases: one, the roughhewn, rapidly written, continuous first draft and, two, the calculated, finely-chiseled, and, finally, polished work.

The Rough Draft

The quality of the finished draft is directly proportional to the usefulness of the rough draft. Here are a few helpful hints and directions for making the rough draft.

When the note cards have been arranged in the order of the topical outline, the student may start writing. If nothing new comes to mind, the note cards should be copied, leaving plenty of white space between lines and using only one side of the paper. When a note is copied or paraphrased, it is followed by an asterisk.*

---

* And the full footnote must be shown between parallel lines, this way, immediately after.

As shown, two parallel lines are then drawn across the width of the page in the next double space following the asterisk, and the full footnote information for the first reference is copied between the lines. These lines may be put in with pen or pencil. They are to set off and safeguard the reference. Later, if it is discovered that this information will serve better in another location, the note can be cut out with scissors and moved anywhere with perfect assurance that it cannot become detached from its footnote reference before it reaches its final position.

Rough drafts may be made on any kind of paper, using ink, pencil, or typewriter. All that is necessary is that the rough draft be a readable copy with enough white space to encourage revision. Crowding not only discourages revision; it makes revision impossible. The more revisions that can be clearly accomplished on the same draft, the better the final paper. This is a point which must be observed: Plenty of white space on the rough draft makes it possible for every word of the final draft to be eventually written on one rough draft. Though it may be necessary to place a few inserts and rearrange some pages, if plenty of white space is allowed for revision, it will save copying the rough draft a second time to produce the final copy.

Revisions of the first draft must not spill over into the space between the parallel lines reserved for footnote reference. Words or phrases trailing off into the footnote territory can be mistaken by the typist for a part of the footnote and thus garble what, up to that time, had been a dependable reference. One should note in the preceding example that rough-draft footnotes are not numbered, that they fall immediately below the point of reference, and that the lines go from margin to margin. (In the final draft, footnotes are accumulated at the bottom of each page.) The asterisk, representing the superscript number to be added later, is indented five spaces, and no space is allowed between the asterisk and the first word of the footnote.

If writing the entire footnote reference interferes too much with the creative processes—and it does for some people—an asterisk alone may serve between the parallel lines until the section has been completed. Every effort should be made to speed up the writing of the rough draft. If the whole paper can be done in one sitting, it tends to improve the continuity and interest.

Dummy space should be left in the rough draft for formulas, graphs, tables, or figures which are to be added within the manuscript.

When the main body of the report has been done, a rough draft should also be made of the other parts of the paper, including the title page, table of contents, list of figures, abstract, and bibliography, and if there is one, an appendix. At this point, it is a good idea to let the rough draft lie. The ideas, all that are available at this time at least, have been captured and tied down by the words on the paper. They will be there when the student returns a little later with an even more finely sharpened pencil. While the rough draft cools, the time should be well spent in completing the drawings, tables, and the graphs which are to be incorporated in the final draft; directions for the preparation of these graphic aids will be given under the study of Form in the following section.

The Finished Paper

In the finished paper attention will be given to three major subdivisions: form, content, and mechanics of expression.

Form. Organizing and presenting information in a standard way is a time-saver for the writer and an aid to the understanding of the report by the reader. Standard form implies logical presentation and accurate documentation, qualities which are found in any report that is of value to others. The form here detailed is widely acceptable; it results in a neat, readable, and easily indexed report, with little left to the imagination and nothing left, it is hoped, to puzzle the reader of the report.

The finished report should not begin as long as one can reread the rough draft and still find spots which need revising. When the last reading turns up no errors in mechanics of expression, no errors in factual data, no additions or deletions in the footnotes; when the subtopics have all been checked against the table of contents; when the figures, formulas, and tables have been checked for continuous numbering; when the graphic art is completed and tied to the text by reference; and when the direct quotations are indicated and marked for single space or double space (see following); then, and not until then, should the student begin typing his finished draft. One should bear in mind that changes in the rough draft can be made in a moment with a pencil; changes in the finished draft may require retyping one or more pages or renumbering all pages or renumbering all footnotes.

The following information is given in the sequence in which it will most probably be needed by the student as he prepares the final draft of the research paper. These fourteen items comprise the specifications for form.

– 21 –

1. Paper, ink: The paper should be plain white bond, #16 weight or better. (Onion skin, Ezerase, or other specially finished paper will not be acceptable here.) Handwritten papers may be in blue, blue-black, or black ink on wide-line composition paper (⅜ inch) or on every other line on narrow-lined paper, but not engineering graph paper.

2. Title page: Unless otherwise directed the title page example should be followed. No cover page is needed.

3. Table of contents: The table of contents follows the topical outline of the paper; Roman numerals are used for the major divisions, but major and minor subtopics are simply indented to the right to show subordination. All topics must match the wording of the topics in the report; pages, too, must be accurately shown.

4. List of figures: Photographs, drawings, graphs, and tables may be included in the list of figures as shown in the example. Graphic aids which are referenced several times are given page numbers, while those referenced only once or twice are mounted facing the page where the first reference is made.

5. Abstract: Two general types of abstracts are used for technical papers: the summary type and the essence type. In this course only the essence type is acceptable. The heart of the paper becomes the topic of the one-paragraph abstract; supporting detail is drawn from the significant ideas of the main subdivisions of the paper. The length is 150 to 200 words. (In general practice the number of paragraphs is not limited, but the word count of the abstract is always limited.)

   The essence paragraph abstracts should include all that is needed for the reader to know the nature of the subject and problem treated, the principal evidence, and the conclusion reached. These should be stated in a straightforward manner, without footnotes. A caution is in order here, however; the abstract should claim no more than is conclusively shown by the paper. The essence type abstract makes no reference to the paper. It is an independent unified statement in miniature of the essential information in the paper. It should be written on a separate sheet, centered within the margins as shown in the example, and page numbered at the bottom of the sheet in lower case Roman numerals.

– 22 –

6. Headings: The subject of the paper may or may not be repeated at the beginning of the text. If it is, it should be centered about two inches below the top of the page. The first Roman numeral subdivision follows four spaces below the title of the paper. Long topics should be broken at logical phrase endings and the remainder of the topic centered on the the next double space below the first line of the topic.

   Spacing of the subtopics within each section is as follows: First-level topics, corresponding to A, B, C, of the outline, are begun at the margin a triple space below the last section, but they are not indented from the margin. These topics are underlined but not followed by a period. A double space is allowed, and a new line of text is begun with paragraph indention.

   Sub-subtopics, corresponding to Arabic numerals in the outline, are indented with the paragraph indention of five spaces to the right of the margin, underlined, and followed by a period. The text continues after the sub-sub without shifting to a new line.

7. Margins: General practice leans toward a neatly spaced open text with margins of 1¼ to 1½ inches on the punched side of the paper and ¾ to 1 inch at the bottom, opposite side, and top. At least two inches should be allowed at the top of the first page of the introduction.

8. Paging: Pages of the introductory material are numbered at the center of the bottom, ¾ inch above the bottom edge of the paper, in small Roman numerals. The title page, however, does not show a number, though a page number is allowed for it. The table of contents begins on page ii. Arabic page numerals are used for the text. They begin on the second page with an Arabic numeral 2 in the right-hand margin, a triple space above the first line of the text but not closer than ¾ inch to the top edge of the paper.[6] If main subdivisions are begun on separate pages, the numeral for that page may be omitted, though one must be allowed.

9. Graphic aids: Graphic aids are used for dramatizing information. They

---

[6] Other styles of manuscript paging may require that page numbers be centered at either the bottom or the top, or that they be spaced midway between the top center and the right-hand margin. Paging for this manuscript example is at the bottom center to prevent confusion with the consecutive page numbers of the text.

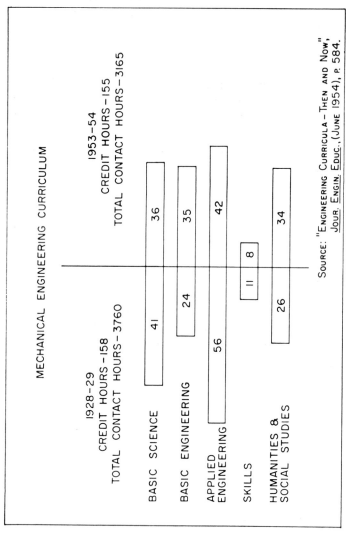

Fig. 3. Bar graph. (Student example)

should aid, not puzzle the reader. In the scientific report they are almost indispensable. There are three or four basic types of graphic aids, each of which will be discussed in turn. The general requirements of all graphic aids are that they be simple, photographically reproducible, adapted to the kind of information displayed, and properly credited to source when borrowed (see Fig. 3).

All graphic aids in the research paper must be drawn in black ink on a good grade of white paper—not vellum, not tissue, not plastic. Completely opaque linen drawing cloth is acceptable, but plain white paper is preferred. In addition to these general requirements, the details of drawings should be held to a minimum. Legends and labels on drawings must be easily read, the smallest letters not less than 3/16 inch high and the main headings proportionately larger. This is to permit reduction in size when graphic aids are reproduced by the photographic process.[7]

Alphabets should not be mixed or the slant changed once the style has been set. If the appearance of the drawing would be enhanced by a frame, then a frame should be added.

The margins of graphic aids should fall within the margins of the text. Graphic aids which are to receive page numbers should have a margin of 1¾ in. on the left; those which are to be mounted facing a page in the text should have the greater margin on the right. Credit for a borrowed graphic aid may be given at the bottom, a little to the right of center within the frame, if there is sufficient room, or it may follow the descriptive caption after the figure number.

Some general hints are in order for preparing graphic aids. When a graphic aid is borrowed, the credit line should give the manner of reproduction; for example, one should say the graph is "redrawn" or "modified" or "traced" or "redrawn in part" from such and such a source, with the figure number and caption of the original given (see Figs. 4 and 5).

---

[7] Pica capital letters made with the typewriter can be substituted for the minimum-sized lettering if carefully made. A light, quick tap of the key, using the back spacer for a second strike, makes a much smoother and blacker letter than one hard clunk of the key.

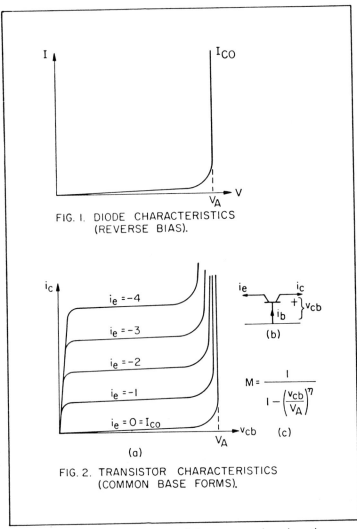

FIG. I. DIODE CHARACTERISTICS
(REVERSE BIAS).

FIG. 2. TRANSISTOR CHARACTERISTICS
(COMMON BASE FORMS).

Fig. 4. Simplified curves. Two small figures are placed on the same
page. (Student example)

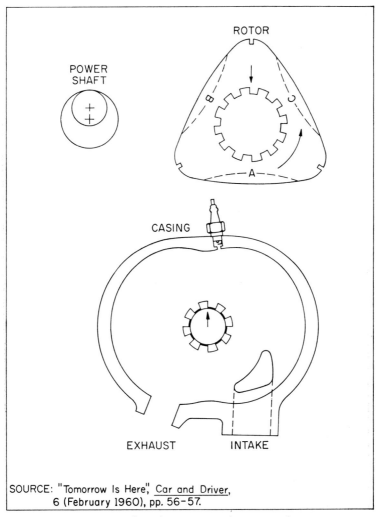

POWER
SHAFT

ROTOR

CASING

EXHAUST   INTAKE

SOURCE: "Tomorrow Is Here", *Car and Driver*,
6 (February 1960), pp. 56–57.

Fig. 5. Outline drawing. (Student example)

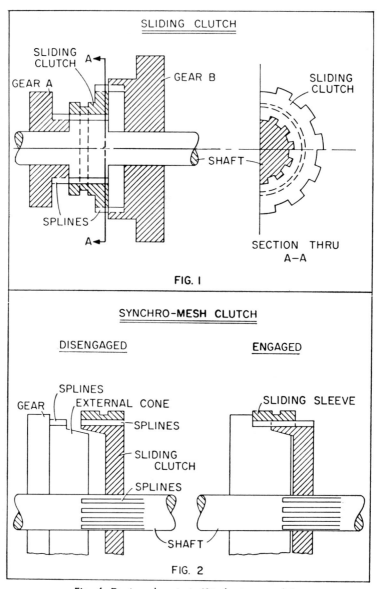

Fig. 6. Design drawing. (Student example)

Layout drawings should be simplified or done schematically (see Fig. 6); raw data should be processed into tables; statistical information should be rendered into pie graphs, bar graphs, or curves. Bar graphs are constructed so that the bars have blank spaces between them. Curves are never drawn on graph paper; plain white paper is used, with the significant lines drawn in with black ink.

Normally graphic aids are placed on separate pages, using the same margins as those set up for the text. Two or more may be placed on a page if they are small and closely related. Information which can be shown in a graphic aid not exceeding three vertical inches, including the double space above and below it, may be placed within the text. Large graphic aids on white paper may be used in standard foldout sizes so that a foldout may be made vertically or horizontally. Drawings on horizontal foldout pages must be oriented so that the reader views them by rotating the paper clockwise. No page number is allotted a graphic aid when it is mounted facing a reference in the text. Page numbers, when assigned, are at the top right hand approximately ¾ inch from the edge of the paper.

For the rough draft copy, graphic aids can be free-hand drawn in pencil and placed in their approximate positions in the text. For the finished draft, however, the drawings must be neatly inked on white paper. If photographs are to be used as graphic aids, they should be given "dummy" space in the manuscript but not pasted in place. Instead, photographs with their figure numbers and captions should be enclosed in an envelope securely mounted on the inside of the back cover. All graphic art should be simple and functional in design, photographically reproducible, and if not orignal with the writer, accurately referenced and credited to its source.

10. Footnotes: The first full footnote, the form used for the first reference to any given source, is placed one double space below the dividing line following the text at the bottom of the page (see examples). Footnotes are numbered consecutively beginning with the Arabic numeral 1. Every important piece of borrowed information which advances the thesis or aids the solution of the problem should be footnoted, whether a direct quotation, a summary, a paraphrase, or an isolated fact. Information which has become a part of every technical man's knowledge, or which at least is common knowledge within the area of specialization discussed, need not be referenced.

Sometimes excessive footnotes can be combined in a general note giving inclusive pages. Or a note to the reader can be made citing a whole chapter or article from which a theory or process has been summarized. Common sense is again the best guide for adequate credit. A direct quotation, a significant fact, a graphic aid, must always be pinpointed to the exact page. Paraphrases or summaries, however, may be referenced either to a single page or to inclusive pages.

The first reference to any source requires a full footnote. Footnote form varies slightly with the kind of source. For a book, the author's full name is given in normal order, followed by a comma; the title is italicized (underlined); the place and year of publication are enclosed by parentheses, followed by a comma; the page number or number of the reference is indicated by a small p for one page and two p's for more than one (pp.). For a first reference to a magazine article the title, enclosed by quotation marks, is followed by a comma; the name of the magazine is in italics followed by a comma; the volume number, with no intervening comma, precedes the date. In this style the date is enclosed by parentheses (see footnote samples in Appendix I). One should note that commas and periods always fall inside quotation marks when these are used at the end of titles. All useful information, whether book, magazine, or other source, should be given in the first reference.

The shortened forms used for the second and succeeding references are less standardized. The important rule of thumb here is to remember that, where there is any possibility the reader might be confused by the shortened form, it should be lengthened. The footnote is for the reader's use, not the convenience of the writer.

In technical papers the tendency is to shy away from the more literary forms of reference, most writers preferring to say simply, Smith, p .21, instead of Smith, op. cit. (opere citato, in the work cited), p. 21. Ibid. (Latin ibidem, in the same place) is used more, though it, too, is restricted. In technical papers Ibid. is similar to a ditto sign; it is never allowed to stand alone or to serve as the first reference on the page. It is always capitalized, since it is the initial word on the line; and it is followed by a period because it is an abbreviation and underlined to show italics for the Latin. Ibidem is used to advantage when it can stand for a long name or a title for which no author has been given. If additional references are made to the same source but to different page locations, ibid. should be followed by the page number, thus: Ibid., p. 22.

Sometimes the beginner is baffled by the problem of maintaining footnote spacing within bottom page margins. The space required for footnotes can be calculated easily from the rough draft. Remembering that the footnotes are single spaced with double space between the individual footnotes, the student may quickly total lines and spaces and then convert them to vertical inches. If the total number of vertical inches needed for footnotes is known, a scale or ruler can be used while the paper is still in the typewriter to find and mark the edge of the paper with a pencil where the last line of text should stop. The point may just as easily be found by subtracting the vertical inches from 11 and measuring down to the same point. When the typist reaches the pencil mark in the margin he can throw the carriage and make the divider line with confidence, knowing that the last line of the last footnote will fall not lower than ¾ inch from the bottom of the page and not higher than 1½ inches from the bottom, the minimum and maximum page margins.

8–1/4"

MEASURED DOWN

For example, one may suppose his particular typewriter moves on the average one vertical inch for each six lines or spaces. Three superscripts have already been encountered on the page; from the rough draft he estimates the first note will require three single-spaced lines, a second note will require two, and a third, one line. Adding these, beginning with the last line of the third footnote and moving upward to the last line of the text, the following sums are obtained:

$$1+2+3=6 \text{ lines for note material}$$
$$1+1+1=3 \text{ spaces, two between footnotes}$$
and one below divider line
1 divider line
1 space below text
—
Total   11 spaces needed below text

*First footnote ....

**Second footnote ....

1–3/4"

MEASURED UP

***Third footnote ....

1" (3/4 MIN.)

Eleven lines (or spaces) on this typewriter equal 1 and ⅚ vertical inches; rounding this to the nearest quarter and adding a one-inch bottom page margin, it is seen that the last line of the text should stop 2¾ inches from the bottom of the page.

11. Direct quotations: Some type of "he said" expression must always precede formal quotations, and the quoted matter must be accurately indicated and referenced. It must also be quoted in its context; that is, the meaning must not be twisted to apply a meaning other than that intended by the quoted author. Changing the intent of a quoted author's statement by quoting fragments of sentences is not ethical and can lead to libel. No wording may be changed in a direct quote. When errors are quoted from the original they are followed by the Latin word <u>sic</u> (meaning "so it was") within brackets (not parentheses), thus: [sic]. Sic is not an abbreviation; hence, no period. When it is necessary to make a comment or to explain something within a quotation, the words of the editorial comment are always enclosed within brackets.

Quoted matter may be shortened by the use of dots (points of ellipsis) to show omitted words, as follows:

Omission at the beginning of a sentence ". . . followed by the remainder of the quotation to the end of the sentence."

Omission within a sentence: "The important thing to remember . . . is that the dots are equally spaced within the sentence at the point of the omission."

"Omission at the end of the sentence. . . ." The fourth dot represents the period.

Omission of a sentence or more within a paragraph: "Four dots will occur at the point where the material was omitted. . . . But the dot representing the period of the preceding sentence will be separated from the other three by an intervening space."

Omission of a paragraph or more is represented by a centered row of five equally spaced asterisks, thus:

*   *   *   *   *

When less than a paragraph is quoted, no paragraph indention is observed. When more than a paragraph is quoted, the beginning is indented whether or not it is the beginning of the original paragraph.

"... by the external resistance of the circuit. This phenomena has been studied rather thoroughly by S. L. Miller in the low signal, junction transistor types (particularly alloy diffused junctions).[1] This research has led to experimentally observed results concerning the multiplication of minority carriers coming from the high resistivity side of germanium step junctions to a value approaching infinity at the breakdown voltage mentioned before.[2] Miller contends that the diode curve in the region well below breakdown is multiplied (near V_A) by an empirical formula

$$M \cong \frac{1}{1 - \left(\dfrac{V}{V_A}\right)^n} \tag{1}$$

where V_A is the breakdown voltage, V is the junction voltage, and n is a number which depends upon the resistivity and resistivity type of the high resistivity side of the junction.[3] For the alloy diffused..."

Fig. 7. Formula within text. (Student example)

But each succeeding paragraph quoted is carefully indented according to the indention of the original paragraphs.

12. Formulas: One of the differences between technical and popular papers lies in the use of mathematics. Formulas may be used when they are needed, though they should never be used when the same story can be better told in words. Simple term formulas may be used within the text as words, or they may be centered on a separate line for the sake of emphasis when it is desired. But complex formulas (any formulas containing terms written above and below the line) must be centered on separate lines with double or triple space below the text and above the explanation, which must always accompany the formula (see Fig. 7). It is much better to use derived formulas and, if necessary, to show the derivation in an appendix. Each formula within the paper (basic formulas, that is) should be numbered on the right-hand margin in Arabic numerals in parentheses, beginning with (1) and going consecutively through the paper.

13. Bibliography: The list of sources in the bibliography must be made alphabetically with the last names of the authors. If articles have no authors given, the corporate author may be used if given (as for technical societies and research organizations). A period follows the author's name. Sources without authors are indexed by the first word of the title (not prepositions, articles, or conjunctions).

Swinging indention is required to obtain the full benefit of the indexed first three letters of the initial word. Three to five spaces after the first letter of the initial word of the item will serve as the return margin for the second line of the bibliography item. Bibliography items are written on consecutive single-spaced lines within the established margins, but double spaced between items. Bibliography items are always closed by a period. Examples of forms for magazines, books, pamphlets, and general references with single and multiple authors are shown in the bibliography at the end of this chapter.

14. Appendix: Any material which has some oblique bearing on the subject, yet is not a part of the main development of the subject, should be placed in an appendix. This might include such things as raw or unprocessed data sheets, test results, maps, tables, definitions, terms, symbols, and formulas. Headings and margins in the appendix should follow the general style of the paper, but the material may be single spaced with double

spaces between paragraphs. Pages may be numbered in the same series as the paper.

Content: Introduction, Body, and Conclusion. The content of a research paper is what is said. It is entirely possible to be so concerned with the outward appearance of the paper that nothing of value gets in, and that what does appear to be of value is later found incomplete and unreliable. To be certain that the paper says what the student intends it to say, a time-tested formula should be used: There must be a beginning, a middle, and an end.

Communication, even on the simplest level, requires some form of <u>introduction.</u> The writer must present the subject, purpose, scope, and plan so that the reader may establish a frame of reference to receive the communication before him. All doubt must be removed from the reader's mind about the exact meaning the writer intends to give his subject. A definition of the subject will often involve a point of view and some indication of the significance the subject has. A statement of purpose should naturally follow the comments on significance. This statement will indicate what the writer expects to accomplish in the presentation of the paper. Announcing the scope of the paper is important, too, since this aids the reader in understanding precisely what ground is to be covered. Adherence to a previously announced scope limits or focuses the reader's (and the writer's) attention on a certain aspect of a subject. A clear indication of scope prepares the reader by marking the boundaries of the discussion so that he is not disappointed when the writer fails to include something expected but which lies outside the established scope. Introductions, for the longer papers, should also include the plan of presentation. The plan gives the sequence for major subdivisions; it should be stated last so that the reader has the first topic already in mind when he has finished the introduction and has begun to read the body of the paper.

The introduction may contain other special instructions to help the reader understand the writer's reasons for his mode of presentation. But to omit one of the elements named—subject, purpose, scope, and plan—is to write an incomplete introduction.

The <u>body</u> of the report must be logically subdivided. The subdivisions must not only seem logical to the writer, but this logical relationship of subdivisions must be clearly indicated to the reader. When the writer has decided upon the most suitable order of arrangement—chronological, simple to complex, cause to effect, or whatever is applicable—this order controls the subdivisions in the paper. Each subdivision in turn should be further broken down into sizes suitable for detailed treatment. Both major and minor subdivisions (indicated by marginal or indented heads, respectively) should be carefully evaluated to determine whether the rank indicated is logical and whether the headings which are of equal rank are parallel. Main topics must be descriptive of the material to be discussed, perhaps even giving a hint of the viewpoint to be taken. Sub-subtopics may be shorter, though they, too, should be well phrased and appropriate.

At the beginning of each major subdivision it is well to write a combination transition and introductory paragraph to serve the double purpose of telling the reader where he has been and where he will be going in the new subdivision. The headings themselves cannot serve as transitions. The text must carry its own transitions in addition to the relationships indicated by headings. Further breakdown in subject should be shown by transitional sentences at the beginning or ending of paragraphs.

In a short paper of this type, 4000 to 5000 words, three to seven major subdivisions are considered normal. If the student has fewer than three or more than seven Roman numeral subdivisions, it is almost certain that his analysis of the problem is faulty, and some of his major subdivisions should be further subdivided or the number reduced, as the case may be.

Not only must the subdivisions of the body seem logical to the reader, but the material within the body must be plausible. Statements of fact must be supported by authority acceptable to the reader—objective tests, the word of an expert, statistical records. To include material in the body of the research paper which is merely the opinion of the writer or to make unwarranted generalizations is to short-circuit the analysis and cancel the effectivenes of the report. Personal judgments should be reserved for the interpretation which follows the presentation of evidence. Opinion has its place, but it will have value only after the writer has shown that he has fully evaluated what others have had to say.

In addition to the qualities of logic and readability, the reader must believe that what he is reading is significant. A statement in the introduction of the significance of the material is not enough. This significance should be referred to occasionally to maintain intellectual suspense and to keep the goal clearly in the reader's mind.

Other characteristics of the body of the paper are unity, coherence, and emphasis. Unity is obtained by clearly marking out the scope and plan of the subject matter at the beginning and then following the plan. Coherence is obtained to some extent by transitional words, phrases, clauses, and entire paragraphs which cross-reference and tie every part of the paper to some other part. Each new idea should lead naturally into the next until the very last one is reached. Without this quality of coherence the material flocculates or falls apart in unrelated clumps. Emphasis may be gained by the repetition of certain key ideas and by arrangement. The topics which are considered of greatest importance should get the most detailed treatment, and they should occupy the positions of most notice. The writer should check to see whether he has inadvertently emphasized an insignificant or less important aspect of his subject. A test for this might well be the reading of the paper by a friend who knows nothing of the subject matter, who is then asked to comment on what he thinks are the most important topics discussed. If his answer coincides with the writer's intentions, it is safe to conclude that the emphasis has been placed where it belongs.

There are two general types of conclusions in technical papers. Where no particular problem has been studied, and where the imparting of information has been the general purpose, a summary type of conclusion is used. In the summary one simply recapitulates, in a concise manner, the important points made in each of the major subdivisions. The other type of conclusion, the conclusion involving a decision, must be studied in more detail.

In a decision type of conclusion it is customary to restate the problem first and then to review the evidence as presented in the report (no new evidence should be presented in the conclusion). A careful analysis follows in which the evidence is weighed and a judgment is rendered. One should note that only at this point, and not until this point, is the researcher permitted to give his personal opinion. Here he may freely do so, provided his opinion can be supported from the evidence presented. The conclusion he reaches may be his alone, or it may be the consensus of authorities which he has made his own, or it may be his own in some respect and in other respects one shared by others. In any case, the opinion expressed should be clearly stated and identified as to source, whether the writer's own or another's.

The conclusions in a research paper are its only reason for being. In industry one of three things happens when the researcher fails to reach a conclusion: He is asked to do additional research so that a decision can be made. His assignment is given to another person for reevaluation and checking, or for additional research as necessary to arrive at a definite decision. Or the subject is abandoned. It is most likely to be the first. Every resource should therefore be exhausted to reach a sound decision before the report is written. (For additional information on introductions, transitions, and conclusions, see Chapter 6.)

Mechanics of Expression. All of the intrinsic and extrinsic qualities of technical style as defined in Chapter 7 are included here by reference as requirements for the research paper. Particular stress will be laid on the extrinsic qualities of style— clarity and compression. This, of course, implies standard use of punctuation and grammar.

In the final reading, one should check to see that all sentences are complete and varied enough in form to prevent boredom. The voice and mood of verbs should also be checked. The indicative mood, active or passive voice, may be used freely, but the subjunctive mood (including modal auxiliaries) should be used sparingly and the imperative not at all, unless the stage has been set for giving commands. The tense, voice, mood, number, and person of the verb should be used in accordance with the accepted technical practice. Though research papers are sometimes written in the first person, they are not so written here. The third person is used exclusively.

From the larger view, every paragraph should be checked for unity. Paragraphs here are generally shorter than in other kinds of writing, but this should tend to improve unity and coherence, not serve as license for unrelated ideas which the writer is unable to arrange in a logical manner. Incomplete paragraphs may be a sign of an incomplete understanding of the subject matter by the writer. Transitions help out here, and standard punctuation can do wonders in speeding up the understanding. The goal, of course, is to write in such a manner that the idea is clear at all times, with nothing to puzzle the reader or cause a momentary wandering of his attention.

VI. Conclusion

This chapter of the text has attempted to answer most of the questions on research procedure and on the form, content, and mechanics of the assigned library paper.

By acquiring the ability to use the research tools of the library to obtain and analyze the published opinions of others in the solution of a technical problem, the student has come closer to the self-reliance and technical competence expected of the professionally trained man. The process of selecting a subject suitable for the practice research paper and of learning the library system for coding and filing published information has shown the student how and where to begin. It has been shown that it is just as necessary to maintain engineering accuracy in references, facts, figures, and graphic aids with which the student deals in a research report as it is to maintain physical tolerances in the fabrication of an engineering structure.

In summary, this section has been devoted to research methods as they affect the advancement of the professional engineer or technical man. It has shown how to find published material on a given subject, how to document that information, and finally how to classify and interpret the published opinions of others in a creditable and effective manner. It has taught a procedure and a form of research paper. Standard form, it has been shown, is that form which the research writer must follow in a given circumstance. If the student has learned to follow instructions here, he has learned to work within the framework of specifications, a lesson every engineer must learn. And further, it may be concluded, the student has gained experience in the sustained concentration needed for some of the longer reports he will soon be called upon to write when he begins his career as a professional engineer.

The format and manuscript style of this chapter are essentially what the student is expected to use for writing a technical research paper. The research paper example following the chapter Appendices may make it a little easier to translate these instructions into practice.

BIBLIOGRAPHY

Hicks, Tyler. Successful Technical Writing (New York: McGraw-Hill Book Company, 1959).

Ives, Sumner. A New Handbook For Writers (New York: Alfred A. Knopf, 1960).

Mills, Gordon H., and John A. Walter. Technical Writing, rev. ed. (New York: Rinehart and Company, Inc., 1962).

Perrin, Porter. Writer's Guide and Index to English (Chicago: Scott, Foresman and Company, 1959).

Schultz, Howard, and Robert Webster. Technical Report Writing (New York: David McKay Company, Inc., 1962).

Sherman, Theodore. Modern Technical Writing (Englewood Cliffs, N.J.: Prentice-Hall, Inc., 1955).

Sypherd, W., Alvin Fountain, and V. Gibbens. Manual of Technical Writing (Chicago: Scott, Foresman and Company, 1957).

Van Hagan, Charles. Report Writers' Handbook (Englewood Cliffs, N.J.: Prentice-Hall, Inc., 1961).

Zall, Paul. Elements of Technical Report Writing (New York: Harper and Brothers, 1962).

APPENDIX I

Sample Footnotes

BOOKS

[1] G. R. Harrison, R. C. Lord, and J. R. Loofbourow, Practical Spectroscopy (New York, 1948), p. 1.

[2] Harrison and others, p. 1.

[3] Frederick E. Terman, Electronic and Radio Engineering (New York, 1955), pp. 672–673.

MAGAZINES

[4] R. W. Powell, "Infrared Tracking," ARS Journal, 29 (December 1959), p. 973.

[5] David Novick, "Mathematics: Logic, Quantity, and Method," Review of Economics and Statistics, XXXVI, No. 4 (November 1954), p. 358.

[6] Novick, p. 358.

[7] E. Niesen and others, "Water Cooling of Low-Power Klystrons Used in the Laboratory," Review of Scientific Instruments, 29 (September 1958), pp. 791–792.

[8] G. E. Jablonski, "Space Charge Neutralization by Fission Fragments in Direct Conversion Plasma Diode," Journal of Applied Physics, 30 (December 1959), p. 2018.

[9] Jablonski, p. 2019.

[10] "Cesium Cell Converts Heat Directly to Alternating Current," Electrical World, 153 (January 1960), p. 64.

[11] Ibid., p. 65.

GENERAL REFERENCE

[12] James Stokley, "Electronics," Encyclopedia Britannica, Book of the Year, 1960, p. 228.

[13] Reference Data for Radio Engineers, 3rd ed. (1949), pp. 228-230.
(No shortened form. Ibid. could be used if a second note to this same source followed next on the same page.)

APPENDIX II

Sample Bibliography (from a student paper)

Bak, Borge. Elementary Introduction to Molecular Spectra (Amsterdam: North-Holland Publishing Company, 1954).

Barnes, R. Bowling. Infrared Spectroscopy (New York: Reinhold Publishing Corporation, 1944).

Cohen, David. "Infrared Emission from High-Frequency Discharges on CO_2," Journal of Applied Physics, 28 (June 1957), 737–741.

Cook, A., and P. J. Taylor. "Simple Mulling Technique for the Preparation of Samples for infrared Spectroscopy," Chemistry and Industry, 1 (January 25, 1958), 95.

Hall, J. D. Industrial Applications of Infrared (New York: McGraw-Hill Book Company, Inc., 1947).

Hallett, L. T. "Analyst's Column," Analytical Chemistry, 30 (April 1958), 55A–57A.

Harris, N. J. "Characteristics of Junctions in Germanium," Journal of Applied Physics, 29 (May 1958), 764–771.

Harrison, R. G., Richard C. Lord, and John R. Loofbourow. Practical Spectroscopy (New York: Prentice-Hall, Inc., 1948).

Hawkes, J. C. "Infrared Spectroscopy as a Quantitative Analytical Method in General Chemicals Manufacture," Journal of Applied Chemistry, 7 (March 7, 1957), 123–130.

Juzycz, M. S. "Fundamentals of Infrared," Electrical Engineering, 77 (August 1958), 704–706.

Klass, P. J. "Infrared Challenges Radar's Monopoly," Aviation Week, 66 (March 4, 1957), 50–61.

Muller, R. H. "Infrared Absorption Spectrum Techniques Are Ideal in Medical Research, Criminological Investigation, or Forensic Tests," Analytical Chemistry, 28 (April 1956), 41A–44A.

Powell, R. W. "Infrared Tracking," ARS Journal, 29 (December 1959), 973–980.

Roberts, D. H. "The Design of Infrared Spectrometers," Chemistry and Industry, 1 (April 20, 1957), 482–485.

Smith, R. A. "Recent Developments in the Detection and Measurement of Infrared Radiation," The Scientific Monthly, 83 (January 1956), 3–18.

STUDENT EXAMPLE

Library Research Paper

Report on

THERMOELECTRIC POWER GENERATION

Technical Communication
Arizona State University
Tempe, Arizona

by
Lawrence H. Stubbe
(Senior Electrical Engr. Student)
December 11, 1961

TABLE OF CONTENTS

LIST OF FIGURES

ABSTRACT

There are three basic phenomena upon which theromelectric power generation is based. These are the Seebeck, the Peltier, and the Thomson effects. Experimentally, relationships have been established for each of these effects. Although the Seebeck effect is the most directly related to thermoelectric power generation, the other two effects are not negligible in an analysis of the subject. Lord Kelvin has derived two equations which give the relationship between these effects. Using Kelvin's two relations and the definition of efficiency, an expression can be obtained for the efficiency of a thermoelectric generator. Based on current device theory, the maximum theoretical efficiency of a thermoelectric generator, working into an optimum load, is about 20%. In order to increase the efficiency of a thermoelectric generator, both the "figure of merit" and the "Carnot efficiency" must be increased. The figure of merit varies as the square of the Seebeck coefficient and inversely as the product of the electrical resistivity and the thermal conductivity. The Carnot efficiency is the quotient of the temperature difference across the sample divided by the average temperature. This information indicates to the designer what properties a material must have in order to be a good thermoelectric element.

I. Introduction

In recent years there has been a renewed interest in thermoelectric phenomena. Thermoelectric phenomena are those effects by which heat energy is converted into electrical energy and vice versa. Electricity obtained reversibly from heat is called thermoelectricity. This renewed interest is demonstrated by the large number of recent publications on this subject and by the amount of effort that is being expended on basic research in this field. The United States government alone, in the past decade, has spent several million dollars for research and development of thermoelectric materials and devices. This renewed interest has been stimulated largely because of the recent advances in space technology. These advances have made it increasingly important to have a source of power which has a long life and a high power-to-weight ratio. Thermoelectric generators using semiconducting materials show promise of meeting these requirements.

The purpose of this report is to give the reader an insight into the subject of thermoelectric power generation. The basic thermoelectric phenomena are discussed first, and then the relationships between them are shown. These relationships are then used in the development of equations in the design of thermoelectric generators. Only those mathematical relationships are given which are considered necessary for an understanding of the subject so that the reader is given a general understanding of subject rather than specific information for the design of a thermoelectric generator.

II. Thermoelectric Phenomena

There are three basic reversible thermoelectric phenomena which have been experimentally observed and studied: the Seebeck effect, the Peltier effect, and the Thomson effect. Although only the Seebeck effect is directly related to the generation of thermoelectric power, there is a definite relationship between the three effects which makes it necessary to study all of them in order to understand the subject.

Seebeck Effect

The Seebeck effect was first observed by Johann Seebeck, a German physicist, in 1821. Seebeck was experimenting with strips of copper and antimony when he noticed that the needle of a magnet deflected whenever he touched his hand to one of the junctions. He correctly ascribed the cause to the heating of one of the junctions, but he was unaware that the magnetic field was caused by an electric current in the circuit. This was the first recorded observation of this phenomenon, which was later named the Seebeck effect after its discoverer. It was later found that the output voltage produced between two given materials was proportional to the temperature difference between the two junctions. This statement can be expressed mathematically as

$$\Delta V = S_{ab} \Delta T \tag{1}$$

where ΔV is the open circuit voltage, S_{ab} is a proportionality constant (Seebeck coefficient), and ΔT is the difference between the temperature of the hot junction T_h and the cold junction T_c. It should be noted that although S_{ab} is commonly

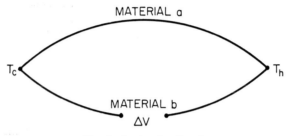

Fig. 1. Seebeck effect.[1]

referred to as the "thermoelectric power" between materials a and b, it actually has the dimensions of volts per degree C and not the power unit of watts. Microscopically, the Seebeck effect arises because the concentration of charge carriers in a conductor depends upon the temperature. The presence of a temperature gradient in a material causes a carrier-concentration gradient, and an electric field is established which causes the net flow of charge carriers under open circuit conditions to be zero. This will be discussed in greater detail in another section of this report. It should be noted that two dissimilar materials are necessary in order to observe the Seebeck effect.[2]

---

[1] Figures 1, 2, 3, and 4 that follow are redrawn from Paul E. Gray, The Dynamic Behavior of Thermoelectric Devices, (New York, 1960), pp. 2-5. In the figures that were reproduced from Gray's book, some of the symbols have been changed so that the terminology is consistent throughout this report.

[2] Abram F. Joffe, "The Revival of Thermoelectricity," Scientific American, 199 (November 1958), pp. 32-33.

Peltier Effect

In 1835, a French physicist, Jon Charles Peltier, observed that when a current flows in a circuit of two dissimilar metals, heat is absorbed at one junction and the same amount of heat is rejected at another junction. This phenomenon is referred to as the Peltier effect. It was experimentally observed that the quantity of heat transferred by this process could be expressed mathematically as

$$Q = \pi_{ab} i t \qquad (2)$$

where Q is the amount of heat, in joules, absorbed or rejected; π_{ab} is the coefficient of proportionality (Peltier coefficient), in volts; i is the current, in amperes; and t is the time, in seconds. Microscopically, the Peltier effect arises because the potential

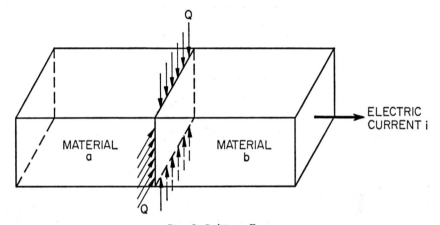

Fig. 2. Peltier effect.

energy of the charge carriers is in general different in the two materials and also because the scattering mechanisms that govern the equilibrium between the charge carriers and the crystal lattice differ in the two materials. Consequently, in order to maintain conservation of energy as well as conservation of charge when charge carriers move across the junction, energy must be interchanged with the surroundings at the junction.[3]

Thomson Effect

William Thomson, who was later given the title of Lord Kelvin in 1857, observed

[3] Joffe, "The Revival . . . ," pp. 32-33.

that electrical energy was not entirely used for transferring heat from the cold junction to the hot junction. Part of it is lost as heat in portions of the same material if a temperature gradient $\Delta T/\Delta x$ exists in it. This loss is small, but not negligible, in thermoelectric devices. Figure 3 shows this effect. The heat that is

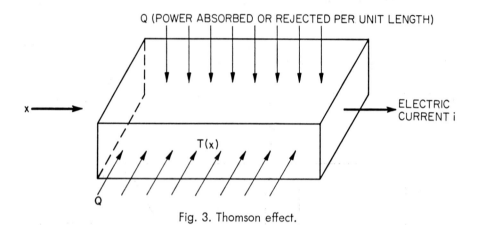

Fig. 3. Thomson effect.

produced over the length Δx in the material can be expressed mathematically as

$$Q = N_a \Delta T i t \tag{3}$$

where Q is the heat loss, in joules; N_a is the coefficient of proportionality (Thomson coefficient), in volts per degree C, for the material a; and ΔT is the temperature difference, in degrees C, across the length Δx. Microscopically, the reasons for the existence of the Thomson effect are essentially the same as those that cause the Peltier effect. In this case, however, the differences in the potential energy of the charge carriers and in the scattering mechanisms are the consequences of the temperature gradient and not the inhomogeneities in the conductor.[4]

III. Kelvin Relations

There is a definite relationship between the three coefficients obtained from the Seebeck (S_{ab}), Peltier (π_{ab}), and Thomson (N_a or N_b) effects. Thomson (Lord Kelvin) showed from thermodynamic considerations that any two of these co-

---

[4] Gray, p. 3.

efficients can be derived from the temperature dependence of the third by means of the following relations:[5]

(1st Kelvin relation) $$\pi_{ab} = S_{ab}T \qquad (4)$$

(2nd Kelvin relation) $$\frac{dS_{ab}}{dT} = \frac{N_b - N_a}{T} \qquad (5)$$

where T is the absolute temperature, in degrees Kelvin. The first Kelvin relation relates the Seebeck coefficient to the Peltier coefficient directly. The second relation relates the derivative of the Seebeck coefficient of the junction between two materials to the Thomson coefficient in each of the junction materials. These two relations can be used to link the various parameters encountered in the design of a thermoelectric generator.[6]

IV. Absolute Thermoelectric Power

The basic thermoelectric phenomena and their relationship to each other have been discussed, and now these will be used to determine the "absolute" thermoelectric power. The Seebeck coefficient or thermoelectric power S_{ab} has been defined only at the boundary of two materials; therefore, the value of this coefficient depends on both of these materials. To describe the thermoelectric power of a given material requires that measurements be made with respect to some reference material. Thermoelectric power is additive with respect to thermocouple materials; therefore, the thermoelectric power can be calculated for any two materials if values for the thermoelectric power of each of the materials referenced to a third material are available. If it is desired to find the thermoelectric power between the materials a and b, which have been referenced to material c, then one merely adds them together algebraically as $S_{ab} = S_{ac} + S_{cb}$. A useful expression can be obtained by integrating Kelvin's second relation (equation 5). This integration yields

$$S_{ab} = \int \frac{N_b}{T} \, dT - \int \frac{N_a}{T} \, dT \qquad (6)$$

One can regard the two terms on the right-hand side of this equation as the absolute thermoelectric power of materials a and b. The negative sign reflects

---

[5] Herbert Mette, "Power Generation and Heat Pumping by Thermoelectric Phenomena," The Solid State Journal (May 1961), p. 23.

[6] Mette, p. 24.

the fact that the Thomson coefficient can have either positive or negative signs. This can be expressed mathematically in the following way:

$$S_a = \int \frac{N_a}{T} \, dT \tag{7}$$

$$S_b = \int \frac{N_b}{T} \, dT \tag{8}$$

where S_a and S_b are the "absolute" thermoelectric power of a and b, respectively. It should be noted that this definition is arbitrary and that only the difference $S_{ab} = S_b - S_a$ has any physical meaning.

In the discussion that follows it should be understood that when the absolute thermoelectric power of a single material is referred to, it will be the thermoelectric power of that material referenced to some standard reference material. The thermoelectric power between any two materials can be found easily by taking the difference between the values of the absolute thermoelectric power for the two materials. In the early days of thermoelectricity, the only materials available for use in the construction of thermoelectric generators were metals. The absolute thermoelectric power S for metals is in general very low compared to that of semiconductor materials. As a result of this low value of S, thermoelectric generators were considered for many years to be of academic interest only.[7]

Comparison of the Thermoelectric Power of Metals and Semiconductors

Recent advances in solid-state physics, namely, the discovery of semiconductors, have given at least a tenfold increase in the thermoelectric power obtainable from a thermoelectric device.[8] This fact can be seen by comparing the values of the absolute thermoelectric power for metals and semiconductors as shown in the following tabulated data. These values in microvolts per degree C are referenced to a "standard silver alloy, Ag + .37 atom percent Au."[9]

---

[7] Abram F. Joffe, "The Revival . . . ," p. 31.

[8] E. W. Bollmeier," An Elementary Design Discussion of Thermoelectric Generation," *Electrical Engineering*, 78 (October 1959), p. 995.

[9] Extracted from Mette, p. 25. For a more extensive table see *Handbook of Chemistry and Physics*, 41st ed., (Cleveland, 1959-1960), pp. 2640-2641. This table uses lead as the reference material.

Metals				Semiconductors			
Element	ATP	Element	ATP	Compound	ATP	Compound	ATP
Bi	−70	Cs	.2	MoS	−770	CdO	−41
Co	−17.5	Y	2.2	AnO	−714	FeS	26
Ni	−18	Rh	2.5	CuO	−696	CdO	30
K	−12	Zn	2.9	Fe_2O_3	−613	$GeTiO_3$	140
Pd	−6	Ag	2.4	FeO	−500	NiO	240
Na	−4.4	Au	2.7	Fe_3O_4	−430	Mn_2O_3	385
Pt	−3.3	Cu	2.6	FeS_2	−200	Cu_2O	1000
Hg	−3.4	W	1.5	MgO_3H_2	−200		
Al	−.6	Cd	2.8	SnO	−139		
Mg	−.4	Mo	5.9	Fe_2O_3	−60		
Pb	−.1	Fe	16				
Sn	.1	Sb	35				

Why is the value of S so much larger for semiconductors than for metals? In the discussion of the Seebeck effect it was mentioned that a temperature gradient across a material causes a gradient to appear in the charge carriers. The reason for this is that the thermal energy of the carriers at the higher-temperature end of the sample is greater than it is at the cold end. This thermal energy causes many of the bound carriers to agitate enough to break their bonds and move around in the lattice structure of the material. The higher the temperature, the greater is the number of charge carriers that are liberated. Since the voltage between the two ends of the material is determined by the difference in the concentration of carriers, anything that will increase the difference in the concentrations will increase the voltage output.[10] Metals have a large concentration of free electrons (except at the temperature of absolute zero), and an increase in the temperature causes only a small percentage change in this concentration. On the other hand, semiconductors have a much smaller concentration of free carriers than metals; therefore, it takes a much smaller change in the number of free carriers to give a corresponding percentage change in the carrier concentration. It follows that, with a given temperature difference, a much larger voltage will be developed across a semiconducting material than there will be across a metal. This is the essence of the thermoelectric advantage possessed by semiconductors. Semi-

[10] Joffe, "Revival of . . . ," pp. 32-33.

conductors possess still another thermoelectric advantage over metals. In p-type semiconductor material the voltage differential between the hot and the cold end is set up, not by the flow of negatively charged electrons but by the flow of positively charged "holes." By proper "doping," semiconductors can be made to produce positive (p-type) or negative (n-type) thermoelectric voltages. Since the carriers in a p-type semiconductor material have a positive charge, they set up a voltage opposite to that in n-type material with a given temperature gradient. By proper "series" connection of n- and p-type semiconductors (see Fig. 4), the voltage output will be nearly twice as great as that obtained by using only n- or p-type material.[11]

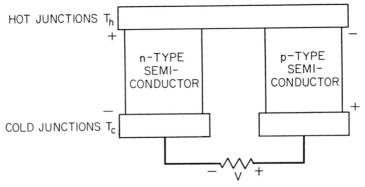

Fig. 4. Thermoelectric generator.

V. Efficiency of Thermoelectric Generators

The efficiency of thermoelectric generators is also an important consideration if thermoelectric generators are to be practical devices. A high thermoelectric power S alone is not sufficient to produce a good power conversion efficiency. If the electrical resistivity of the material used is too high, the thermobattery will have a high internal resistance, and little useful power can be obtained. On the other hand, if the thermal conductivity is high, heat will flow directly through the legs of the thermocouple, thereby reducing the efficiency of the energy conversion. Since thermal and electrical conductivity vary approximately together, it is obvious that a compromise must be made in designing any practical thermoelectric device. Joffe has defined the thermoelectric efficiency as "the ratio of the useful electrical

[11]Abram F. Joffe, "Revival of . . . ," pp. 32-33.

energy delivered to the external circuit to the energy consumed from the heat source of the thermoelectric generator."[12] Mathematically this can be expressed as

$$n = \frac{W_{out}}{W_{loss}} \tag{9}$$

where n is the efficiency, W_{out} is the power delivered to the load, and W_{loss} is the total heat power supplied to the generator. Consider a thermoelectric material with resistivity ρ, cut to the shape of a cube, with a side length of 1 cm as shown in Fig. 5. A cube of this dimension is chosen so that numerically the resistance, in ohms, between opposite faces of the cube is the same as the resistivity, in ohm cm, of the material. Electrical contacts are placed on two opposite faces which are

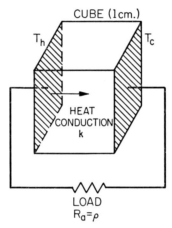

CUBE (1cm.)

Fig. 5. Derivation of power generator efficiency.[13]

kept at constant temperatures T_h and T_c, respectively. The cube then acts as a thermoelectric battery with internal resistance ρ and an open-circuit voltage $V = S\Delta T$, where $\Delta T = T_h - T_c$. Assuming perfect matching (maximum power output by an external load $R_a = \rho$), the maximum power which can be drawn from the generator is

[12] Abram F. Joffe, Semiconductor Thermoelements and Thermoelectric Cooling (London, 1956), p. 38.

[13] Redrawn from Mette, p. 26.

$$W_{out} = \frac{V^2}{4\rho} = \frac{S^2(\Delta T)^2}{4\rho} \tag{10}$$

where ρ is the resistivity and S the Seebeck coefficient. Equation 10 is derived in Appendix I. There is also a heat loss from one side of the sample to the other by direct heat conduction. This can be written as

$$W_{loss} = k\Delta T \tag{11}$$

where k is the heat conductivity. Since thermal conductivity is analogous to electrical conductivity, the numerical value of the thermal conductance between the faces of the 1-cm cube is the same as the conductivity of the material.

Criteria for Improving Efficiency

Neglecting, for the moment, other heat losses, such as Thomson heat, it can be seen by referring to equations 9, 10, and 11 that in order to have a high conversion efficiency, a material should have a high thermoelectric power output W_{out} and a small heat loss W_{loss} by heat conduction. This conversion efficiency can be obtained in terms of S, ρ, and k by substituting equations 10 and 11 into equation 9. Carrying out this operation gives

$$n = \frac{W_{out}}{W_{loss}} = \frac{1}{4} \frac{S^2}{\rho k} \Delta T \tag{12}$$

In this expression it will be noted that the terms S, ρ, and k are essentially constant for any given material. This led Joffe[14] to make the definition

$$Z = \frac{S^2}{\rho k} \tag{13}$$

where Z is the "figure of merit" of a material. Since the terms on the right-hand side of equation 12 are constant for a given material, it follows that Z is a constant for the material. Substituting the value of Z into equation 12 and multiplying by T/T gives the expression

$$n = \frac{1}{4} ZT \frac{\Delta T}{T} \tag{14}$$

where T is the average temperature between the hot and cold contacts. It is seen that high efficiency of thermoelectric power conversion depends on two factors: One is that the material constant Z be large over the temperature range

---

[14] Joffe, Semiconductor Thermoelements . . . , p. 38.

considered, and the second is that the Carnot efficiency[15] $\Delta T/T$ be high; that is, the device should be operated with a maximum temperature difference between its two junctions. At the present time the best materials have values of Z around 3×10^{-3} deg^{-1} over small temperature ranges.[16] The efficiency currently obtainable from experimental thermoelectric generators is 20%. As technology progresses, this value should continue to rise. There is information in the literature that indicates how to choose the optimum values of the appropriate parameters which will allow a thermionic converter to be operated at the maximum efficiency at a given temperature.[17] It is clear from equation 14 that the higher Z is made, the higher the obtainable efficiencies from the generator. It can also be seen from the definition of Z (equation 13), that S enters in as a squared term. Therefore, when looking for materials with high thermoelectric figures of merit, it would seem reasonable to search for materials with a high value of thermoelectric power. In the 19th and early 20th centuries, when only metals were known to be electric conductors, bismuth and antimony were used as thermocouple materials. It can be seen from the preceding tabulated data that these two materials have a difference in Seebeck coefficients of 105×10^{-6} volts per degree C. These early converters operated with a maximum conversion efficiency of 1.5%.

A big breakthrough on theromoelectric devices came with the advent of semiconducting materials. Such materials combine a high thermoelectric power with a low resistivity, which inherently gives them a high figure of merit. The value of S for an extrinsic semiconductor[18] can be shown to be a linear function of the logarithm of the electrical conductivity, while the thermal conductivity is a linear function of the conductivity. This means that the figure of merit Z will have a maximum value at a predictable value of S.[19] The magnitude of Z at its maximum value is assumed to be a function of the mobility of the free carriers, the three-halves power of the density of the free-charge carriers, and the thermal resistivity. Based on these assumptions and on solid-state theory, a derivation of the theoreti-

---

[15] F. W. Sears and M. W. Zemansky, University Physics (Massachusetts, 1957), pp. 352-353.

[16] R. M. Jepson and G. G. Messick, "Designing Low-Current Thermoelectric Coolers," Electronics, 34 (April 21, 1961), p. 58.

[17] John H. Ingold, "Calculation of the Maximum Efficiency of the Thermionic Converter," Journal of Applied Physics, 32 (May 1961), p. 769.

[18] An intrinsic semiconductor is one in which impurities (dope) have been added.

[19] F. J. Donahoe, "Theoretical Bound on the Thermoelectric Figure of Merit," Electrical Engineering, 79 (June 1960), pp. 489-490.

cal upper limit for Z has been obtained.[20] This gives a value of 17×10^{-3} reciprocal degrees at 300°K. If the resistance of the branches of a thermoelectric generator (Fig. 4) are matched to give Z a maximum value, then Z becomes a function of the material constants of the two branches. This can be expressed as

$$Z = \frac{(S_a - S_b)^2}{(\rho_a k_a + \rho_b k_b)^2} \qquad (15)*$$

where $S_a - S_b = S$ and $k = (\rho_a k_a + \rho_b k_b)^2$. Although S has been considered to be a constant, in actual practice is is very difficult to get materials that will give a high value of S over the entire range of temperatures of interest (25°C to 700°C). This is true because S has a maximum value which depends on the temperature gradient and the average absolute temperature in the sample. As shown in Fig. 6,

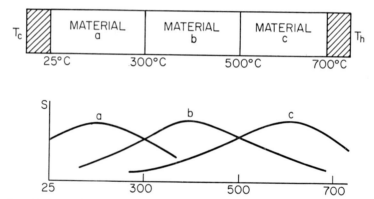

Fig. 6. Principle of sandwich arrangement of materials along the branch of a power-generating thermocouple.[21]

several materials which have maximum values of S within the specified temperature range can be connected so that each material operates within a narrow temperature range where its optimum S value is located. Thus by "sandwiching" materials between 25°C and 700°C, each material can operate within its optimum

---

[20] Donahoe, pp. 488-490.
* Donahoe, p. 996.
[21] Figure 6 redrawn from Rosi, et al., p. 452.

range.[22] Since the methods of measuring the Z values of a material are beyond the scope of this paper, they are not discussed. The interested reader is referred to the literature on the methods used to make these measurements.[23, 24]

VI. Prospects for the Future

In the foregoing sections the various parameters of the thermoelectric generator have been discussed. In this section, consideration is given to the future prospects for these devices. Laboratory devices with efficiencies of 20% have been fabricated, but they are too small for commercial application.[25] There is reason to believe that these laboratory devices can be made large enough and with high enough efficiency to be of practical commercial application.[26] The question is asked, "But how can the thermoelectric generator with an efficiency of 20% compete with the steam and gasoline engines which operate with efficiencies of 40%?" The answer to this is that the thermoelectric generators have no moving parts; therefore, they require very little maintenance. This makes them especially adaptable to remote areas, where maintenance is difficult and expensive. It is, therefore, the aim of considerable research efforts, supported by both government and private funds, to increase the figure of merit and the operating range of materials suitable for use in these generators. Metallic oxides are being studied for possible high-temperature applications. Some believe that "the thermoelectric power may increase by many orders of magnitude beyond its theoretical value, due to a peculiar interaction of the lattice thermal vibrations with conducting electrons."[27] This interaction comes about through the use of the "phonon drag effect." This effect has previously been found only at low temperatures, but recent

---

[22] F. D. Rosi, J. P. Dismukes, and E. F. Hockings, "Semiconductor Materials for Thermoelectric Power Generation Up to 700° C," Electrical Engineering, 79 (June 1960), pp. 451-452.

[23] E. H. Lougher, "Measurement of the Parameters in the Thermoelectric Figure of Merit," Electrical Engineering, 79 (June 1960), pp. 358-360.

[24] H. L. Uphoff and J. H. Healy, "Semiconducting Properties of Inorganic Amorphous Materials," Journal of Applied Physics, 32 (May 1961), p. 951.

[25] G. G. Messick, "Heat and Cold from the Same Source in a New Device," Electrical Engineering, 80 (May 1961), pp. 395-396.

[26] R. W. Porter, "Adventures in Energy Conversion," Electrical Engineering, 79 (October 1960), pp. 803-804.

[27] Mette, p. 30.

measurements on certain materials have revealed that this effect exists even at room temperature. Though it is beyond the scope of this report to discuss these special effects, it is clear that there are many unexplored possibilities for extending the capabilities of thermoelectric generators. There is, therefore, good reason to believe that high-power and high-efficiency thermoelectric generators may be fabricated and be competitive in particular applications with steam and gasoline power plants in the not-too-distant future.

VII. Conclusion

There has been an ever increasing interest by both government and private organizations in the use of the thermoelectric phenomena for the conversion of heat to electricity. There are three basic effects which enter into this conversion of energy: the Seebeck, the Peltier, and the Thomson effects. The Seebeck effect is the voltage that is produced by a temperature difference set up across a sample as a result of a current flow through the material. There is a definite relationship between these effects which is expressed in the two Kelvin relations. This inter-relationship can be used to solve for the voltage produced between the output terminals of a thermoelectric generator. Using this voltage and the values of resistivity of the thermoelectric materials, an expression for the efficiency of the device is derived. This expression is used to determine which parameters are to be varied in order to maximize the power and efficiency of the generator. Laboratory thermoelectric generators with efficiencies of 20% have been produced. This does not appear to be competitive with the steam and gasoline engines, which produce 40% efficiency, but it should be remembered that there are no moving parts in a thermoelectric generator and thus maintenance is kept at a minimum. This fact makes the thermoelectric generator especially adaptable to remote locations. If thermoelectric generators capable of supplying sufficient power at about 20% efficiency can be fabricated, they will probably replace many of the smaller steam and gasoline power plants in a number of applications. It is highly possible that a breakthrough in thermoelectric technology will occur in the not-too-distant future which will revolutionize the generation of power and make the fabrication of these higher-power devices possible.

BIBLIOGRAPHY

Bollmeier, E. W. "An Elementary Design Discussion of Thermoelectric Generation," Electrical Engineering (October 1959), pp. 995-1002.

De Groot, S. R. Thermodynamics of Irreversible Processes, 2d ed. (North-Holland Publishing Co., Amsterdam, Netherlands, 1958).

Donahoe, F. J. "Theoretical Bound on the Thermoelectric Figure of Merit," Electrical Engineering, 79 (June 1960), pp. 488-90.

Gray, Paul E. The Dynamic Behavior of Thermoelectric Devices (New York: John Wiley and Sons, Inc., 1960).

Handbook of Chemistry and Physics, 41st ed. (Ohio: Chemical Rubber Publishing Co., 1959-1960), pp. 2640-41.

Ingold, J. H. "Calculation of the Maximum Efficiency of Thermionic Converters," Journal of Applied Physics, 32 (May 1961), pp. 769-72.

Jepson, R. M. and G. G. Messick. "Designing Low-Current Thermoelectric Coolers," Electronics, 34 (April 21, 1961), pp. 58-60.

Joffe, Abram F. "The Revival of Thermoelectricity," Scientific American, 199 (November 1958), pp. 31-7.

Joffe, Abram F. Semiconductor Thermoelements and Thermoelectric Cooling (London: Infosearch Limited, 1956).

Lougher, E. H. "Measurement of the Parameters in the Thermoelectric Figure of Merit," Electrical Engineering, 79, (May 1960), pp. 358-64.

Messick, G. G. "Heat and Cold from the Same Source in a New Device," Electrical Engineering, 80 (May 1961), pp. 395-6.

Mette, Herbert. "Power Generation and Heat Pumping by Thermoelectric Phenomena," The Solid State Journal (May 1961), pp. 23-30.

Porter, R. W. "Adventures in Energy Conversion," Electrical Engineering, 79 (October 1960), pp. 801-7.

Rosi, F. D., J. P. Dismukes, and E. F. Hockings. "Semiconductor Materials for Thermoelectric Power Generation Up to 700°C," Electrical Engineering, 79 (June 1960), pp. 450-9.

Sears, F. W. and M. W. Zemansky. University Physics, 2d ed. (Reading, Mass.: Addison-Wesley Publishing Co., Inc., 1957), pp. 352-3.

Uphoff, H. L. and J. H. Healy. "Semiconducting Properties of Inorganic Amorphous Materials," Journal of Applied Physics, 32 (May 1961), pp. 950-4.

APPENDIX I

Derivation of Equation 10

A simplified equivalent circuit of a thermoelectric generator is shown in Fig. 7. Solving for the current i gives

$$i = \frac{V}{\rho + R_L} \tag{16}$$

where R_L is the resistance of the load. The power P_L dissipated in the load is expressed as

$$P_L = i^2 R_L = \frac{V^2 R_L}{(\rho + R_L)^2} \tag{17}$$

The derivative of P_L with respect to R_L will be zero for the value of R_L that gives

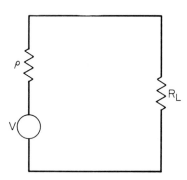

Fig. 7. Simplified circuit diagram
of a thermoelectric generator.

maximum power output W_{out}. Taking the derivative of equation 18 with respect to R_L and equating to zero gives

$$0 = \frac{(\rho + R_L)^2 V^2 - V^2 R_L (2) (\rho + R_L)}{(\rho + R_L)^4} \tag{18}$$

Simplifying equation 19 yields

$$\rho = R_L$$

When this relationship is substituted into equation 17, an expression is obtained which is equivalent to equation 10.

10
Writing for Publication

For the man beginning a technical career, writing offers an interesting hobby. It gives personal pleasure through the contacts it brings with others of similar interests; it keeps one in close touch with his field of specialization; it enhances one's professional standing; and it adds appreciably to one's income—not in the sale of articles but in the pay raises that follow publication. The term "writing for publication" in this context means writing for any periodical published primarily to inform rather than entertain, from popular factual magazines to the most sophisticated professional journal.

The whole range of technical periodicals could be subdivided into formal and informal. But in this discussion, instead of a division into formal and informal, all technical periodicals are considered to be either magazines or journals. These two categories are far enough apart at the base to be plainly recognizable, and any slight overlapping along the intermediate zone will not conflict with the purpose here to present the fundamentals of nonfiction writing. Writing for technical magazines will be considered first, followed by a discussion of the general requirements for journal articles.

WRITING FOR NONFICTION MAGAZINES

The technical presses of the country are anxious to consider factual articles of the type which a technical man is qualified by training and experience to write. The range of subject and format are practically unlimited. Anyone with something to say who has met the minimum requirements of a course in mechanics of expression and technical style can write an article suitable for publication, provided he follows the simple directions to be given here.

Choosing a Subject

In fiction writing an author who has a good imagination and a passion for research may write realistically about something he has never actually seen or physically experienced. The technical man, who deals only in demonstrable facts, must choose a subject he knows something about. The technical student knows enough about many subjects to write well on each of them. The catch is to find a subject about which the writer has a strong feeling as well as information. Nonfiction writing, as it will be shown later, is definitely affected by the writer's emotions.

The first requisite, therefore, in choosing a subject is to *please the writer.* The next requisite is to decide upon an angle of treatment which will *please the reader,* the reader in this case, until a specific magazine is selected, being the average intelligent man. What the average intelligent man is interested in is reflected in the sales of the popular periodicals. The third requisite in choosing a subject for publication is to find a subject which will *please the editor.* But it is not possible to know what will please the editor until a specific magazine has been selected.

Choosing a Magazine

If one is in possession of a novel idea or an insight into an old process of current interest, he will find a hundred magazines waiting for the article he will write. The engineer as a writer is in a competitive position with the professional writers because he knows his material from first hand experience; he may in fact be the one who made the discovery or conceived the invention he will be describing.

After a tentative subject has been selected as just described, one may go to the periodical desk of the nearest library to find articles similar to the one being planned. It has been observed that librarians are more helpful in supplying the desired technical magazines when the student asks for magazines which might have articles on a certain subject. He does not need to reveal his full purpose; announcing the intended authorship is not calculated to impress the librarian. From a dozen or so magazines supplied by the librarian the student is able, by scanning the tables of contents in each of them, to see which magazines come nearest to publishing what he has in mind. Once the magazine has been selected, the back issues for at least a year should be checked for a thorough analysis. The student should first see whether a title similar to the one he contemplates has been used. If he discovers that his idea has not been treated in the past year, he may take courage. If further research reveals nothing in the past two years, or better yet, nothing at any time so far as he can learn, his subject is a good one. He can then check out the three most recent issues and begin his detailed analysis.

As a preliminary step it is not a bad practice to write a note to the editor of the chosen magazine, giving a résumé of the proposed article and asking for special instructions to contributors. This may result in a letter from the editor showing interest in the proposed article, with special instructions for writing. But editors are not always able to reply to such inquiries. There is really no reason to wait for a reply from the editor. The student can actually learn more by studying the magazine than any editor would have time to write. Every fact needed for writing—length, style, subject matter, field of interest, reader level—can be deduced from the last three issues. The subjects of the three issues will bear a remarkable resemblance. After studying them a while, one may even predict the length, subject, range, and format of the articles for a typical issue.

Analyzing for Reader Level and Style

The reader and his tastes are most dependably derived from a study of the advertising the magazine carries. This will also serve as a guide to editorial policy. Nothing speaks so loud to an editor and to his publication staff as the dollar value of his advertising, since it is from its advertising that a magazine gets its life's breath. To confess the truth, it is the advertisers who are the first and last arbiters of the subjects and content of the printed articles in the magazine. A two-page spread from Company X is a better index to what the magazine will publish than all the articles put together. An article containing a derogatory or uncomplimentary statement about Company X, or a statement which gives favorable treatment to something opposed by Company X, would cause that article to be rejected if the passage could not be deleted or satisfactorily rewritten by the editor.

After the student has read most of the articles in two or three issues, has classified them, and has made careful notes on reader level by studying its advertising, he is ready to analyze the articles for style. A good way to see the difference between ordinary technical reports and magazine articles is to read all of the opening paragraphs of the articles in two or three consecutive issues. It will soon be apparent that magazine articles do not follow the same organization that is used for scientific reports. If the student outlines some of the articles, he will find that what might correspond to the introduction is delayed until the reader's attention has been attracted and his interest aroused. The student will also see by further analysis that many illustrations and transitions are used, more perhaps than he, so well acquainted with the subject, thinks are needed. Last of all, the conclusion may not be a conclusion in the technical sense at all; the article may just have a natural stopping place.

But after several articles have been closely studied, an order will begin to evolve. It will be found that the nonfiction article follows a flexible but nonetheless essential plan. Professional writers carry out this plan so smoothly that the reader is not aware that a plan exists until he tries to imitate the style.

The Nonfiction Formula

Every article accepted for publication in a nonfiction magazine with a paid circulation will be found to have a regular plan of presentation. Since this is a demonstrable fact, it follows that the logical first step in writing for magazine publication is to recognize the outline and elements of the plan and then to adhere to the plan while writing the proposed article.

The essential elements of nonfiction writing reduced to their lowest terms can be represented by the following formula:

$$P = (ART)^r E$$

where P = publication possibility,
   A = attention of reader,
   R = relation of topic to reader,
   T = technical information,
   r = reader's response,
   E = emotional factor.

It will be observed that P increases with the exponent small r and decreases to a small quantity when small r becomes negative. Moreover, E is a major factor which must be present in nonfiction articles intended for the paying publisher. This formula, properly understood and applied to one's own writing, can hasten the day of acceptance of a first article by many months. One has only to understand the terms, which will now be defined more fully.

From the formula it will be observed that magazine articles invariably begin by catching the reader's attention in the opening sentences or opening paragraphs. The exact nature of the opening sentences depends on the reader level and reader interest as determined from the magazine. If the reader level is known, it is possible to select a statement from some portion of the article that can be put first to catch his attention. The attention-getting sentence or paragraph may suggest conflict, a discovery, a shocking fact. It must be sharp and barbed, giving just a hint of what is to follow.

If the reader is stopped by the attention device in the first sentence, it indicates that he has a spark of interest which may be readily fanned into curiosity by the second term in the formula, the element R, or the relation of the subject matter to the reader. This must be known soon, however, or attention will be lost. Everyone enjoys reading when he feels that the material he is reading has some particular application to him personally, or that the subject is one which he should know, or even better, a subject which it will be worth his while to know. If, as soon as attention has been arrested, the writer immediately relates the material to the reader, showing the relevancy to the reader of what is about to be said, the R factor insures that the reader will continue to read on until the next term T has been employed. The T factor represents the point at which the author gets down to cases and starts his idea sequence, which, if expertly sustained, will hold the reader's attention to the end.

The sequence of question and answer (of cause and effect, or of fact after fact) will depend to some extent upon the kind of material presented. Transmission of the technical information in a magazine article corresponds to the point where in more formal writing the subject, purpose, scope, and plan of the particular article are given; but not all of these elements of the introduction need be given in a single breath, or for that matter spelled out precisely at any point, if in doing so the reader's interest may be given a chance to lag. It is better to suggest rather than give in detail all that is to be covered in the article.

In arranging the technical material represented by the T factor, one must pay close attention to the sequence of ideas so that the reader is always being told what he would like to find out next. It will be remembered from previous discussions that cause and effect, induction and deduction, and time sequences are the devices most commonly used for maintaining unity and coherence in the paragraph. Combinations of these are used in magazine writing, the surest for holding attention being the time order. The time sequence, one of the simplest unifying devices, is perhaps the one to use first in laying out the technical information. This has the advantage of inducing the reader to pick up enough facts in the narrative portion to make him curious enough to read on into the expository paragraphs.

The use of the active voice in the time sequence brings the reader directly into the article as a witness to the discovery or the demonstration of the facts being presented. The reader keeps on reading because he has a sense of discovery. If the reader *sees* evidence unfolding before him, follows the author to discover facts, he will read to the end without stopping. His interest, in other words, is much greater when he is *being shown how and what* rather than merely *being told what* the writer discovered. Unless the writer reveals his facts to the reader in this way, so that he is held fast by the desire to learn what happened next, the reader is almost certain to stop before he reaches the end.

The total quantity, *ART,* produces a reader response. The reader's reaction is shown in the formula as an exponent because the publication value of an article increases with positive increases in reader reaction, the *r* being a measure of the reader's reaction. The reader's reaction can be expected to be positive and energetic if he has been given an interesting, coherent series of facts.

In journal writing, to be discussed later, the *E* factor is suppressed, but not in magazine writing. The facts must be tempered by feeling. When the detective said "Just the facts, ma'am, just the facts," in a once popular TV series, he may indeed have wanted only the facts, but the TV cameraman was focusing his machine on the emotions— the bloody knife, the tear-streaked face, the uncombed hair of the bereft wife, the grubby suspects. Finally the trap is sprung. The rat fights, runs, trembles in fear, then breaks, a guilt-confessed murderer awaiting trial. The detective got the facts all right. That was his job. But it was the cameraman who captured the feelings and held the audience.

A scientific article is written and read strictly for the facts. It is like a field of grain purposely planted in rows to be purposely harvested for a specific use. A magazine article is a blend of fact and feeling, like a hillside of wild flowers sown by the wind to be enjoyed or not as one passes by. If the writer *appeals* to his readers, as he must surely do in all but technical journals, he must engage the emotions as well as the intellect. The ratio of information to emotion varies with the reader level, reaching about a fifty-fifty ratio with the average intelligent but uninformed reader and disappearing entirely in the formal scientific article. The *E* factor must be present in the opening paragraph, where the reader's attention is obtained, and it must be continued throughout the article in the proper ratio to permit the reader to have an emotional experience with the facts. The emotional factor is always present to some extent, even in old-line trade magazines of technical information like *Metals Progress* and in newcomers like *Astronautics*. It rises to something like 40 or 50 percent in the technical articles of a popular magazine such as *The Reader's Digest*.

A few paragraphs analyzed from the magazine selected for publication will reveal the approximate ratio of fact and emotion for that particular level. Words that arouse emotion (all of them) should be counted against those which are strictly factual in determining the ratio of fact and emotion. The following example, which appeared in a popular space magazine and was condensed for the average intelligent reader, is about equally balanced between fact and emotion. The randomly spaced emotion words are italicized here to permit the student to note them readily:

> But the facts of science, *priceless* though they are, tell only part of the *story. Across the seas of space* lie the *new raw* materials of the *imagination*, without which all forms of *art must* eventually *sicken and die. Strangeness, wonder, mystery, adventure, magic*— these things, which not *long* ago seemed *lost forever*, will *soon* return to the *world*. And with them, perhaps, will come again an age of *sagas* and *epics* such as *Homer never* knew.
>
> Though *we may welcome* this, *we may* not *enjoy* it, for it is *never easy to live* in an *age* of transition. *We must* prepare *ourselves* for *painful* shocks that will involve *our* philosophical and *religious beliefs. We now* take it for granted that *our* planet is a *tiny world* in a remote *corner* of an infinite universe, and have *forgotten* how this discovery *shattered* the *calm certainties* of medieval faith. Space will present *us* with facts that are even more disconcerting.[1]

Thus, it has been shown that each of the terms of the nonfiction formula represents an essential element in the style and plan of magazine articles. These elements have been combined in a handy

[1] Arthur C. Clarke, "Space Flight and the Spirit of Man," *Astronautics*, October 1961, quoted by permission from the condensed version in *The Reader's Digest*, February 1962, p. 75.

formula to accommodate the technical man who has learned to grasp relationships through mathematical symbols. It is easy to recall that the publication possibilities P increase as the favorable reader response, small r, increases and without the prime factor E the publication possibilities are adversely affected. With the E factor present, facts are much more interesting and easier to remember.

The Finished Manuscript

When the nonfiction article has been roughed out according to the formula just given, it should be allowed to age awhile before its final polishing. When the student returns to the article in a few days or weeks, his attitude should be that of the editor of the magazine selected. Then he can pounce upon the errors with a blue pencil in an objective manner. As an objective editor of his own work, he should blue-pencil the unnecessary words and write his criticisms along the margin for a later, more deliberate revision. Any item which is not in good technical style, whether an intrinsic or an extrinsic quality, should be noted; and any deviations in the use of abbreviations, numbers, and formulas from the style sheet of the magazine he has selected should also be noticed and blue-penciled.

A resourceful engineer can go even further; he can observe the style and quantity of the graphic aids—diagrams, charts, drawings, photographs—printed in the magazine. And by following the few simple instructions which are given in the succeeding paragraphs, he can prepare attractive and usable graphic aids. With a little thought it will be realized that these graphic aids are reproduced by a photographic process. Every graphic aid should therefore be submitted in black ink on a separate sheet of white paper, unless a color process is used by the magazine. Certainly the advantages that color offers in a drawing would be lost in the black-and-white reproduction process.

The drawings should be done, one to the sheet, about twice the size they are expected to be when reproduced on the printed page. Vellum and other translucent materials are not suitable for magazine reproduction processes. Graphic aids should be designed to show only the kind of information needed by the text reference. If the graphic aid involves curves to be drawn on graph paper, the significant lines of the graph paper should be reproduced on white paper, and the curves should then be drawn on the white paper. Graph paper, which does not reproduce well by the photographic process, should not be used.

Photographs are not treated the same way as other graphic aids. They should be styled to match the magazine, whether human interest shots or equipment shots. It is often a good idea to send two shots of the same general area. One should contain action, such as the operator at work or other human interest elements; and the other should contain equipment with the human element submerged in the extreme background or omitted entirely. If it is within the means of the student, he should obtain 8 by 10 inch black-and-white glossy prints of his photographs.

The top of the photograph should be indicated by writing *TOP* in the white margin above the picture. The illustration number and legend should be lightly penciled on the back of the picture; a ball-point pen or a fountain pen should never be used to write on the back of a photograph. A still better method, and one that is standard practice throughout the publishing industry, is to type the illustration number and legend on a separate slip of paper, which is then attached by cellophane or masking tape to the white margin at the bottom edge of the picture. The bottom edge is the bottom with reference to the way the picture is to be printed. No instructions should be written on the photograph. Anything written on the photograph, even if out of range of the subject, will be lost when the editor crops the picture for proper reproduction and layout. The photographs with their legends should be assembled in the order in which they occur and placed separately at the close of the manuscript, usually in a separate envelope; but in no instance should they be fastened together with wire clips or staples. This practice is a sure sign to the editor of the writer's lack of professional training.

One of the editor's greatest joys is to find a well-written article on just the subject he has been looking for, especially one with plenty of sharp black-and-white photos and drawings that are ready to be reproduced without retouching. An engineer who has had training in mechanical drawing and lettering has all the talent needed to produce professional graphic aids. Certainly, sloppy drawings prepared by an engineer should never be sent to editors with the thought of publication.

When the graphic aids are completed, the manuscript should be typed. The first page should start a good third of the way down to allow space for the editor's comments to the writer or the printer if the article is accepted. The manuscript should be on white paper and doubled spaced, with the pages numbered consecutively beginning with the second page; and it should be mailed flat in a manila envelope with a self-addressed stamped return envelope enclosed.

Cover Letters

A short one- or two-paragraph letter to the editor is generally favored as a means of transmitting the manuscript. The letter should simply state that the article (with its title in quotation marks) is being offered for publication in the chosen magazine (properly spelled and underlined to show italics). If there has been previous correspondence with the editor, this makes a good opening point; if there has been none, the purpose in sending the article to the editor might be of some interest, and any unusual circumstances under which the article was conceived or written may also be stated. A long letter is a bad omen for an editor. The least said that will serve the purpose of transmission is the best. After three months, if the student has heard nothing of the manuscript, he is fully justified in inquiring about its status. Failure to receive a manuscript back within a few weeks should be considered a good sign rather than a bad one.

Rejections

When the manuscript is returned (and there is a good chance that it will be, especially if it is the first attempt), it may have the editor's comments or his request for a revision. If it has neither of these, it will be well to consider sending the same manuscript without further revision to a second magazine. Any pages that have been spoiled, however, should be redone before the article is sent out the second time. It is difficult to determine in advance how far the student should go in circulating his article. One thing, however, is certain: duplicate copies should never be sent simultaneously to two or more magazines; to do so is considered nonprofessional conduct. If after several attempts there is no comment on the manuscript and no request for revision from any of the editors, the student should throw the manuscript into his inactive file (not into a wastebasket) and start a new one. He can rest assured that the rejection of his paper was due to one or more of the following reasons:

1. The manuscript was not acceptable to the magazine's advertisers.
2. The manuscript content was not of current interest to the readers.
3. The manuscript was not acceptable to the magazine editor.

The student can profit from his experience in the writing of his next paper by deciding which of these reasons it was.

The three items just named sum up, in effect, what was said in describing the procedure for writing a nonfiction article for a technical magazine. The student should know from his analysis of a magazine in what ways the advertisers limit what the editor can print. Any would-be contributor who has failed to analyze the tastes and range of interest of the advertisers has missed his first hurdle. The second hurdle is the current significance of his article to the reader audience of the magazine. If the material is of current interest and well organized, he has taken his second important hurdle. But after successfully jumping the first and second hurdles, he may still be stopped at the third—the hurdle of format and style. The editor must be able to use the article very nearly as written, except in those rare instances when the material is so appropriate for the editor's use that he is willing to make some revisions or is willing to point out shortcomings and return the material for the author's own revision.

If the engineering student, however, has done his work well and has not aimed too high in his first attempt, he may soon see his article in print and have the satisfaction of knowing that he has been able to share his knowledge with a great many others. The technical man might remember that the progress of technology in a democratic country is geared to the man-in-the-street level of understanding and appreciation of science. Science is supported by people, not by scientists. People like to know what their scientists and engineers are doing. Time out from work to write an article for publication helps in a small way to raise the national level of scientific knowledge, and it may teach the writer something he would not have discovered otherwise.

In the next section, writing for technical journals is discussed. Journal articles, as it will be shown, are a little above the technical means of the undergraduate. Nevertheless, a study of the journal article will help the student in the advanced research and writing that will become necessary soon after he is in graduate school. And some transfer of the information gained here may carry over into the early years of the student's employment, when he may wish to attempt the technical journal article.

WRITING FOR TECHNICAL JOURNALS

Nationally organized technical societies are publishing, monthly and quarterly, thousands of specialized reports in just about every branch of modern science and technology. The prestige journals are backlogged for a year or more in advance, with elaborate review boards to screen only the faultless papers for publication; while the struggling-to-be-heard journals are pulling papers from the older societies and beating the bushes to get enough to meet the next deadline. All have high standards, but some have greater regard for form than content. If an IBM-typed manuscript with two copies has the right number of charts and graphs and the correct ratio of integral signs, some journal is sure to publish it. Articles of this kind are sometimes produced by college professors who have nothing to say but, knowing that they must publish to be promoted, have learned to say nothing quite well.

Journal articles mark the path where discovery has been; contrary to popular belief, they are not the vanguard of science. The scientist or the engineer who has no interest in patent rights, and whose work is not classified, may reveal some new discovery in a journal article, but such an author is rare. Generally the journals bring up the rear of the advancing technological front by publishing what has been known among scientists for some time but could not be released for proprietary or security reasons. The frontier in a given science has moved on six months to two years before the average journal article is printed.

The greatest service of the journals is that they store documented facts which can be indexed and retrieved by others who later need to know what has been done in any branch of science. A scientist or an engineer who is already a specialist in his field will often find his best ideas coming from informal news articles or magazine articles written by inventors or newshounds. The journal, though, will be his reliable source of information on the techniques his colleagues are employing to solve the kind of problem which he faces. And aside from their other uses, journals raise research standards and promote the specialized interests of a professional group. A man expecting to become recognized in a professional calling should certainly subscribe to the journal of his society and read it regularly. As soon as he has the time and opportunity he should attempt to write a technical paper suitable for journal publication. Technical articles of this category are truly the badge of distinction for the career man.

The following directions for writing the journal article will be helpful to students as a complement to the only dependable guide for publication in a journal—the journal's own author's manual. Nearly all journals will send free or at a very nominal cost their specific directions for publication. After the style manual for the chosen journal has been received, the student must perform an analysis of several issues in somewhat the same way as he analyzed the magazine in the previous section.

Technical journal articles may be classified according to their level of specialization or the degree of difficulty in deciphering them. Or they may be classified by content as original research, feasibility studies, or state-of-the-art reviews. Or they may be classed as dealing with pure science or as dealing with applied science. The convenient though less scientific classification used here places all reports in two categories: those written primarily to be spoken or read and those written primarily to be printed. Papers written for oral presentation are further subdivided into student contest papers and conference papers. These subdivisions are discussed in the order named, after which the section is concluded by a few remarks on professional ethics.

Student Contest Papers

By the time the technical student reaches his upper-division courses he should begin to read a journal which publishes on subjects near his field of specialization. Reading articles of this kind broadens the student's knowledge and helps him to develop an appreciation of the objective technical literature which he must himself eventually be called upon to write. Though the average undergraduate student will not have sufficient mathematics to understand all of the articles he attempts to read, he will gain some facts and some valuable orientation toward a technical man's way of formally expressing his ideas.

As soon as he gets the chance, the career-minded technical student should join the local chapter of his professional society. One of the many benefits derived from such an association is that it makes the student eligible to compete in society-sponsored contests for technical papers. The participant in a student paper contest, even when he fails to win a prize and immediate recognition, has nevertheless gained experience in formal writing which will make it easier for him to prepare a journal article once he has begun his employment. For the student who wishes to go immediately into career work in some specialized field, the writing of a contest paper as a term project in his course is a more valuable experience than writing a library research paper or a nonfiction article, valuable as these projects are in acquainting the student with the techniques of research and writing. The contest paper increases the student's knowledge and at the same time seasons him in public speaking. It can, and often does, bring professional recognition, free trips to regional and national meetings, and even money.

The first step in writing the student contest paper is to check one's eligibility for competing. The professional society sponsors located on university campuses or in nearby cities may permit nonmember students to compete, though membership is generally required for winning. The guide lines for preparing the papers are supplied by the sponsoring groups well in advance of the contest deadline. If these are not readily available, they may be obtained through any faculty member who happens to belong to the society sponsoring the contest. The contest announcement usually includes suggested subject fields or, in some instances, the general subject upon which papers are to be prepared. The instructions usually limit the subject to some area of vital interest to that particular professional discipline; that is, if the American Society of Civil Engineers is sponsoring the contest, the subject will certainly be limited to problems concerning civil engineering. The scope may be further limited to current and significant problems, problems which are at the moment of widespread interest to the profession as a whole. Of course, the exact angle of development and the content of the paper is the responsibility of the individual student, yet nothing can be lost by talking over the subject of a prospective paper with one's professor, a practicing engineer, or even one's acquaintance. Above all, there must be a personal interest in any contest subject selected. Without a deep and abiding interest, the student will not put forth a winning effort.

If the contest rules permit a *choice of subject,* the student will find his best subject near the center of his present activity. Work done in advanced courses involving laboratory projects can serve as the basis for a contest paper. Sometimes technical subjects grow out of the student's independent researches or inventions. If no laboratory or private research project appeals, and the contest rules permit, the student may elect to write a state-of-the-art review in some specialized field of interest to the sponsoring society. This kind of subject demands wide reading and sharp analysis. It resembles somewhat the library research paper, but it is shorter, usually about three thousand words.

If the winning paper is to be published, the judges will be inclined to favor the best form and style, other qualities being equal. In any case the work must be well documented, and it must be displayed in an interesting manner. The degree of documentation will indicate the student's familiarity with the periodical literature dealing with the contest subject. The mechanics of style and the manuscript format for both the laboratory research paper and the state-of-the-art paper should follow the style of the technical journal which will ultimately print the winning contest paper. If the papers are not to be published, or if the instructions do not specify the manuscript style, the student should use the form of the research paper (Chapter 9) for the state-of-the-art paper and the form of the short report (Chapter 8) for the laboratory-type contest paper.

It must be remembered in any case that the oral presentation will not be an actual reading of the paper, or at least it should not be. What makes good sense on paper will need a good deal more explanation when presented orally. The oral presentation should make use of the distinctions between oral and written reports discussed in Chapter 11. The judges will have a copy of the student's paper for reference before he speaks and from that will know a great deal about the subject beforehand; but they will judge the student on how effectively he communicates with the audience, which in all probability will not be as familiar with the subject as the judges. This means that a judicious reduction in the number of topics must be made for oral delivery and that more time must be allowed for explanations and transitions and for graphic art if slides or posters are to be used.

Anything the student can do beforehand to cut down the awkward rattling of papers and to eliminate fumbling to find a place in the prepared text will increase his chances of winning. The paper may be kept on the rostrum, but it should not be used unless it is evident to the student that the oral communication is in danger of breaking off completely. Facts, figures, and other data intended to be given verbatim may be copied on 3 by 5 cards, which are held in the hand while the speech is going forward. Likewise, any quotations from others writers, which must always be read verbatim if they are read at all, should be copied on cards for handy reading.

In the preliminary contests the audience in the room may be quite small, so that one may speak in a conversational tone. But if one is fortunate enough to win a state or regional contest, he may find himself speaking before an audience of 1000 people. In the semifinals or finals, as the competition grows keener and keener, every little thing becomes important. For this reason the student should polish and repolish his oral presentation until it is the best that he is capable of delivering. The techniques for public speaking presented in the next chapter will be found applicable here. An effective speech deviates somewhat from the written contest paper. Selected topics are expanded and illustrated, and transitions are made to replace the omitted material. In this way the student can make a more interesting speech and say more that will be remembered in his allotted fifteen minutes than if he read the entire paper in the same length of time.

A final caution should be given on graphic art used to dramatize information in contest papers. It must be good. One has only to attend a technical conference of the "big league" scientists to gain a proper appreciation of the artful use of slides and posters. Simplicity is the guide word, and large scale is the law. Prepared slides that are useful in a small room become a distracting irritant in a large auditorium because the audience is too far away to see them clearly. If the people in the back row cannot see, they shuffle chairs and feet. Thin lines, excessive detail, lettering too small, poor-quality photographs— these should not have to be called to an engineer's attention. In presenting slides the student should know that he will not be heard if he speaks while he is facing away from the audience, but in the excitement of making the speech he loses some of his presence of mind. Judges note this and grade the student down on poise. If it is necessary to point to display material, one simply speaks, then points, then turns back to speak again with his face to the audience.

To the winner of a contest there is almost certainly afforded some level of publication. If the contest is national, it could be a technical journal. Publication at any level demands a careful recheck of factual data. Before the winning paper is sent to the printer the student should ask one of his professors to help him recheck it for errors. Having a winning paper published is probably the greatest thing that will happen to the student before his professional career is begun, and he cannot afford to make a mistake.

The Technical Conference Paper

The comments here on the symposium paper (or, as it is more often called, the conference paper) are included for the guidance of students who may soon find themselves eligible to compete for one of the speaker places on the agenda of a forthcoming conference. The stakes are higher for the conference paper than for the contest paper because the student has in all probability now finished his formal schooling and has begun his professional career as an engineer or a scientist.

The conference paper is like the contest paper in being written for oral presentation, but it differs in most other respects. It is initiated when one or more technical societies or other organizations decide to sponsor a technical conference. A committee works out an agenda of subjects which is usually published some months in advance of the meeting date. The open invitation for papers on the agenda subjects ordinarily accompanies the announcement. Any qualified engineer or scientist may compete for a speaker's place at the conference by submitting an abstract within the allotted time on one of the proposed subjects. The conference papers may be selected from the abstracts and the authors notified of their selection, or the final decision may be withheld until the paper deadline has passed before notifying the successful participants. Conference papers are usually written by specialists within a particular field. Although most papers report research studies, some may be state-of-the-art reviews.

Since the selection of speakers is made well in advance of the meeting and since the subject is one the engineer or scientist is well versed on, there is absolutely no excuse for the presentation of a half-baked, disorganized paper. As with the student contest paper, there are actually two assignments—a scientific paper and a speech based on that paper. In preparing the conference paper the first requisite, of course, is to observe the word limit for the written paper and the time limit for its oral presentation at the conference. If the topic is one of the writer's own choosing, it is assumed that a great deal of the research has already been done and that perhaps the paper has been sketched out in rough draft. If one has kept systematic notes on his research and has these available, the research phase of the conference paper should be much simpler. Nevertheless, he will still need to systematically run the indexes of periodical literature to be fully conversant on his subject and to be completely up to date at the time the conference paper is presented. On the other hand, if the paper he is to write, either by invitation or by his own choosing, is a state-of-the-art review, search of the literature may be the biggest single task in writing the paper. Reading and note-taking in the preparation of the state-of-the-art paper can be done in the same way as outlined for the writing of the technical research paper in Chapter 9. The manuscript style, however, is that of the sponsoring agency's journal or, in the event of cosponsors, the style of the one having the publishing privileges of the paper.

Again it should be emphasized that, in formal scientific papers, the high standards of technical style as described in Chapter 7 are the essential minimum. The professional man with some years of experience is expected to do a better job organizing and presenting his facts than the undergraduate student in a technical school. He should be resourceful enough, even in his first paper, to find the necessary information on format and style and to write within the specified word limits.

When the paper has been completed, including the graphic aids, the writer should make use of the advice on the preparation of slides in the previous discussion of student contest papers, and he should look forward to the material in Chapter 11 on public speaking in the preparation of the speech which will be based on the written paper. The better speeches are not necessarily synopses of the written papers.

It is wiser to select certain topics which can be effectively illustrated, and which make a more dramatic presentation orally, than to spend the entire speech time recapitulating what is in the paper. The slides, for example, to be used in the oral presentation of a conference paper should be even more expertly made, if possible, than those for the contest paper. When the lights are dimmed, the audience expects to see something on the screen. If a blurred or puzzling slide is flashed before them, the audience shows about the same negative reaction that they do toward a mumbling speaker who cannot be heard. Communication simply breaks down, and it may be impossible to resume even when the lights come on again (if the projector is not the new type which does not require dimming of the lights). In contrast, well-prepared slides (colored, if possible) are a delight to any audience, and they can compensate for some dullness on the speaker's part. In fact superbly made slides speak even louder than words, and they are easier to understand and remember.

A first appearance on the rostrum at a scientific conference is, in a sense, a sacred trust, and it demands one's very best effort. Failure to write a worthwhile paper or to make an interesting speech when the opportunity has been afforded in this way is pretty sure to lower one's professional standing, and it could result in one's being bypassed when the speaker roster is made up for the next conference. But the engineer or scientist who muffs his speech in his first experience at a conference may take consolation in the hope that his printed paper will be good enough to redeem him.

The Scientific Paper

The universally accepted standard for the measure of a man's professional achievement is the scientific journal paper. Has the man's work appeared in a reputable journal? For some this is the only standard of accomplishment. The man may have made an epoch-making discovery which was reported in the newspapers and magazines, but until he has appeared in a respectable journal he has not achieved full standing among his fellow scientists. When the writer once asked a well-known scientist what he thought of a certain man's work, he said, "For me it doesn't exist." And when asked why, he was quick to add, "I don't believe it. And I won't believe it, until it has been thoroughly documented and published in some professional journal."

If the scientific paper has this effect on the status of professionally oriented people, it is not too soon for the student to be introduced to this form of writing. Even if he is not ready to produce a scientific paper, it is high time he become familiar with the style and format so that meanwhile he can make use of journal articles to supplement his specialized upper-division textbooks. Technical students are not introduced early enough to the great body of periodical literature. Some will be found ready for graduation as far as core courses are concerned who have never read a journal article and who could not name three professional journals. Great amazement is often expressed when the student discovers that technical journals exist for just about every branch of learning and many of them for multiple fields of learning. A journal, for example, like *Solar Energy*, may draw on many kinds of science and several branches of engineering. A man about to receive a Bachelor of Science degree in any field of science should be familiar with at least the journal of his specialized field.

The purpose of this introduction to scientific writing has been to give the student a fuller understanding of journals as a significant means of communication between scientists and other technical people and, if possible, to encourage the student to begin the reading of journal literature as soon as he is academically able. It is hoped also that this discussion will challenge the student to try his own hand at writing a scientific paper—if not while he is still in school, at least at as early a date as feasible after he has begun his employment.

It will be noted from this briefing on the scientific paper that the writing instructions for the various journals differ a good deal in minor points of style and format. The student is advised to procure the instructions for authors (guide lines) from the journal for which he expects to write his article and to follow these religiously. The concern here is not so much to offer a detailed procedure for writing as it is to make some distinctions between the characteristics of the formal paper and those of the informative nonfiction article discussed at the opening of the chapter. Another purpose is to assist the student in understanding journal style so that he may begin earlier to read current periodical literature as a necessary part of his professional training. Earlier reading of journal literature and earlier attempts to write a scientific paper will shorten the time before professional standing is achieved. For until that first paper is accepted for publication, the young engineer or scientist will not have won his professional spurs.

What then is so difficult about the scientific paper? Nothing really difficult—just different. Aside from its qualities of style and format the scientific paper has these important distinctions of content: 1) something significant has been done; 2) what has been done is accurately described; and 3) what has been done can be duplicated by others. These three distinctions will be discussed in the order named.

SOMETHING SIGNIFICANT HAS BEEN DONE

As was previously indicated, undergraduate students are rarely able to do anything scientifically significant because their available time is spent earning a living or the opportunity for research is too limited. One research institution, realizing the untapped potential of superior students, has begun a summer research program using undergraduate students. Significant discoveries, however, are not often made by undergraduate students. When laboratory research projects are done in college courses, the work is not sufficiently documented or thorough enough to be suitable for journal articles. Still, it can and does afford opportunity for student contest papers, as the example at the end of this chapter will show. A few students, however, do have something significant to say about scientific discoveries made before graduation, and they are able to get journal space for their contributions.

Though the presentation of something significant has been given as the chief criterion of a scientific paper, it does not follow that all scientific papers are significant. In reviewing the papers of several national conferences and one worldwide technical conference this author has found by conservative estimate that more than half of the total word count was a needless proliferation of what was already known. In some conferences the count would probably run a great deal higher than this. Since there is no absolute way of knowing what is significant for either the present or the future, it is to be expected that some reports devoid of significance should be written and printed. But it is regrettable that such a large volume of this material finds its way into print. The fault of the system lies in the fact that the only person competent to evaluate the conference papers is the scientist himself, who unfortunately does not have the time or inclination to serve in this way. Hence the entire proceedings of the conference are more than likely bundled up and sent to the printer (at a cost per member of $10 to $15). The indiscriminate printing of worthless scientific papers is a waste of the nation's communication resources. It is a hindrance rather than a help in the pursuit of knowledge because the wheat is buried under a pile of straw.

In both federally and privately sponsored research, one may estimate that approximately 10 percent is added to the cost of the basic work to pay for the writing of reports. With something approaching $15 billion annually for research—a figure expected to reach $20 billion annually in five years or six years—it means that from $1 to $2 billion is or will be spent annually for the production of scientific reports. Editorial boards for technical journals are set up to screen out the papers which have nothing significant to say, but there is no such safeguard in sponsored research which pays for the printing of the reports in the basic contract. It is estimated that four to five thousand technical reports are being produced monthly. How does one code and file this mountain of printed matter so that it can be found again when next year's mountain falls on top of it?

Electronic cataloguing and retrieving techniques are beginning to be employed in some areas on a rather large scale. More research, however, needs to be done on ways to keep from losing a significant fact once it has been discovered so that the same work will not be done twice or even three or four times. Information clearing houses for all sections of industry might prove the solution to the problem of duplication. For example, the Power Information Center at the University of Pennsylvania, sponsored by six branches of the Armed Services, has been set up to collect and dispense information to government agencies and government contractors on a need-to-know basis. The work done on research contracts involving certain unconventional power-conversion projects (several hundred) is reported to the PIC, where it is coded and briefed. The power-conversion industry is kept informed on what has been achieved through short summaries, called project briefs, which are mailed periodically to those concerned.

But there is still far too much effort wasted in duplicated research. More of the nation's brains and communication resources should be assigned to devise better means of untangling the mass of scientific knowledge already stored and to keep a more up-to-date and accessible listing of all that is being done at any given time. When a man undertakes what he thinks may result in a significant contribution to the nation's scientific advancement, he cannot be sure someone else has not already done the same thing. So far, the efforts to coordinate research done in private laboratories and by government-sponsored research organizations have been ineffective. Even between branches of the Federal Government there is no overall cognizance of research in progress. The author recalls, for example, two translations of a Russian book made not long ago and published within a few weeks of each other. Neither of the government agencies knew of the other's work until the translations were out.

Not only is there a need for better ways of coding, storing, retrieving, and coordinating research, but somehow the volume of printed pages must be reduced. This is basically a twofold problem: reevaluation to reduce or eliminate rehashes of old papers and correction of the mistaken belief that reports with negative results should be full-fledged 40-page reports with all the trimmings. Instead of being padded to make the research effort look impressive, all reports should be ruthlessly pruned of insignificant warmed-over hash. This must be done by the writers themselves.

The responsibility goes even further back—back to a reeducation of the public from its preference for volume and complexity to a preference for intrinsic value and simplicity. Research with negative results should be reported, not at length, but in summary form. Scientists would preserve in these summaries a record of their failures to keep others from wasting time finding out the same thing. Only what are considered significant discoveries would be described in detail. By this expedient the total volume could be cut at least in half, and countless hours spent by librarians in cataloguing and abstracting scientific papers would be greatly reduced. Perhaps the research organizations themselves could encourage shorter, more significant reports by stipulating in their awards and contracts that unless something significant was discovered the report should be reduced to a bare outline of the procedures used.

This will not be easy. The habit of writing long reports is deep rooted. A successful consulting engineer confided to the author that the size of his report depended a lot on the scientific understanding of his client. If, for example, he were asked to investigate a simple foundation failure, his cost might run as high as $200. On a single page he would make to a technical man a full report of the cause and recommend the cheapest way to save the building. A technical man would understand the significance of the procedures used, and the difficulties encountered in obtaining the data for the report, and would consider the fee a reasonable one while appreciating the brevity of the report. On the other hand, if the client were not a technically trained man, he would prepare a 20-page document to say the same thing so that the client would not complain about the fee. It is believed that a great deal of sponsored research is being reported on the same principle as the reports of the consulting engineer. The researcher probably assumes (rightly, it must be admitted) that the sponsoring agency regards the size and complexity of the report as a measure of its significance. Since it is the taxpayer or the stockholder who must pay for this unnecessary waste, the reform movement should probably begin with those responsible for appropriations in the Congress and the large research institutions.

On the other hand, additional funds might be allotted to pay for translations of scientific papers into the laymen's language so that more of the general populace might understand the significance of the papers. News agencies and public relations departments of industrial corporations, as well as the information services of various governmental agencies, have made a good start in this direction, but the coverage is still not wide enough.

Oftentimes a significant discovery is reported which turns out, after wide acclaim, to be a rediscovery of something which was discovered earlier but which was not widely publicized because it was not thought significant at the time. Discoveries of pure research should be indexed in a form suitable for electronic retrieval whether they have apparent significance or not. The value of indexed research is illustrated by the work the German scientists did on carbides. During World War I, when they could not obtain African diamonds needed for making drawing dies for tungsten filament wire, the German research scientists scanned indexes until they found an extremely hard substance produced by Henri Moissan, a Frenchman, thirty years before in his attempts to produce aluminum in an electric furnace. Moissan had recognized these extremely hard intermetallic compounds and had catalogued their properties. The Germans, after considerable experimenting, found that tungsten carbide particles could be bonded in a cobalt matrix to form a substance hard enough to replace diamonds. Today industry would be at a standstill without carbide cutting tools.

The judges of what is significant in reports are the editors and reviewers of professional journals. When articles do not meet the publication standards of the journal, they are generally lost to scientists. Some journals have moved to preserve interesting discoveries not written in journal style, and not sufficiently documented or described to be given journal status, by including them as *technical notes*. This practice ought to be encouraged.

WHAT HAS BEEN DONE IS ACCURATELY DESCRIBED

If the scientst or the engineer considers writing a professional-level paper about something he has done, he may as well dismiss the thought unless the work has been done under standardized reproducible conditions which can be accurately described. To fail to account for every significant factor is to run counter to the acceptable scientific procedure. A discovery, to be accepted at face value by the scientific world, must be reproducible, and it cannot be reproduced until all the variables have been accounted for in such a manner that the reader can conclude with certainty that the writer has isolated the *true cause* or the *true result* by the experiments performed. This is a lesson the young engineer may have to learn through trial and error, but it need not be learned that way. By reading the scientific papers in his own society journal he can observe how others have described and verified their findings to the satisfaction of other professional people. By following the instructions in this text on the writing and documenting of factual reports and by using the knowledge gained from the preliminary briefing on the scientific paper, the student can describe his work so that an editor or reviewer will be able to accept it. One must not overlook the admission of mistakes and hypotheses which were found to be false. Scientists are skeptical of research which reports no errors.

WHAT HAS BEEN DONE CAN BE DUPLICATED BY OTHERS

It follows that what is not accurately described cannot be duplicated. Perhaps a patent is pending which the writer wishes to protect. Then perhaps he may as well delay the writing of the scientific paper, because professional people take a dim view of partial reports. It is especially objectionable for a writer to indicate by the title and abstract that something important is to be said and then dodge the vital issues with the excuse that information is being withheld pending patent protection. Though it may seem unfair to the inventor, the scientific paper must tell the whole story and tell it in such a manner that any competent researcher could reproduce the entire results from the procedure described. If any steps are omitted which the researcher performed, it may well be that the procedure could not be duplicated by another researcher with the same results.

The three criteria just described control the scientific paper. They do not, however, control another kind of paper that is given limited space in journals—the state-of-the-art paper. Such a paper is essentially a literature survey written by an acknowledged authority in a particular field, often at the request of an editor, for a year-end issue or by invitation of the technical conference chairman for an opening session. The state-of-the-art paper is prepared in much the same manner that the student research paper is prepared: the writer makes a survey and an analysis of the existing scientific papers in a particular field of specialization. It generally includes his personal appraisal and a statement of the probable future trends in the field.

Accepted Journal Articles

When the journal article is accepted, the author receives notification and probably a form requesting a preferred address where he may be reached when the galley proofs of the article are sent for the author's correction. At the same time, the notification may contain a form on which the author can request reprints if any are desired. With the galley copy the author may also receive the editorial proofreading guide with illustrations for marking copy. In all probability the galley will have been read at least once and will have proofmarks already made along the margins. It is not good practice in proofreading to change from the original version. These copy changes are expensive to make, and they should be limited to correcting overlooked errors. If the editor's proofreading instructions do not come with the galley copy, standard proofreader's marks can be found in most dictionaries. One should note that the marks are made in the margin nearest the error, either the right or left margin, and it is not a bad idea to use a direction line from the marginal correction to the position of the error in the line. The best advice is to read the galley and return it to the editor on the same day it is received.

Professional Ethics

A great deal has already been said about intellectual honesty in formal reports (see Chapter 7, on technical style), but a few more words about professional ethics may save the young engineer a lot of grief. A natural desire to obtain recognition and a sincere belief in the truth of his assumptions have led many a young man to draw conclusions from insufficient evidence which were later proved false. Modesty is a virtue most becoming to the technical man. Another point of professional ethics involves the demarcation line between a healthy professional jealousy and plain spite with respect to a colleague's work. If the writer *enjoys* the process of revealing errors in another man's work, he has departed from the scientific style. His emotions are coloring his language, and any attempts he makes to sound benevolent will not deceive anyone. The only right thing he can do is to omit references to the other man.

Another question: how does one distinguish between the inspiration received from another man's work and the actual stealing of the other man's idea? If there is any doubt, a credit line should be given. Also, when does an idea cease to be the possession of one man and become common knowledge of the science? When the idea ceases to be footnoted in the writings of reputable scientists. Or again, how much can a man reveal about his work without endangering his proprietary rights? Or, put another way, how much can a man conceal and still be reporting scientifically? Proprietary subjects are not suitable for scientific reports. They should probably be reported in news magazines. Here the young man may seek the counsel of an older man in his field, if he has such a man for a friend, or he may seek the advice of a competent patent attorney. Professional ethics can be put in a nutshell by saying that one should not engage in practices which are contrary to the best interests of his group.

From this brief discourse on scientific papers it may be seen that the young scientist or engineer, ready to try his first scientific paper, must have something significant to say and he must describe his work accurately so that it can be duplicated. Though the scientific paper is somewhat beyond the opportunities of the undergraduate, he should be encouraged to try it. A few will succeed.

So far in this text, writing has been the chief concern. In the next chapter the student will find some methods he can use to improve his oral communication.

No exercises are included at the end of this chapter, since its use is optional. However, an example of a student contest paper is given for the guidance of those who decide to choose this type of report for a term project. Student contest papers, as it will be observed from the example, may be done jointly and may extend across society boundary lines. The names of the coauthors are shown on the title page of the student paper.

STUDENT EXAMPLE

Contest Paper

ANALOG COMPUTER TECHNIQUES
FOR STUDYING TRAFFIC PROBLEMS

Arizona State University
March 24, 1962

James A. Kirsch and Charles R. Moores
Student Members, AIEE
(American Institute of Electrical Engineers, Advanced to
First Place, District 8, May 5, 1962. Monterey, California.)

(Institute of Radio Engineers, Advanced to First Place, Seventh
Region, May 25, 1962. Seattle, Washington.)

TABLE OF CONTENTS

LIST OF ILLUSTRATIONS

ABSTRACT

In an attempt to find an improved method of solution to the problem of traffic congestion, analog computer techniques were developed by the authors to simulate intersection control. Originally undertaken as a term project at Arizona State University to study a simple two-street intersection, it has been expanded to include more complex intersections.

Most of the time devoted to the project thus far has been spent designing, building, and testing circuits to accomplish the desired computer operations. These operations include stop-go signals, accumulation of traffic, and regulation of movements. With the computer performing these operations, the operator can determine the optimum settings of intersection parameters. Circuits currently being tested will automatically determine the signal cycle length and phasing.

Actual intersections have been simulated and the computer results have been checked and found accurate. During these simulations it became evident that the analog computer is a valuable tool in the study of traffic congestion.

I. Introduction

This project was begun in connection with a course in analog computers at Arizona State University. The simulation of traffic problems was undertaken since one of the authors was involved with traffic congestion problems while working for the Arizona Highway Department. The objective was to find an accurate, easy, and efficient approach to the problem of traffic congestion. Thus far the studies have been limited fo single urban intersections where distances to adjacent intersections reduced interaction to a minimum. Furthermore, simulations have been restricted to "peak hour" traffic volumes.

History shows that traffic on our nation's highways increases exponentially, with a corresponding increase in associated problems. The increase in traffic volumes has caused many streets and highways to overload above their design capacity. The basic problem is congestion. This problem concerns not only the traffic engineer, but anyone traveling from one point to another.

In urban or suburban areas, the congestion problem is centered at the signalized intersection. The most obvious solution is to provide more traffic lanes, thereby increasing the number of vehicles that can pass through the intersection during any given time. However, due to buildings, real estate costs, and other factors, this solution is not always feasible. Consequently the need exists to obtain the maximum efficiency from existing facilities.

The Bureau of Public Roads recognized this problem and developed a mathematical and graphical approach based on manual intersection studies. Although this was a step in the right direction, it still leaves much to be desired. A person employing this method must work with a fixed set of parameters. Changing any one of these requires a complete reworking of the problem. Furthermore, each intersection must be worked separately, and the presence of special conditions at the intersection greatly increase the complexity of analysis. All of this takes time and reduces the effectiveness of the traffic engineer. Therefore, an additional need exists to find a faster, more efficient approach to the problem. This report is the result of the authors' efforts to develop analog computer techniques to meet this need.

II. The Problem

Capacity studies necessarily depend on what information is known and what is desired. Generally, a traffic volume is used to determine the intersection requirements. These requirements include the signal cycle length and phasing, necessity of special signals for turning movements, and the number of lanes for each approach. Included in this is the amount of overload that can be handled efficiently. The reverse process is also possible: finding the capacity of some specific intersection configuration. In some cases it is desired that the queue length be approximately equal for different approaches. This becomes a rather involved problem using conventional methods.

The capacity of a signalized intersection is limited by several factors. Some of these can be simplified by making assumptions allowed by the physical system. For this project, it was decided to work on a "critical lane" basis, a "critical lane" being the lane in each approach requiring the most time. All left turns were assumed to be of a critical nature, as that volume is determined by gaps in the opposing traffic.

It was also assumed that all vehicles had passenger car characteristics with regard to acceleration. Factors have been developed which relate this passenger car equivalent to actual volumes, once the percentage of commercial vehicles is known. This assumption allowed departure rates to be determined by the formula

$$R = \frac{(G)\ (H)}{G - D - 2H}$$

where R is the departure rate in seconds per vehicle, G is the green phase in seconds, D is the starting delay of the first two vehicles, and H is the time-headway of the third through last vehicle of the queue. Typical values are $D = 5.8$ sec, $H = 2.1$ sec, and $R = 2.15$ sec/veh. These average values were determined by manual intersection studies.[1]

With minimum pedestrian interference, right turns may be included in the through movement, since both require about the same time.[1] In cases of substantial pedestrian volumes, right turns must be considered separately.* Consideration of right turns as a separate movement has not been necessary in simulations conducted thus far.

With the nature of the traffic portion of the problem developed, the next step was to implement it in the computer. The computer must provide a stop-go signal, accumulate the traffic, and regulate the movement of vehicles. Most of the time devoted to the project thus far has been in the development of circuits to perform these functions. The nature of the high-gain computer amplifier is ideal for these operations, requiring only a change of the input or feedback impedances to change the overall characteristics of the amplifier.

[1] A method of including right turns is discussed in the Appendix.

Fig. 1. Equipment used. (The authors are also shown in the photograph.)

III. Basic Program and Circuit Logic

Equipment Used

The equipment used in the simulations to be discussed is shown in Fig. 1. The computers used are GEDA Analog Computers, Model L-3. On the right is a Sanborn Recorder, Model 350. The equipment shown provided a capability of 48 amplifier channels and six recording channels.

Block Diagram

The basic program[2] for simulation of through traffic and left turns on one street is shown in Fig. 2. The function of each block is summarized below:

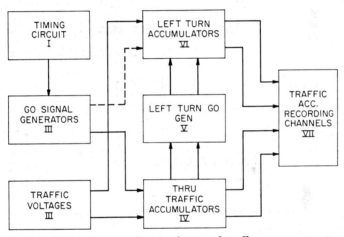

Fig. 2. Block diagram for simulation of traffic on one street.

Block I—The outputs of the timing generator control the time of the total stop-light cycle and the distribution of green time to each street. Only one unit is necessary for a complete intersection simulation.

Block II—In the GO signal circuits, the timing signals are combined to provide up to four properly sequenced green phases. Four channels are required to provide all of the GO signals. The GO signal to the left turn accumulators is shown by the dotted line. As will be shown, this signal path is usually optional.

Block III—This block represents the various driving functions which can be used to represent traffic. Normally, d-c signals are used to represent average traffic rates. After the time settings have been made based on average rates, time-vary-

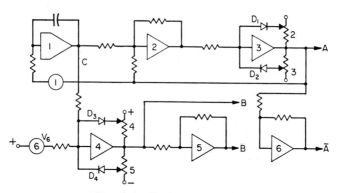

Fig. 3-A. Timing generator.

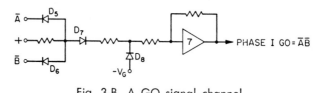

Fig. 3-B. A GO signal channel.

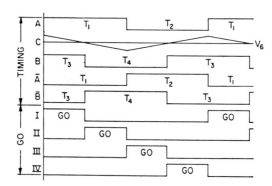

Fig. 3-C. Timing and GO wave shapes.

ing signals can be used to test the response and modify the initial settings if necessary.

A planned extension of present techniques for representing traffic is to use a tape recorder to record the pulses of an electromechanical traffic counter as it is actuated by vehicles crossing a "rubber hose" extended across the approach. This tape can then be used as the traffic input to the computer. This will, in effect, bring the actual intersection into the laboratory.

Blocks IV, V, and VI—The outputs of the accumulating circuits represent the number of vehicles stopped at the stoplight. The through traffic and left turn blocks each consist of two accumulating amplifiers. One of these is used, for example, for northbound traffic, while the other is used for southbound traffic. The action of each accumulator is such that the traffic voltage causes an increase in the output voltage. Application of a GO signal correspondingly causes a decrease. The left turn GO circuits provide a GO signal to the left turn accumulators whenever the opposing traffic accumulation is almost zero. For example, as the northbound through traffic becomes nearly zero, the associated left turn GO circuit allows left turns to be made freely from the southbound left turn lane. One IV, V, and VI Block is needed for each street being simulated.

Block VII—This block is a Sanborn Recorder, shown in Fig. 1. By means of this device the accumulations of vehicles can be <u>continuously</u> monitored. A permanent record of the results is also made.

Timing Generator

The timing circuits are shown in Fig. 3-A. Amplifiers 1, 2, and 3 comprise a free-running multivibrator which is the basis for all timing signals. Amplifier 4 is a limiting amplifier, which is driven by the action of the free-running circuit. The cycle lengths are the same for both circuits, but the shapes and relative phase of the outputs are different. Amplifiers 5 and 6 are inverters. These amplifiers are needed to provide necessary signals to the GO signal circuits, which are discussed in the next section. The timing waveshapes are shown in the upper portion of Fig. 3-C.

The effects of circuit adjustments on the waveshapes are summarized below:

(1) Potentiometer 1 controls the total length of the stoplight cycle. Increasing the amount of feedback increases the frequency and thus shortens the cycle.

(2) Potentiometers 2 and 3 control the relative pulse widths, T_1 and T_2, for signal A. For example, increasing potentiometer 2 shortens T_2 without affecting T_1. Such an adjustment also has a secondary effect on frequency.

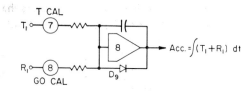

Fig. 4-A. Traffic accumulator.

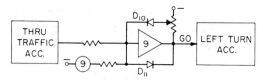

Fig. 4-B. Left turn GO circuit.

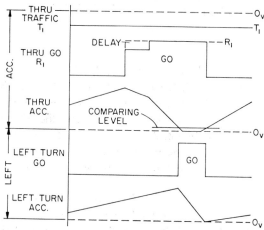

Fig. 4-C. Accumulator and left GO wave shapes.

(3) Potentiometer 6 controls the relative pulse widths, T_3 and T_4, for signal B. Signal B changes polarity whenever the input C crosses the voltage level V_6. Potentiometer 6 has no effect on frequency.

(4) Potentiometers 4 and 5 have no effect on timing but merely adjust the voltage levels of signal B.

GO Signal Generator

The GO signal generator consists of four channels. Each channel contains a diode matrix and associated limiting circuits. One channel is shown in Fig. 3-B. The diode matrix consists of diodes D_5 and D_6, and a resistance R. In order to get a GO signal, both inputs must be negative. When this condition occurs, a positive GO signal is produced at the output of limiter amplifier 7. Since adjustments in the timing circuits cause the voltage levels of the timing signals to change, the limiters are necessary to insure that the GO signal voltage level will not vary at the output. The sequential generation of GO signals is illustrated by waveshapes shown in the lower portion of Fig. 3-C. The action of the circuits may also be summarized by the switching equations.

$$\text{Phase I} \quad \text{GO} = \overline{A}\,\overline{B}$$
$$\text{Phase II} \quad \text{GO} = \overline{A}\,B$$
$$\text{Phase III} \quad \text{GO} = A\,B$$
$$\text{Phase IV} \quad \text{GO} = A\,\overline{B}$$

When less than four separate GO phases are needed to simulate an intersection, GO signals can be combined to form either two or three phases. An advantage of phase combination will be illustrated in the next section.

Traffic Accumulation Circuits

An example of a traffic accumulator is shown in Fig. 4-A. Amplifier 8 is an integrating circuit. The output is given by

$$\text{Acc.} = \int (T_1 + R_1)\, dt$$

where Acc. is the accumulation of vehicles stopped at the light, T_1 is the arrival rate in vehicles per second and R_1 is the departure rate in vehicles per second. Arrivals T_1 occur continuously, but departures occur only during the time the stoplight is green. Since a negative accumulation has no physical meaning, diode D_9 is provided to limit the accumulator output to values above zero. This provision also furnishes a reference for measuring accumulation. Potentiometers 7 and 8 allow the calibration of the traffic and GO signals. The accumulator waveshapes are shown in Fig. 4-C.

Because of the phase reversal of the amplifier, the arrival rate is represented by a negative voltage. Thus the arrival signal causes the accumulator output to increase. The GO signal is positive during green time, which causes the accumulation to decrease.

When two GO signals are combined, it is possible to adjust their amplitudes to account for starting delay. The through GO signal shown in Fig. 4-C illustrates GO signal combination. During the first portion of the green time, a GO pulse of reduced amplitude is provided to the accumulator. After the initial delay period, a GO pulse of higher amplitude is applied. This represents the flow of vehicles through the intersection at full speed.

Left Turn GO Circuits

An example of a left turn GO circuit is shown in Fig. 4-B. Amplifier 9 is a comparator multivibrator which monitors the accumulation of the through traffic in the direction opposing left turns. Potentiometer 9 is used to set the comparing level shown in Fig. 4-B.

When the opposing traffic accumulation goes below the comparing level, a positive GO pulse is furnished to the left turn accumulator. During this time, left turns are permitted and the left turn accumulation will diminish as shown in Fig. 4-C. When the light controlling the opposing traffic accumulation turns red (represented in the computer as the absence of a GO pulse) the opposing traffic accumulation builds up above the comparing level. This causes the left turn GO signal to return to zero. No further left turns are permitted until the opposing traffic again goes below the comparing level.

If the through traffic and/or left turn volumes are sufficiently heavy, the amount of GO time provided by the method of this section may be too short to keep the left turn accumulation from overloading. In this event, a GO phase must be provided for left turns only.

Calibration and Scaling

During the studies to be discussed, a time scale of 10:1 was used. Thus a peak hour simulation can be run on the computer in six minutes. A magnitude scale of two volts per vehicle was the standard at the outputs of the accumulators. To calibrate a traffic arrival rate, the GO signal is removed from the input to the accumulator, and the recorder paper speed is set at a convenient rate. This causes a high accumulation of traffic to occur as shown in Fig. 5.

The average arrival rate can be determined by the relation

$$\text{Arr. rate} = \Delta V_a / \Delta t_a$$

where ΔV_a is the number of vehicles arriving in the interval Δt_a. By removing the traffic signal and replacing the GO signal, the departure rate can similarly be calibrated.

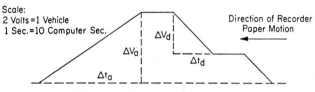

Fig. 5. Calibration procedure.

IV. Results

The computer results must be accurate to be of any value in traffic simulation. Accuracy was checked by setting the departure rate to 2.11 sec/veh, the approximate departure rate of the graphs published by the Bureau of Public Roads.[3] The computer results showed the capacity to be 1706 vehicles per lane per hour of green time. For the same conditions the graphs yield a total of 1730 vehicles, giving a difference of 1.4%. Thus the computer results are of sufficient accuracy. Furthermore, the computer departure rate is completely flexible, an attractive feature not offered by the graphs.

Of the several intersections simulated, the intersection of Washington and 40th Streets in Phoenix, Arizona, will serve as an example. This intersection is illustrated in Fig. 6. Volume data was obtained from the Arizona Highway Department. Arrival and departure rates were set using methods previously outlined.

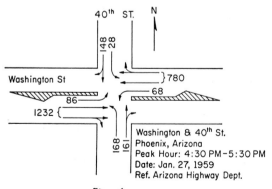

Fig. 6.

The critical lanes on Washington Street were assumed to carry 55% of the traffic, excluding left turns. Since a maximum of 6 pedestrians were observed crossing any approach during the peak hour, right turns were combined with the through movements.

The traffic volumes shown did not cause the intersection to operate at maximum capacity. The phasing was adjusted to provide equal queue lengths for the heaviest approach on each of the two streets. With a 45 second cycle, Washington Street received 30 seconds and 40th Street received 15 seconds. These times include the caution phase.

The maximum storage on any approach was three vehicles. A separate left turn phase was not required since all left turn accumulations reached zero during each cycle.

To determine the additional amount of traffic that the intersection could efficiently handle, the arrival rates were proportionally increased until maximum capacity conditions existed. It was found that the intersection could handle a 50% increase of the volumes shown in Fig. 6. With the proportional increase, the limiting movement was found to be the westbound left turns on Washington Street. This was due to the increase in opposing (eastbound) traffic limiting the time for the left turn movement.

Intersections approaching maximum capacity were observed in two other simulations. One of these involved the estimated 1975 peak hour volumes at the intersection of Interstate 17 and Peoria Avenue, north of Phoenix. It was determined that I-17 must have three through lanes plus left turn lanes in each direction. Peoria Avenue required one through and one left turn lane in each direction. Since a total of four lanes (no left turn lanes) currently exists on I-17, the highway department must decide whether or not to provide the additional lanes. The computer can assist in this decision by checking the capacity of intersections on alternate routes to determine if existing facilities can accommodate the total volumes. Digital computer techniques have been developed which distribute the traffic among several alternate routes.[4]

The other simulation was the more complex intersection of Grand Avenue, Indian School Road, and 35th Avenue, located in northwest Phoenix. This simulation required a three phase GO signal. The intersection was found to be operating just below maximum capacity for present traffic volume. A separate left turn phase was not needed, although a slight increase in left turns on Grand Avenue will require such a signal. The optimum phasing gave Grand Avenue 40% of the green time, with Indian School Road receiving 33%. The remaining 27% of the 86 second cycle went to 35th Avenue. The next step will be the simulation of this intersection using estimated traffic volumes for some future year. If a left turn phase is necessary, the computer will indicate this. The effect on the through movements of time given to a separate left turn phase can also be determined.

Application of the computer results to the actual intersections has not yet been accomplished by the authors. However, Dr. F. V. Webster of the Road Research Laboratory, Great Britain, has done similar work in this field.[5] He was able to check his results on actual intersections and concluded that intersection efficiency was definitely improved by applying the computer results.

V. Conclusions

The computer approach to the problem of traffic congestion definitely showed several important advantages over the graphical and mathematical approach. Of prime importance is the flexibility offered by the computer. The operator is allowed to change any parameter, either singly or in combination, to determine optimum operating conditions. Rapid solutions of similar intersections can be accomplished by simply changing the inputs and adjusting to optimum conditions. Since the adjustments consist primarily in changing potentiometer settings, relatively unskilled personnel can do this work. Special conditions, such as offset intersections, can be simulated by additional circuitry. The computer also permits the simulation of unrealistic situations, which may provide insight into actual problems. The greatest advantage is that the operator has complete control over the intersection variables, and the effect on the entire system of changing any one of these can immediately be determined. Thus the operator is limited only by his knowledge and imagination.

REFERENCES

1. Capacity Study of Signalized Diamond Interchanges, Donald G. Capelle and Charles Pennell, Texas Transportation Institute, Jan. 9, 1961, pp. 8-9.
2. Analog Computation. Albert S. Jackson, McGraw-Hill Book Company, Inc., New York, 1960. (Used as a programming handbook.)
3. U. S. Department of Commerce, Bureau of Public Roads, June 24, 1959: Circular memorandum, Chart 2B.
4. A Mechanical Method for Assigning Traffic to Expressways, E. Wilson Campbell, Traffic Engineering, Vol. 28, Number 5, February 1958, pp. 9-14, 35.
5. Traffic Signal Time Setting, F. V. Webster, The Engineer, Vol. 209, April 1, 1960, p. 653.

APPENDIX

Extending the Basic Program

When necessary, right turns can be included in the intersection simulation. This need would arise if pedestrian movement interfered with right turns. A circuit for considering right turns is shown in Fig. 7-A. Northbound right turns N_R are used as an example, as shown in Fig. 7-B. In Arizona right turns are allowed on RED, provided that eastbound through traffic E_T and pedestrians crossing in the east-west crosswalk do not interfere.

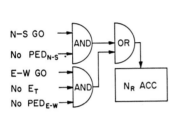

Fig. 7-A. Right turn GO generator.

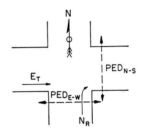

Fig. 7-B. Movements affecting right turns.

The conditions under which right turns are allowed are summarized in the switching equation

$$N_R \text{ GO} = (\text{N-S GO}) (\text{No PED}_{\text{N-S}}) + (\text{E-W GO}) (\text{No } E_T) (\text{No PED}_{\text{E-W}})$$

To develop the additional signals required for generation of the N_R GO signal, it would be necessary to provide pedestrian accumulators and to monitor them in the same way in which through traffic is monitored to provide for left turns. The E_T accumulator would also have to be monitored. Consideration of right turns, while involving additional circuitry, is merely an extension of the techniques discussed in this report.

ACKNOWLEDGMENT

The authors wish to thank the Arizona Highway Department and Mr. J. W. Morrison, faculty adviser at Arizona State University, for their help in the development of this project.

– 11 –

The technical conference. Opening session of the United Nations Conference on New Sources of Energy, Food and Agriculture Organization Building, Rome, Italy, August 21, 1961.

11
Public Speaking
for Technical People

Communication by sound is a strange and interesting process. In its elementary stages of development it probably corresponded very much to the coming of speech to the newborn child—first only grunts and cries concerned primarily with the needs of the body. Then came the goo and blub stage. Some of the most primitive words in the language may go back to this time; the word *mama*, for example, made by intermittent cries while nursing, is probably the oldest word in human speech. Then came words for the emotions. Pain may have been primitively expressed as a simple aspirated groan, such as o-o-o-o. With fear added and the stomach muscles tensed to receive a blow, an explosive grunt with the nostrils distended probably originated the negation *N-o-o-o!*

Next after emotions came imitative sounds of things in nature, with gestures to indicate direction. Modern speech still preserves the convenient communicative motions—a closed fist, for example, to indicate strong opposition. Actions were also named from sounds either in nature or man-made: snip, twang, buzz, zoom, bang, scratch, cut. And at a much later time modifiers were added—many of these in not-too-distant times—to resemble natural sounds. The sound of an arrow passing close to one's ear is heard in the German word *geschwind* (pronounced ge-shvint) and to some extent in its counterpart, *swift*, in English. Much later in human history came the invention of audible sounds representing abstractions. By etymology, *home* and *love* are related to *lair*, a lying-up place where the animal took his kill and where man later took his possessions, including, of course, his family. The oral language has thus grown as a system of audible *symbols* by which men understand ideas. The sound itself, or the word, is not the idea; it is only the symbol for the idea. If the sound were the idea, only one language would exist, and there would be no misunderstanding.

Understanding a neighbor across the backyard fence on a subject like the weather or fishing or the kind of fertilizer on the lawn will not offer very much difficulty—not, that is, if both speak the same language. But if neighbor A, who is a mechanic, shifts the subject to the difficulty he had locating a crack in the pump housing of an automatic fluid-drive transmission, the chances are that neighbor B, who is not mechanically inclined, will be bored and will find some excuse to get on with his lawn mowing. The difficulty is, as one can readily see, not one of physically making audible sounds. The difficulty lies in the speaker's ability to make sounds which the listener will not only physically receive but understand.

Because the technical man must on occasion dispense highly specialized information, he should take time to make himself an effective public speaker. The material in this chapter is provided as an engineering shortcut to give the minimum training and practice to those who may not have had time for a formal speech course. In this brief, practical approach, the subject has been limited to a discussion of three topics: the technical man as a public speaker; adapting material for oral presentation; and the types of oral communication.

THE TECHNICAL MAN AS A PUBLIC SPEAKER

Technical people understand their facts. They understand the mechanics of sound by which the idea symbols are transmitted. They compose readable reports. They draw accurate diagrams. Why can they not speak? Some can. But, by and large, communication by audible symbols is not the technical man's strong point.

How much a few public speaking techniques could do for technical people is realized by attending a large symposium or technical conference which brings together diverse personalities and disciplines of technical study. Some papers are presented with clear enunciation, good audience eye contact, well-prepared slides and other graphic aids. These speakers catch and hold the interest of a thousand men for fifteen minutes with hardly a foot moved. Other speakers, mediocre by comparison, are not able to hold attention; there will be coughing and moving of feet and chairs, and occasionally one may observe whispering between members of the audience. Then comes the mumbler. Without looking at the audience he mumbles his way through fifteen pages of data and concludes with no one the wiser. This is a time to sleep or to go out for coffee; the man's printed paper can be read later.

Last comes the jaunty young "brain" wearing an open T-shirt and slacks. He runs through his technantics (needlessly long strings of specialized terms), pokes fun at the serious efforts of his colleagues, tells ribald stories, and facetiously explains the arrangement of subatomic particles. The audience is bored because both speaker and speech are out of context; they are not in harmony with his surroundings. The speaker has succeeded in showing his contempt for convention, but instead of being funny and informative he has succeeded only in being tiring and disgusting. Neither the mumbler nor the "brain" has taken seriously his responsibility for communicating with his technical colleagues.

In one respect technical communication is easier through the spoken word than it is through the printed page. By voice inflection, timbre, tone, pitch, and volume, the speaker can indicate shades of meaning that are impossible in writing. The speaker must face the discouraging fact, though, that the spoken word has two disadvantages which more than offset the one advantage mentioned: 1) personality traits of the speaker may distract the listener; and 2) the spoken word, unlike the printed one, is gone forever an instant after it is spoken. Nonetheless, the man who has already learned from his skill in writing how to organize his ideas into a logical order and support them by plausible evidence can make and deliver an effective speech of any length to any audience, if he remembers these important differences between speech and writing:

1. Audible symbols must have pleasing inflections, tone quality, and sufficient volume to be heard at the back of the auditorium by the person with normal hearing.
2. Personality traits, pronounced mannerisms, or facial or bodily gestures must not be allowed to distract the audience.
3. The speech must be simplified by increasing the ratio of illustrative material and transition beyond what is normally encountered in writing.

These differences between speech and writing form the basis for the technical man's practical training in public speaking.

Communication by Audible Symbol

In normal conversation the difficulty of being heard is not present, and the difficulty of being understood is reduced by *facial gestures* and by motions of the eyes, head, hands, and other parts of the body.

For some people these gestures are almost as much a part of communication as the audible symbol itself. But when a man becomes a technical speaker before an audience he may have difficulty making himself heard and making his words understood when they are heard. One of the first things a speaker should do when he learns that he will make a speech is to find out the size of the auditorium and whether he will have amplifying equipment or will have to speak without it. Also, if possible, he should get an estimate of the number of persons expected to attend. A full auditorium will require twice the volume that the same auditorium would take if half filled. And a very large auditorium will have a decided effect upon the rate of speech— that is, upon the amount of daylight needed between the words to permit the sound to carry to the farthest parts of the auditorium without serious interference from reverberation and the overlapping of sound. If nothing can be learned in advance, the auditorium can be sized up during the preliminaries before one is called upon to speak. The amount of reverberation and the strength of the public address system can be tested at the beginning of a speech by telling a humorous anecdote and observing whether the people in the back rows laugh at the punch line as heartily as those in the front rows.

Without going into the details of voice culture, there is a great deal the technical man can do for his voice, to make himself understood, by using his own good sense. The poet Burns' prayer, "O wad some power the giftie gie us/To see oursels as others see us!" was answered long ago in the silent films; now the power to hear one's self has also been granted. The tape recorder is the most effective speech-teaching device ever invented, and one can be borrowed or rented for very little cost almost anywhere. A few trial recordings of the voice played back will do more to eliminate objectionable speech qualities than many hours of classroom instruction. The student will not develop the elocution of Laurence Olivier, but he can take enough of the objectionable qualities out of his voice to keep it from distracting those with whom he would like to communicate.

In speaking, one should strive to match pitch, tone, and inflection to the meaning. If a recording of one's voice sounds flat—and it nearly always does—one simply hums through his nose and, without moving anything, opens his mouth and groans out a few words. If these words have the desired resonance, he has only to continue placing his tones in the resonating chambers of the sinuses to correct his trouble. But if the voice sounds anemic, it can be strengthened by laughing like

Santa Claus until the same muscles can be felt pushing the words out (this may take some practice). If the *s* sounds tend to whistle, this can be stopped by a conscious effort to put less stress on the *s* sounds (this sentence, for example, will show up the whistling difficulty if one exists.) Breathiness can be partially controlled by opening the throat more while inhaling, or by speaking a bit louder and moving farther from the mike.

If words cannot be understood well because they are run together, they can be separated by giving greater stress to the consonants and slowing the pace of delivery. Americans are noted for their slovenliness of speech. This can be largely corrected by making the lip and tooth air stops distinctly. A lazy use of lips, teeth, and tongue does not interfere much with informal conversation, but when technical people stand before a public address system in a large auditorium, the sound symbols must come out clearly, with every word understandable. If the audible symbol is being received, yet is not understood, it may be the consonants that need cleaning up; if the audible symbol is not being heard at all, it is the vowels which need pushing out more.

Anyone who has had military training will recognize the devices that are used to obtain greater carrying power for audible signals. The infantry command "right oblique," becomes "rhīt-ho-blhīk" when given by the experienced officer. The meaning, "turn right at a 45-degree angle," remains the same, but the symbol is changed to one which carries better in the open. Repetition of the new sound soon fixes the new symbol to the old meaning. This does not, however, license the technical man to change the standard sounds of words when the audience is within easy range of the public address system. A technical man's only recourse is to be certain that he speaks loudly enough to be heard and that he enunciates clearly enough to be understood.

Practice in reading aloud a sentence like "Wasps build nests on fence posts" will help, but reading aloud a specialized technical description will be almost as good. The enunciation (distinct pronunciation) of technical words is also improved by reading aloud (to anyone who will listen) from textbooks, technical journal articles, poetry, and novels (older novels, preferably, that were written to be read, not mentally syphoned by speed readers). The same people are poor speakers who are poor readers. Anything which will improve reading ability will be reflected favorably in one's ability to speak well. When the tone, the pitch, the inflection, and the enunciation have been practiced enough, the audible symbol approaches the meaning of the printed symbol. In other words, a properly read paragraph, when played back on the recorder, should have almost the same meaning as the printed page.

The Use of Gestures

A recording device is good for the voice, but the elements of personality, including body movements, are best practiced in front of a mirror. If the motions and mannerisms of a speaker are meaningless, they can distract the audience sufficiently to block hearing and understanding. On the other hand, meaningful bodily movements, called gestures, can help the audience interpret the speaker's meaning. Though facial gestures may go unnoticed in a large auditorium, a simple movement of the head or the hands can be seen almost as far as the speaker himself. Transitions in thought which would be indicated in a small auditorium by a slight shifting of the body weight are indicated in the large auditorium by a short step, if the public address system permits it. All bodily gestures are calmed down as the auditorium decreases in size. In an ordinary classroom, vigorous gestures are not becoming to an objective presentation; gestures should be limited to the face or a turn of the hand, with the body remaining in a comfortable, but not slouched, position.

When practicing before the mirror, one should watch for mannerisms—for such things as picking the nose, smoothing the hair, pulling at the trousers, twiddling the thumbs, adjusting the spectacles, gazing at the ceiling, clearing the throat, and pacing back and forth. Once the speaker is aware he has these mannerisms, he can eliminate them quickly. In their place he can adopt the gestures appropriate to the subject matter and to the size of the auditorium.

ADAPTING MATERIAL FOR ORAL PRESENTATION

Like technical writing, technical speaking is done primarily to inform. The basic kinds of writing and the techniques of oral presentation are parallel. The inherent difference lies in the fact that audible symbols are illusive and transitory. This brings about significant changes in style which must not be ignored. It is the evanescent quality of the human voice that can make a well-written paper hard to follow when read aloud to an audience. Disregarding the elements of personality already treated, the required changes in style are described next under the headings "Expanded Ideas" and "Rhetorical Devices."

Expanded Ideas

The significant difference between a fifteen-page speech and a fifteen-page technical paper on the same subject is that a great deal more information is included in the paper. The techniques for compressing the language are not so much involved as the necessity for adding illustrative material, better and more frequent transitions, and more repetition. The problem of most concern to the speaker is to decide what should be given up to make room for the added material. Nothing really essential should be eliminated. The minor details of the paper are bridged over in the speech with summarizing transitions, and the basic ideas are lifted from the written text and turned to the audience, first one way and then another, until all have been understood. This means that one may have to use informal definition more frequently. He must develop hypothetical cases and make comparisons and contrasts. He may even have to describe some parts of the equipment in greater detail. Certainly he must take every opportunity to link ideas in chronological sequence.

The level of technical specialization of the audience will determine to a great extent which basic ideas need expansion. The tendency of most speakers is to forget how much more difficult it is to understand by the audible symbol than it is by the printed page. The superiority of eye over ear in translating symbols and ideas is obvious in a foreign language class. The French sentence spoken by the instructor is much harder to translate than the same sentence when read from the text.

When key terms are encountered in speaking, they require more expanded definitions than when encountered in the written paper. It is also advisable to use the new term two or three times after it has been defined. The tendency is not to repeat ideas often enough in spoken language. Soap opera writers know the need of repetition for a listening audience. When anything is mentioned of importance to the plot, it is named or stated in different forms at least three times. For example, the man asks, "Where is my knife?" The woman says, "What?" The question is repeated, "My knife! It was right here on the mantel." And she says, "Oh, your hunting knife. Charley's killing hogs today and wanted to borrow it." "Charley!" he says, "How come you didn't tell me this sooner?" And so on. The attentive listener has already heard the word *knife* three times and has marked its importance. If he is a really sharp listener, he knows the next sentence is going to repeat the word *Charley,* an even more important word in the plot. This same technique of repetition, in a milder form, is used effectively in technical public speaking. The inexperienced speaker will find it difficult to believe that his audience is not able to comprehend at a faster rate than it actually does. The classroom instructor, on the other hand, knows that it is beyond hope that all students will be listening all the time. Even when the same ideas are restated in three or four different ways, some student by an irrevelant question will reveal that he failed to understand even on the fourth time around.

Rhetorical Devices

The other matter to consider in making the style change that is needed to transform an effective paper into an effective speech is the addition of rhetorical devices. Devices used to influence or persuade, though out of place in formal technical papers, are permissible in speeches, their use depending on the formality of the occasion. The rhetorical devices used in a speech to expand and illustrate ideas make the big difference. The technical speaker may use anecdotes, hypothetical cases, illustrative comparisons or contrasts, and some figures of speech. Hyperbole, of course, is excepted; exaggerated forms of speech are not in keeping with technical speech style. Metaphors and similes are also used sparingly. Anecdotes are generally limited to the introduction, but they may also be used at other points in the speech when it is desirable to relate the experiences of other persons.

The one indispensable rhetorical device for the technical speaker is the use of overlapping questions to create a kind of listener suspense. This technique of sustaining the listener's interest was described earlier in the text (see Chapter 7). It is a technique especially useful in public speaking because it helps to focus attention on the words of the speaker. Nothing can be communicated to anyone without his attention. If the information is technical or strange to the listener, it will take concentrated attention on his part to understand it. The speaker should always keep at least one unanswered question before the audience until the very end, when the last question is answered without raising a new one.

In addition to the attention-getting anecdote at the beginning and the use of sustained questions to hold attention, some provision should be made for recapturing the attention of persons whose attention has been lost for one reason or another. For this purpose a strange or surprising fact may be placed at the beginning of each major subdivision in the speech and at any other point where the interest might be expected to drop. Partial summaries are also useful for getting the inattentive listener back into the speech.

It goes without saying that good composition, which is by extension included in the subject of rhetoric, is the most vital of all considerations in adapting material for the speech. What has been said about composition in Chapters 1 through 7 is noted here only by way of reference. Two or three admonitions, however, will bear repeating from those chapters: The speaker should prefer familiar nouns for things and limit the use of strange or unfamiliar terms wherever that can be done without obscuring the meaning or reducing the degree of accuracy. Shorter nouns are substituted wherever possible because they are more easily understood. Concrete nouns are better than abstract ones. Evidence is better than general inferences. The listener prefers being shown to being told. He likes to be made an eyewitness and to take sides with the protagonist in the discovery. For this reason active, specific verbs and the active voice, indicative mood should be used to relate all processes. Conditions, side effects, suppositions, opinions, and the like may be given in the passive voice, using the indicative or subjunctive moods as desired.

TYPES OF ORAL COMMUNICATION

Classification of every kind of utterance made by the technical man would serve no useful purpose here. Three general types, however, are so often used that they should be singled out for special attention: the group discussion, the technical conference speech, and the popular lecture.

Group Discussions

Group discussions may range from the high-level formal conference involving top-level management to the informal shirt-sleeve powwow over a lab table. They may be announced well in advance, like the monthly sales or production meeting, or they may be precipitated by a hot wire from an angry client or customer. The "boss," who may be anyone from a group supervisor to the plant manager, calls the meeting and usually acts as chairman. Each man is asked to contribute his wisdom to the wisdom of the group in order to meet the new emergency. A clear distinction must be made, though, between what one knows and what one thinks. Transcriptions of such conferences are sometimes circulated. The group discussion is not an uncontrolled bull session or a disorderly name-calling session. These could be differentiated, but since both are out of place in business and scientific circles, no useful purpose would be served.

The group discussion provides the stimulation for drawing out the best thoughts on a given subject from those participating. Every effort should be made to hear from all those present, even the less articulate ones. If the chairman requests the remarks of each person to be confined to the subject of discussion and the time to be limited to three minutes, these restrictions must be observed by the speakers. Because time is usually limited, the speaker should go directly to the point and be as brief and succinct as possible. If the group becomes too emotionally involved to make a sound judgment, the meeting should be recessed for coffee—or if there is excessive display of emotion, until the next day. To maintain poise and self-control under fire is a mark of maturity which will not go unnoticed by one's superiors.

Technical Conference Speech

Technical speeches are of two general types, the state-of-the-art paper and the report of work done in a specialized field. If one has already written and delivered a student contest paper, he has a pretty good idea of what it means to deliver a technical speech for a critical, well-informed audience.

The conference speech is derived from the paper which has been written for the occasion. The bound papers, being a desirable by-product of the conference, are circulated to libraries and others interested in the general conference subject. The conference speech is often referred to as "presenting a paper." This may be the way of least resistance for the busy man, but if enough time could be scrounged to prepare a speech from the written paper, the conference audience would appreciate the difference. Published speeches are too expanded for written technical style, and written papers intended for publication are too compressed for oral presentation. If all participants realized this, the total amount of information exchanged through the oral presentation of papers would be considerably increased.

Popular Technical Lecture

The popular technical lecture is one of the favorite kinds of entertainment for the high school and college forum, the celebrity series, and various types of club programs. It is characterized by the display of scientific materials, slides, motion pictures, posters, and so on; and it is delivered with humorous anecdotes. It requires, besides a pleasing personality and a good voice, a profound knowledge of the scientific subject and the ability to translate this knowledge into the common language of the audience.

Invitations to deliver a popular scientific lecture are usually extended to persons who have become well known in their specialized field of study. The young engineer or scientist, however, who accepts an invitation to speak to a neighborhood science club of fifth to eighth grade children is getting a foretaste of what the popular lecture assignment of five or ten years in the future will be like. If he holds the attention of these lively youngsters, he need not fear either the technical lecture platform or the popular lecture assignment. Such neighborhood assignments, incidentally, are the responsibility of professionally trained people, and they should be accepted willingly. Sharing the strange and wonderful facts of science with those who do not know the language, but who are intelligent enough to appreciate the knowledge, is one of the compensations of the scientist or the engineer that is not included in his paycheck.

In this chapter some distinctions have been made between the oral and written modes of communicating technical information. It has been shown that the rate of idea transfer is much slower by audible symbols than by written symbols. This fact makes it necessary to expand the main ideas and to abridge minor details in adapting written material for oral presentation. Another distinction was made between oral and written communication regarding the effect—either positive or negative—of the speaker's personality on the reception and understanding of the audible symbol. Some pointers were given on ways to improve speaking skill, and some specific instructions, were given for preparing and delivering the technical speech.

In Chapter 12 some observations are made about the technical man's business communication.

EXERCISES

1. Select and purchase one of the technical papers presented at a recent technical conference on a subject of interest to you. Blue-pencil the portions which would be included in a ten-minute class speech on the subject. Hint: papers ordered through members are usually half price.

2. Make a ten-minute class speech on the subject selected for exercise 1.

3. Attend a popular scientific lecture. Take notes. Write a 200- to 300-word critique on the speaker's performance, covering the techniques observed that you think increased your understanding and enjoyment of the speech. Any points for improvement should also be noted.

4. Prepare and deliver a ten-minute class speech on some interesting aspect of your term project. The whole project should be explained in the introduction, but you should then go directly to the portion of most interest and expand it to life size, including, if desirable, material which was not a part of your written project. Do not make your ten-minute speech a synopsis of the entire project. After the ten-minute delivery, you will be asked to remain as chairman of a discussion period of five to ten minutes to answer questions from the instructor and other class members. Your performance will be judged according to the standards for technical speaking described in this chapter.

12

Forms of Technical Communication in Business

The previous eleven chapters have provided sufficient instructions and practice to insure attainment of the minimum goals in technical communication and readiness to fill that first job. But for many of the class who are already working, and eventually for all, there remain a few more problems. These additional after-employment problems are grouped loosely under the title of this chapter because all of them are directly or indirectly concerned with business and because they are wholly or partially the responsibility of engineers and scientists. The extent of involvement for the individual, of course, remains an unknown until the job situation has been formulated.

In the first group of communications are the business-related reports which the technical man is not usually asked to write but for which he is almost always asked to supply information. This group is followed by the letter of application and other business letters and by telephone and teletype message forms. The third group are the business-related reports which the engineer does write, either alone or with the assistance of a technical editor: facility studies, engineering proposals, and technical surveys.

WRITTEN DOCUMENTS INVOLVING THE ENGINEER'S COLLABORATION

In some smaller companies the engineer may actually write the reports discussed in the following paragraphs. Generally, however, the engineer serves only as a source of information, or he checks the technical accuracy of information gathered by others.

Sales Brochures

The original idea of a few sheets of printed matter stitched together has just about disappeared from the word *brochure* as used in modern business. A sales brochure is a dignified sales pamphlet—restrained, factual, attractive, but definitely "pitched" to create a desire for the item to be sold. It can be a land development in the Great Smokies or a gas turbine design to start a jet airliner, one page or a hundred, and still be called a brochure. It is varied in length and in content, and the style and layout, including typography, are designed to suit the nature of the item and the reading level of the potential customers. Although the brochures are produced by specialists in this kind of advertising, the engineer is often responsible for the specifications or factual statements about the product in the brochure. Engineers must sometimes also supply the graphical means of illustrating the product.

If the untrained technical man finds himself with an assignment to write a brochure, he may be able to do a pretty good job of it. The same general procedure can be followed to appeal to a prospective customer as that used to catch and hold the reader's attention in the popular nonfiction article. The *P* in the nonfiction formula, when applied to brochures, simply becomes *purchase probability*:

$$P = (ART)^r E$$

The purchase probability of a commodity described in the sales brochure can be estimated from the effectiveness of the other elements of the formula: The *A*ttention of the prospective customer, the *R*elation of the customer to the subject of the brochure, and the *T*echnical description needed to give the customer the information to understand the new product. The exponential *r*eaction factor shows the effectiveness of the "sales pitch." If the reaction factor is large—and it will be large if a sufficiently large *E*motion factor has been included in the *ART* of the formula—the *P*urchase probability becomes large.

The reader level has much to do with the ratio of fact to feeling in a brochure. A new model automobile brochure might be 90 per cent feeling; a brochure for a new type of pyrheliometer might be 90 per cent fact. The best advice to a beginner, of course, would be to have half a dozen examples of this kind of writing at his elbow for models as he writes. He will find, however, that a much higher percentage of emotion-charged words are used in brochures than may appear at first reading. On the other hand, sentimental or hackneyed appeals degrade the brochure to the level of hawking; it degenerates into an undignified and overanxious "sales pitch." But an engineer trained in factual reporting should have no difficulty steering away from the pitfall of sentimentality.

Purchase Agreements

Although engineers as a rule do not write purchase agreements, they most certainly do assist in writing the terms of performance for a production item of complex design. They write the specifications which bind the manufacturer and set up the terms for the maintenance and servicing of the items produced. They prepare, in fact, any documents of a technical nature pertinent to the design of the purchased item which are included by reference in the terms of the purchase agreement. The contracts department of the seller will also require engineering assistance in reviewing the probable costs incurred by the specifications for producing and field-servicing a product.

Since the responsibility for checking the terms of purchase contracts rests with the legal department and the engineer's job is only to supply specifications, instructions for writing the terms are not included here. One thing is certain, though. If the project engineer of the buyer and the project engineer of the seller were given a chance to talk over the specifications before the purchase agreement was signed, a great deal of misunderstanding and many costly rejections could be prevented.

Medical Opinions

Medical men, by and large, are highly qualified scientists, but they too must rely at times upon engineers and other nonmedical specialists in writing their opinions. For example, an engineer may be called upon to evaluate the safety hazards in a given industrial situation, or a chemist may be asked to supply analyses and to give his opinion regarding the toxicity of chemicals that may contribute to occupational diseases and accidents. Other nonmedical scientists may have to assist the doctor in writing an opinion involving the use of complex diagnostic equipment. Some doctors use the opinion of the pathologist, for example, who is a scientist but may not be a medical doctor. But although the engineer and the scientist may supply evidence for the doctor's medical reports, the medical opinion itself must be written by the doctor.

Legal Opinions

Lawyers and judges write legal opinions; engineers and scientists write opinions that are legal evidence. Personal damage suits growing out of structural failures (involving the extent of damage caused by storms, earthquakes, fire, and criminal negligence) and similar suits lean heavily on evidence supplied by engineers and scientists. In one instance at least, the patent application, the engineer or scientist writes the legal document itself. The writing of a bona fide patent application is recommended as a term project option in this course. The specific conditions under which the application must be written and submitted to the Patent Office should be worked out with the instructor before it is selected as a term project. The discussion following is intended to supplement the information furnished by the Patent Office.

The United States Patent Office was conceived as a spur to invention. By law, the patent holder is given an exclusive right to produce and sell his invention for a period of seventeen years. The Patent Office, however, does not furnish legal assistance in making application or in defending against infringement. Its primary function is to judge the merits of patent applications, to grant patents, and to make existing patents available to search by inventors or their agents. Patents are granted for patentably novel ideas and inventions or for novel improvements on existing inventions, which may have some value to civilized people; thus patents can be obtained for toys as well as for oil-well rotary bits. The Patent Office is not infallible; it may grant overlapping patents. And it is entirely possible to be sued for infringement with an issued patent in hand and to lose one's patent rights after a patent has been granted. Nevertheless, the Patent Office makes a very determined effort to insure that this will not happen. But though an inventor is given protection for the use of his invention, it is not for a dog-in-the-manger purpose.

Patent litigations can rob an inventor of all the monetary value of his patent. When a really good idea emerges from the research or inventive efforts of an engineer or a scientist, the safest course is to divulge the "secret" to a reputable patent attorney. Such a man is not only ethically bound but, what is even better, of necessity bound to keep secrets. A patent attorney who gave away inventors' secrets would soon be out of business. If the inventor is not financially able to carry a patent application to its completion, a letter with the full disclosure can be mailed to a patent attorney, who will acknowledge the letter with a date, and this can serve as proof of the time the idea came, an important factor in obtaining patents. The inventor could also write the same letter to himself, register it, and leave it unopened until he is ready to develop the idea, or until he is financially able to engage a patent attorney. These are measures which give some priority, but the courts tend to favor the man who, forging ahead, completes the development and produces the invention.

If one has invented a useful device, the writing of a patent application offers a good challenge in communication and a real-life adventure of some practical value. The student begins his application by first procuring and carefully reading the following Patent Office Bulletins: *Patents and Inventions, an Information Aid for Inventors,* 1959; *Rules of Practice of the U. S. Patent Office in Patent Cases,* June 1960; *Guide for Patent Draftsmen,* May, 1961. Then he should make a drawing of his device as specified in the patent instructions, making certain that all parts are numbered exactly as shown in the examples given in the instructions. Next he should write his claims in the recommended tabular form to conform in style with current patent practice. The patent search to show whether others have prior claim to the invention can be made in at least three ways: the inventor can hire a patent attorney, as suggested earlier; he can make the trip to the Patent Office and do the search himself; or he can request the Patent Office itself to supply the needed information. The Patent Office does not make a search service available to inventors. Some help can be obtained indirectly, however, by making the claims broad enough to include prior art references which are closely related to the subject matter described and claimed in the application. When the application is denied, the Patent Office discloses the numbers of references upon which the claims appear to "read" (conflict). The inventor then orders these patents, which he can purchase for a few cents each, and studies them very carefully to see in what way his own invention is novel. Next, he amends or changes his claims so that they do not conflict with any of the claims in the related existing patents. After that he resubmits his amended petition, which entitles him to a second consideration. If his claims are still too broad, his patent will be denied for the reasons noted, and he can continue to amend and to petition until he either succeeds in making his claims novel or until he discovers that his invention has already been patented by someone else.

Once the patent application has been processed and the patent is granted, the next step, of course, is to find someone who will produce the invention at a fair price to the inventor. A few inquiries may turn up a manufacturer in the hometown. Here the inventor needs to exercise caution. For instance, an offer for a percentage of the gross sales should be very carefully examined, preferably by the family lawyer.

Auditors' Opinions

Discussion of the professional opinion written by a certified public accountant would be beyond the scope of this text. The auditor's opinion is almost a stereotyped form, unchanged for well over a hundred years. In fact that may be the reason why the more progressive and enterprising CPA's in Arizona recently held a two-day communication clinic to study ways of writing more concise and understandable reports to clients and to write better letters. When preparing a financial statement, however, the CPA must often seek the collaboration of a scientist or an engineer in trying to arrive at the exact worth of property owned by its clients. The reports of engineers and scientists are used to determine the exact status of research and manufacturing operations which affect the worth of a corporation. The engineering information used by CPA's must be at the professional level, accurate (absolutely), and concisely and objectively written. For example, in order to establish a reasonably accurate statement of loss for tax purposes, an engineer is often called upon to make an appraisal of property which has been damaged or which has radically changed in value due to a technological change in its construction or intended use.

The foregoing have been examples of business reports which the engineer does not write but to which he must often contribute his services. The next section is a discussion of business reports written by engineers in carrying out their regularly assigned duties.

BUSINESS CORRESPONDENCE

Once an engineer has shown an aptitude for technical communication, he rises rapidly in the management level of his company. But long before he has reached the higher levels of management the engineer begins to touch the vital lifeline of profit and loss. His first sales brochure is his letter of application for employment, in which he sells his services to his prospective employer. From then on the engineer's reports gradually increase in complexity and financial value until the seasoned engineer touches every important decision made in the industrial operations of his company. Some of these after-employment communication problems are described in this section.

The Letter of Application

The most important letter any engineer or scientist will ever write is the one which brings him a job. The first job in all probability will not be permanent, but eventually his ability to write a good application letter may lead him to that career job where he will spend most of his working years. Hence it is a mighty important letter, one which needs special care in writing.

Application letters have settled down somewhat in recent years to a pretty standard content. The challenge to the engineer comes in being resourceful and interesting in the manner in which he supplies the standard information. The application letter generally consists of a standardized résumé and a cover letter, to be discussed in that order. Before he begins the résumé, the student should decide at least the kind of employment he wishes to seek—still better, the very employer he hopes will hire him. Having in mind a particular employer will make some difference in the qualifications the student emphasizes. The résumé is simply a logical and convenient form for telling the prospective employer the pertinent things about oneself. These include personal data, educational background, experience background, and personal references attesting character and ability.

The *personal data* section of the résumé should contain only what is of vital concern to the prospective employer. Personal data should include such things as age, condition of health, marital status, draft status, place of birth, race, and citizenship (religion may be omitted unless it is known to be a factor in the applicant's favor), and as much physical description as is considered in good taste and fitting for the kind of employment sought. If physical handicaps are not directly involved in the kind of work the applicant will be doing, they need not be mentioned—for example, facial scars or other blemishes of a physical nature; but if the body activity is impaired or limited by the blemish, such as an eye or limb or back injury, these defects in all fairness should be made known. A one-armed man applying for a job as a bouncer must say that one arm is missing, but at the same time he may wish to stress what he can do with the steel hook that replaces his left arm. A model for men's clothing must admit that one leg is shorter than the other, but he may also offer a picture of himself to show that as a live manikin in a display window he can make the short leg an advantage. To some employers physical description is more important than to some others. The personal data section must be governed by the kind of employment the applicant is seeking.

The second section of the résumé should be devoted to the *education* and special training of the applicant. Generally this section begins with the place and date of graduation from high school, followed by the place, date, and highest degree received in college and university or special schools. In a separate sentence following his education the student may wish to list several courses which he feels have specially prepared him for the job he has in mind. Some such statement as this may serve the purpose: "In reviewing my transcript you will note that the following courses taken at Cornell in animal husbandry are directly related to the zoo keeper's job I am applying for." Then should follow the list (without grades) of four to six subjects, never more than ten. In this way the employer will know in advance that the applicant's education is adequate, and the employer will tend to overlook any bad grades in other subjects when the transcript arrives. If the technical degree is from a reputable college or university, the individual grades are not too important. The overall grade index, how-ever, is important if it is high. A low or average index is just as well left out.

The *work history* or experience section begins with the present job, if any, and goes back as far as the prospective employer could be interested. Five years is a good round figure, though some govern-ment jobs demand what amounts to a life history, going back as far as twenty-five or thirty years. The best way to write the work history is to list the jobs held, beginning with the present one and giving for each job the date, the name of the company, the position held, the immediate superior if known, and the reason for leaving. The salary, unless required, should be omitted. On older forms, when the purchasing power of the dollar was fairly stable, the preceding three-year salary average was a pretty good indication of a man's technical worth. At present, due to the sudden inflation of the salaries for scientists and engineers, a three-year salary average would impose an unfair penalty. Three years ago, for example, the applicant, while working his way through college, may have had a job as a cowboy, a theater usher, or a pin setter, or some other service job which paid from ten to twenty-five dollars per week. Also, in the work history, the reason for leaving should be stated with care. It is better to say "Resigned for a better position" than to say "Couldn't agree with the boss," or "I wasn't going to take that kind of stuff from anybody," or "I didn't like my job." Gaps in the work history should be noted as "Unemployed" or "self-employed—pest control contractor."

The list of *references* completes the fourth section of the résumé. Persons listed for reference should be contacted, if possible, prior to the inclusion of their names as references because an unanswered query letter is considered an unfavorable reply. Three or four, never more than six, names should be given with the full first name, the middle initial, and the last name spelled correctly; and for each the correct street, city, and state address should also be given. The names should represent a fairly good cross section of the people the applicant has worked with. Previous employers, pastors, teachers, neighbors, and professional colleagues all make good references. Naturally the applicant will not make the mistake of selecting as a reference a man who is known to be hostile toward him and who would write an unfavorable letter.

The résumé is an accurate, factual document, but it is not intended to include all possible information of interest to the employer. It may or may not have a photograph attached. If it does, the photograph should be attached in the upper-right-hand corner alongside the personal data. The employer will want to know other things about the applicant if a personal interview is granted. The chance of such an interview may depend largely on the cover letter which accompanies the résumé.

When the résumé is finished and has been carefully checked for errors, the student should begin the rough draft of his *cover letter*. The cover letter of the application is not a summary of the résumé. It serves as an introduction to the applicant's qualifications and as a sales letter (of the low-pressure type). It should be designed to attract the employer's attention and to make a favorable impression, at least favorable enough to gain the personal interview. It begins with the regular business heading and ends with the complimentary close. The sender's address may be either in the upper right-hand corner (older style) or along the left-hand margin, as long as it is in keeping with business practice. It is important, however, to include both the complete address of the sender and the complete address of the employer. The proper salutation is *Dear Sir* or *Gentlemen,* followed by a colon or, better still, *Dear Mr. Blank,* with the name of the personnel director supplied. Effort spent to obtain the correct name of the personnel director will not be wasted.

The cover letter, whether couched in one, two, or three paragraphs, should include the following essential elements: the referral, the inducement, the availability, and the references.

The opening paragraph of the letter relates the form of *referral,* that is, by what means the applicant learned of the job opening. News of the job opening may have come by an advertisement, from a visit to an employment agency, or through a personal friend or relative. Telling the employer the means of referral is not vital to the application, but it does help to hold the employer's attention and keep him reading. Employers spend thousands of dollars to locate and interview prospective employees. They like to know which medium of advertising is most effective. In this game of job or no job, even to keep the employer reading through one short paragraph is worth something.

The employer is now reading on to see what other favorable things the letter has to say. The *inducement* should begin with a further statement about the employer. The best way, of course, to proceed is by degrees of favorable impressions—the inductive method. In the first paragraph the favorable impression was that the company was so well known or had been so favorably spoken of by an employee that someone else became interested in making an application. This is favorable impression number 1. The second favorable impression comes when the employer at the beginning of the inducement paragraph discovers that the applicant has more than superficial knowledge of the employer. If something the student has read can be casually mentioned to show that he has done some research on the company, it will be a pleasant way of letting the employer know that the applicant made up his mind to seek employment with this particular company by a methodical process, not by just picking a company at random.

If it can be done unostentatiously, it will be well to refer to some aspect of the company's growth or to plans for future operations which are of special interest to the applicant. A good way to learn a lot in a little time is to obtain a copy of the company's annual report. This can be obtained prior to the application letter by writing the public relations department, or it may be found in the public library. An interview with a friend or relative employed by the company can also be the source of the applicant's information. Any oblique reference which will show that the applicant has knowledge of the employer's operations is better than an outright statement. But in any event it must be evident that the applicant knows something about the company before he can make convincing the belief that he, the applicant, has useful skills which the company can use.

A new paragraph may be started for the second half of the inducement, or the belief in one's worth or suitableness for the position sought can be worked in as a logical sequence to knowledge of the company to make a single paragraph. The applicant is about ready to say that as a result of the company's future plans (or its employment policy or its sound financial backing or some other thing), he has decided to seek employment with Electro-Optical (the employer's firm name) because he feels that his education and experience particularly fit him for a position in the low-temperature adhesives group (the specific area of interest, if known). He immediately supports this generalization by making a general reference to his special preparation for this particular job. His next statement should hit smack in the same place: that because of his training and experience he believes he could reach a stage of productive activity within a minimum length of time. And a third hit on the same nail should point out that further information about his experience and education is shown in the attached résumé. If these statements are made with moderation and in good English, the employer may now be regarding the applicant, if not eagerly, at least with enough interest to finish reading the cover letter and perhaps to read the pertinent sections of the résumé.

Personnel directors are nice people, but they lose charity in a hurry if the letter takes a sentimental turn; that is, if the applicant attempts to persuade the employer to hire him on any but an individual merit basis. Favorable impressions gained by real merit are lost quickly if anything is said to give the employer the idea that the applicant is thinking only in terms of what he can get and has no thought of what he can give in return. The applicant may have a wolf at the door and a stork on the chimney (so destitute, in fact, that he may even have to borrow a friend's suit for the interview, as one man known by the author did recently), but the financial needs of the applicant must not be allowed to creep in or to make the applicant sound overanxious.

So far the application letter has shown two good reasons why the applicant should be considered for employment: 1) the particular company was deliberately selected; and 2) after due consideration the applicant believes that his education and experience will enable him to render service to the company. The third reason he should be hired is that he is available.

As soon as the employer begins to take an interest he is concerned about the applicant's *availability*. Sometimes a student will not be available for several months. If the applicant is changing jobs, a thirty-day notice may have to be given. Availability for interview will also need to be stated. The applicant should simply say that he will be available for work after graduation in June or that he will be available after a thirty-day notice to his present employer. Then he should say when and where he will be available for interview. If the interview is to be at the university, the student should suggest the most convenient day and hour which he can be available. But if the interview is to be at the employer's office or plant, which may be out of the city or state, the student may say that he is available on any Saturday or on a special holiday—Christmas, New Year's, or Easter, or between semesters. This will indicate to the employer that the applicant has a good sense of the value of his school work and is not willing to drop everything and fly off at a moment's notice for an interview. It will be evident from his statement of availability and his willingness to meet for an interview that the applicant is a man of dignity and honor, willing, even enthusiastic, but not fawning. Most firms are quite willing to pay the transportation for personal interviews that are arranged at their convenience. But the applicant is not expected to drop important work that he has underway at the convenience of the employer when some other date could be arranged just as well. If there is no urgency, the applicant might suggest that he would appreciate an opportunity to talk with the company's representative on his next visit to the university or to the applicant's hometown.

In the very last statement of his last paragraph, immediately following the statement of availability, the student should mention the attached résumé and the personal *references*. It might run something like this: "In the attached résumé of my education and experience, I have included the names of several persons who have expressed a willingness to answer questions about my character and general ability." Any enlargement of this statement is rather risky. A descriptive title or occupation given to each of the references will show their probable relationship to the applicant. After this fourth element of references nothing should follow but *Yours truly, Very truly yours, Yours very truly,* or *Sincerely yours.* The word *your* or *yours* must occur in the complimentary close. The neatly written signature in ink should be followed by the typed name.

The cover letter including these four elements (referral, inducement, availability, and references) in simple, precise language, accurately typed and spaced on an 8½ by 11 inch sheet of white paper (not onionskin or Ezerase), or neatly handwritten in the same format, is the applicant's surest way to gain a personal interview; in fact, a cover letter with résumé, including a picture, has gotten many students jobs without even a request for an interview.

Other Business Letters

Aside from the routine technical reports covered elsewhere in this text, the new employee, perhaps sooner than he expects, will have to write a letter. The first one may be just a simple request for information or service. The engineer will have no difficulty saying what needs to be said in a terse, yet friendly way; he may have some difficulty, though, about the business letter format. Only one style of business letter should be written, whether by a relatively new employee or the executive vice-president, and this is the style established by the company practice through the years. Any deviation from this style should be left to top management. This settles, then, the matter of format. The new employee has only to obtain a model of the business correspondence of his employer and follow it. If this cannot be done, any standard form which occurs in an English or secretarial handbook is acceptable.

Another kind of letter assignment often given to the new employee is to request certain technical information or to prepare an answer to such a request. Letters of this level are written by the man who digs out the information, though they may not be signed by him. Supervisory personnel usually review and send out the letters written by beginning employees. When the new employee can write letters that require no further changes before they are signed and sent out by his superiors, he is pretty certain to be promoted or given authority to sign his own letters. Engineering correspondence between the seller's and the buyer's engineering departments is usually routed through purchasing or sales to insure overall cognizance of all transactions. On very large contracts, all correspondence may be routed through a project manager.

The number of letters an engineer or a technical person may have to write in his first years of employment will depend largely on the branch of engineering he happens to be employed in. Sales and service engineers, for example, write a great many more letters. For these engineers a special course in letter writing is often required, since they must employ diplomatic language and deal directly with the customer. Generally speaking, an engineer has little difficulty with his business letter writing, especially one who has completed a course in technical communication at the level of this text. His habit of being certain of the facts before he speaks helps a great deal. What he has to guard against is failing to say enough. Putting oneself in the reader's place may help solve this problem. A critique from a supervisor may point out ways in which the new man can improve the understandability of his letters.

Telephone Conversations and Telegraphic Messages

Telephone and telegraphic messages are too often taken for granted as something anyone can do well. This, unfortunately, is not true in practice. Engineers, like any other persons, are sometimes awkward or discourteous on the telephone, and too frequently they can be completely obscure in a telegram, commonly referred to in business as a "TWIX" (TWX, a leased-wire telegraphic service). A few pointers and some advice on how to use the telephone and the wire service can be of great benefit in getting off to a smooth start in a new position.

The *telephone ring* in business is like the ring of a cash register. It means money—money going out or coming in. A notebook record of important phone calls should be kept just as surely as a letter file. If the employee has a secretary available, he should dictate a note when the call is completed, giving the subject and purpose of the call, the name of the person called (or calling), and the gist of any agreements reached. A telephone record can save much time, and it may save embarrassment. Notes made at the time of the conversation are convincing evidence, as well as a dependable source of information needed for writing the confirming letter, if contractual matters are discussed by telephone.

A business telephone is not to be used as a device for aimless talk; it is a means of transacting business. To insure the best use of one's telephone call and to get the information needed, one should jot down a list of questions before the call is placed, and one should have by his elbow every fact, figure, drawing, or document relating to the topic to be discussed. It is certainly not good business to interrupt a telephone call numerous times to look up additional information. A little advance planning can cut the cost of the telephone call and improve the temper of the person calling. Telephone questions which cannot be readily answered should be answered by a return call or perhaps by return wire or letter posted the same day. The telephone that sits on the engineer's desk or in the office nearby is a means of business correspondence. It should be used in a friendly and courteous but businesslike manner.

Nearly everyone has been puzzled at some time or other by a telegram "clipped" to the point of being unintelligible. Telegraphic messages as a rule are less expensive than telephone calls. In some areas it may be worthwhile to compare the cost of telegraphic and telephone messages. A three-minute call from Europe, for example, is a great deal cheaper than a 50-word cable. But it is not always a matter of cost. A signed telegram is considered a legal document, whereas a telephone call can sometimes be successfully contested. Telegrams are shortened forms of writing which leave out the words not necessary to the reader's understanding of the message.

Telegraphic style is always more compressed, but it will be observed that the number of words which can be omitted drops noticeably as the dollar value of the information increases. A wire contract for ten million dollars' worth of jet airplane parts might occupy several typed pages with hardly a preposition dropped. Ordinarily, however, nouns and verbs do the talking. As Mr. Paladin says, "Have gun, will travel." The prepositions, articles, conjunctions, most adjectives, and adverbs are omitted unless they are needed to keep the meaning clear. Leaving these out of Mr. Paladin's remark in no way obscures the message. In transmitting messages on complex technical subjects it might be better to spend a little extra money and have the message understood. Nothing has been saved if it is necessary for the receiver to place a telephone call to find out what the telegram means. Engineers and scientists should very carefully proofread all telegraphic messages. Teletypists sometimes unconsciously substitute common words for the technical terms which they resemble. If the typed message is not read carefully by the man who understands the difference in meaning, the wire he sends may have an error that will puzzle the receiver or misdirect him in performing some operation. Obvious errors are an annoyance, but it is the ones which *could be right* that create the havoc because they get by undetected.

If telegraphic style seems difficult, one should obtain some of the high-level telegraphic correspondence and study it carefully. Then he should try to imitate it. As a final safeguard it is a good practice for the new employee to hand his first few wires to a colleague and ask him to interpret them. If only one interpretation is possible, the wire is ready to send.

ENGINEERING REPORTS INVOLVING FINANCIAL TRANSACTIONS

The break-in period for a new technical man corresponds roughly to the testing of a new material. If he has enough tensile and compression strength, he fits into the "structure" of the organization. If he tears easily or is too soft, he may be used as padding or insulation. Many kinds of material are needed. If the technical man has shown good judgment in his business-related correspondence, has become familiar with company procedures, and has proved his technical knowledge in performing routine assignments and writing reports, he is showing signs of being structurally useful to his employer. Writing and interpreting specifications which control the design of products, writing test procedures and technical bulletins, designing test fixtures, searching for technical literature on a research project—any or all of these are likely assignments for the new man during the proof-loading or break-in period. If he dispatches these assignments creditably, there is no doubt that he is in the "structural" category, though it may take some years and hundreds of reports before his employer knows his ultimate tensile and compression loads.

Technical reports are a necessary by-product of an engineer's professional activity. The engineer may not always have to write them, but on many occasions he must, because he is the only one with sufficient technical understanding of the problem. There are occasions when the engineer's assignment requires a kind of report he has never seen before. Here he must rely on the work of others and on his own wits to devise the format most suitable to his purpose. The old adage that "experience is a dear teacher" cannot be gainsaid; but, being an educated man, the engineer knows it does not have to be his own experience. He shows his wisdom—not his ignorance—by asking questions and searching the files when he is confronted with a new kind of report. In the remaining pages of this chapter four types of reports are introduced for which experience is no doubt the best teacher, but a little prior knowledge can soften the shock of the first exposure.

Facility Studies

Facility studies are made by prime contractors charged with the overall procurement, tooling, manufacturing, and delivery of complex structures involving interchangeable parts or subassemblies. When major subassemblies or other large lead-time items are to be procured from subcontractors, the prime contractor makes an evaluation of each prospective subcontractor's plant to decide which of several bidders has the best prospect of producing and delivering the item within the required time. In other words, the subcontractor may have the best of intentions and a reasonable price, but a facility incapable of building and delivering the item by the time it is needed.

The General Shebang Corporation, for example, has a prime contract to deliver a certain missile to the Air Force within a given period of time. The contract specifies that, in compliance with Executive Order Number so and so, 42 percent of the missile is to be placed with subcontractors in depressed employment areas. These are probably the most risky areas in the nation for close tolerances and uninterrupted work. The prime contractor's only recourse is to choose, under the limitations imposed, the subcontractor who appears, after a careful evaluation, to be the best risk. This evaluation, since it involves a survey of the subcontractor's whole organization, may be made by a team of specialists, but it may also be made by a single project engineer who is well aware of the kind of facility needed. Prime contractors have learned from experience that the lowest bidder may not have the plant facilities or the experienced personnel to insure satisfactory completion of a job. The General Shebang Corporation, for example, has learned from previous experience that it takes more than skilled workmen, machine tools, and floor space to build a close-toleranced interchangeable subassembly for a missile. Going to a depressed area with GSC's kind of work is extremely hazardous anyway, because the automotive shops in the depressed employment area have never done this kind of missile manufacturing. Evaluation of the bidders' facilities is the prime contractor's only means of judging which facility in the depressed employment area is most likely to manufacture the needed subassemblies in time for them to be installed without holding up the delivery of the ICBM.

When the visit is made to the prospective subcontractor's plant, every item which would affect the performance of the subcontract should be checked. The project engineer, or any other responsible management representative making the survey, should enter the items to be checked in a pocket notebook so they may be checked off as the study progresses. This means a fine-comb treatment if this plant is to be the sole source for the missile subassembly. The subcontractor's representative may wish to escort the prime contractor's representative during the survey. An experienced man, however, needs no help; in fact, if the offer can be declined gracefully, the prime contractor's representative may complete his evaluation in less time. On the other hand, one must recognize the fact that he is a tolerated guest and his conduct must be above reproach. If the subcontractor does not wish to allow an outsider a free rein in his plant, or in some particular department, the investigator will have to obtain his information by other means. The eyes and ears can reveal a lot if they are open.

Probably the first item on the checklist is management—straight line or dotted line, working relationships among executives, evidences of internal friction or of disrespect from subordinates. Next on the list should probably be departmental organization. Is responsibility well defined between departments? Who will administer the proposed contract, and what has been his experience and training? How are the planning orders originated? Who determines the lead time for the procurement of materials called out on the drawings? Is quality control under management, engineering, or manufacturing? Are inspection people capable and enthusiastic in their work, or are they browbeaten and perfunctory? Do they think quality is built into the product or inspected into it?

Another department high on the checklist, if the missile subassembly requires jigs, fixtures, and checking tools, is the tooling department. This group has more to do with the performance of a contract on schedule than even the subcontractor may realize. The line responsibility should be traced from the man in the tooling shop to the plant manager. The basic philosophy on tooling is best understood by observing the designs of tools under construction, particularly those intended for use on interchangeable assemblies similar to the proposed missile work. Do the check fixtures provide adequate safeguards for holding master gauged points? Do the jigs and fixtures look sturdy and convenient to use, or do they resemble Rube Goldbergs? Is enough tooling provided to insure the production rate? Is the tooling department on schedule? Are the tooling engineers draftsmen or qualified engineers?

When management and the departmental organization have been charted, the investigator should then turn his individual attention to the production worker. The general competence and mental attitude of the man who runs the press are just as vital to a quality job as the general competence and attitude of management, and more important than the quantity or quality of the machine tools. The worker is probably the most critical point of the whole survey. What he thinks and feels can be learned indirectly by simply asking the man on the machine what he is doing. If the man knows exactly what the part name is, why it must be made just so, because it will eventually be used as this or that in service, morale is high; labor-management relations are good. Job knowledge is more than knowing how to operate a machine tool. Knowledge of the use that will be made of the product of his hands shows that this workman has dignity and pride. He will do high-grade work regardless of the job he is assigned to. If the average workman is like this, the chances for a good performance, even on a new kind of product, are greatly increased. If none of the men knows what part he is building and seems surprised that anyone would ask, the chance of getting close-tolerance work of any kind through that shop is meager.

The stability of the working force, also a vital factor in the uninterrupted performance of a contract, may be learned from responsible union officials. These representatives may not say much about the employer; but, again, the observer learns as much from what the union officials will not say as from what they do say. If it is evident that there are important areas of disagreement brewing that could cause a crippling strike, this would increase the procurement hazard, especially if this company is considered as a single source.

In addition to assessing the management and labor force, one should observe the physical plant and its equipment, particularly the necessary specialized tools. It will be of interest to find out what percentage of the proposed contract would be done in the subcontractor's plant and which parts, if known, would be done by further subcontract with outside sources. It is also useful to have an indication of the subcontractor's financial standing. In this connection it is good practice to pick up all the available organizational charts, facility brochures, and the like.

Then, in the quiet of a hotel room or a private office, the engineer should organize his information into a meaningful statement of the company's potential. Although he may be convinced that the company is a potentially good source for the missile subassemblies in question, he must also report any items he has observed which could affect adversely the performance of the facility. A report of this type, after a brief introduction, is organized around the major subdivisions of the company, beginning with top management and proceeding in the order just discussed. The departments are evaluated individually. The company-furnished documents may be used as exhibits, supplemented, at the writer's discretion, by any other graphic means available. A conclusion is reached, after all the evidence is considered, whether, in the judgment of the investigating engineer, this facility is or is not a good risk for the proposed subcontract.

Because the report written after such a study will affect the lives of many people, it must be written in as objective and analytical a manner as one is capable of. A well-documented facility study is a high-level confidential means of removing as much risk as possible from the placing of subcontracts involving interchangeable assemblies or precision equipment in plants unaccustomed to the kind of job the prime contractor is doing. The hypothetical case just described may give the young engineer a better understanding of the close coordination and interdependence of all line and staff departments needed for the successful operation of an industrial plant.

Engineering and Research Proposals

Proposals almost always involve the expenditure of money. When an individual or a corporation wishes to obtain funds to do research, to sell something already conceived, or to take any action which requires formal review, a formal document is prepared which outlines the objectives and presents the idea, item, or action for approval. The proposal lines up all of the favorable aspects and reaches a conclusion in the affirmative that some action should be taken, and in this respect the proposal resembles the recommendation report (see Chapter 8).

The proposal differs, however, in the manner in which the evidence is presented and in the manner in which the emphasis is shifted from conclusions and recommendations to the feasibility of the operation.

The *engineering proposal* is limited to proposals made by engineers. This would include the city engineer's proposal for a storm sewer but exclude the real estate broker's proposal for a zone change. All of the factors involved in the engineering undertaking are analyzed, usually with the aid of charts and graphs, and often with "live" presentation by one or more engineers. The best advice on format is probably to follow a successful model proposal. When the proposal is presented, personally written or typed copies are prepared in advance and distributed to those present. After the proposal has been presented, there is usually a discussion period led by the person responsible for the proposal. Charts, graphs, slides, models, or other dramatic means of selling the proposed idea or item are used with good effect, especially in the personal presentation. A few dollars spent in preparing graphic aids can make the difference between a proposal's acceptance and its rejection. Fifty dollars spent for a color drawing in perspective could be the deciding factor in winning approval for a new wing on the administration building.

The engineer who has prepared a successful proposal is regarded with a new kind of respect by his employer. Government contracts are often obtained through the engineering proposal. When a new product is needed, an agency of the government sends out bid forms to manufacturers who are known to be capable of producing items similar to the new item needed. Proposals showing basic designs are then prepared and submitted to the procurement agency's engineering staff by the bidder. With the increasing complexity of government purchasing, the engineering proposal has taken on a new significance. Often twenty or thirty proposals for a project are carefully reviewed and evaluated before the government agency makes its decision to award a contract.

In writing the engineering proposal one is guided by the budget committed and by the agency of the government which is doing the purchasing. The format of the proposal has some elements of the facility study because it must review plant facilities and the qualifications of persons who will be assigned to the project. It also resembles the recommendation report because it must justify the conclusions reached on design and on the methods to be used in performing the task of manufacturing the item. It is like a sales brochure because it must make a reasoned appeal to convince the buyer. It is, finally, a financial document because it commits the employer on the amount of money the proposed item will cost. The language is formal but on the technical level of those who are expected to review the proposal.

The *research proposal* is somewhat more stereotyped than the engineering proposal. Competition for research funds has become so keen that mass production methods must be used in reviewing the proposals. Arbitrary criteria of form are therefore used to reduce the number of eligible proposals to that which can be evaluated by the foundation's staff. Because of this method of selection, research students, engineers, scientists, and teachers submitting research proposals to foundations should request proposal instructions from the particular foundation. The National Science Foundation, for example, has prepared a guide—*Grants for Scientific Research*—which is sent free on request.

Some effort may be saved by making an informal proposal by letter to the director of the foundation expected to be interested in providing the funds. This will result in contact with the foundation's specialist assigned to the general subject. He may indicate an interest, or he may say that he has no interest whatever in the proposed idea. Whatever his answer, he will in all probability enclose the instructions needed for making the formal proposal. One may also gain valuable time and assistance by sending a preliminary form of the proposal to the foundation for comment before the proposal is duplicated in its final form. If there are defects in such items as the secretarial assistance, manpower, or equipment to be used, or even in the statement of objectives, this may be pointed out by the granting agency so that the necessary revisions can be made before the twenty to fifty copies of the finished report are formally submitted.

Consulting Reports

The third in this series of engineering reports involving the spending of other people's money is prepared by the professional specialist. The scientist or the engineer who sells his services to a client is practicing his profession in the same manner that a doctor is when he writes a prescription. A consulting report is any form of information prepared by the professional man in return for a fee. The consulting specialist has already mastered the kinds of report forms needed for his practice. The student, however, who may in future years be faced with the writing of consulting reports, will profit by the following suggestions.

In the writing of consulting reports, two guiding principles should be remembered: the consultant must speak the truth as he sees it, even when he knows his findings may disappoint his client; and, second, the report must be written in a language the client can understand. The objectives of the report are described first. Then follows an outline of the procedures that were used in gathering the evidence upon which the conclusions are based. Any data useful to the client should be listed in the body of the report; this is especially true if physical tests are performed. The conclusions and recommendations, if any, are generally stated at the close of the report.

Consulting engineering firms, such as Leland S. Rosner of San Francisco and the Austin Company of Cleveland, employ hundreds of engineers who are assigned to research and the subsequent writing of consulting reports with multimillion dollar price tags. Testing laboratories, research laboratories, and medical pathological laboratories are examples of other agencies where consulting reports are mass produced. Any qualified person whose services are obtained through consultation may write a consulting report.

Land and Other Surveys

Statistical reports, land descriptions, and geological reports are typical of a class of professionally written reports called surveys. They are included here because they are technical reports involving financial transactions. Like other reports, the survey has its introduction, body, and conclusion. It requires a thorough technical knowledge of the science involved and the use of a specialized technical vocabulary. The geological survey, for example, often classed as a consulting report, is written by geologists. The survey is mentioned here also because it is one of the options for a term project recommended for use in this study. A short example of an actual geological survey done by students as a class project is given at the end of this chapter.

In conclusion, it should be remembered that these four types of technical reports and surveys are not specific or absolute forms which can be identified by outward appearance. Their differences are chiefly in the purpose for which they are written. All are alike in the fact that they directly or indirectly influence the spending or making of money.

No exercises follow this chapter, since the student is not expected to have occasion in the near future to write any of the four types. Some advanced students, however, particularly those already employed in industry, may be interested in the writing of the engineering proposal. This chapter of the text has been included as a means of informing engineers and scientists of some of the report forms which they will encounter in their careers in industry.

The next and final chapter of the text begins a new subject important to all who are interested in making a professional career of engineering or science.

STUDENT EXAMPLES

Letters of Application

M.O. Best Hall "A"
Arizona State University
Tempe, Arizona
June 8, 1962

Mr. J. B. Willson, Chief Engineer
Station WHO-AM-FM-TV
1100 Walnut Street
Des Moines, Iowa

Dear Mr. Willson:

Mr. Rod Gelatt, a longtime personal friend and a past employee of WHO, referred me to you concerning an opening on your engineering staff in the television facility.

As a native Iowan, I grew up knowing the sound and sight of WHO—Des Moines. I am aware of the station's high caliber of programming and great popularity throughout the Midwest and Central Iowa. As indicated in my enclosed résumé, my broadcasting experience has been here on the A.S.U. campus. I feel that this training will be highly beneficial to me and my employer in this field.

I plan to be visiting in the Des Moines area during the week of July 4. If possible, I would like very much to visit your new studios sometime while there.

Also indicated on the résumé are some of my personal acquaintances in the Central Iowa area, as well as those here in the Valley, who will be happy to supply character recommendations upon request.

Sincerely yours,

James A. Blank
James A. Blank

PERSONAL DATA

NAME: James Albert Blank
AGE: 23
RACE: Caucasian   PHOTO
RELIGION: Protestant
MARITAL STATUS: Single
DRAFT STATUS: 1-D (reserve)

EDUCATION

Graduated

HIGH SCHOOL: Perry High School, Perry, Iowa	DATE: May 1956
COLLEGE: Arizona State University, Tempe, Arizona	DATE: June 1962

SPECIAL TRAINING: Various military communications courses

EXPERIENCE

DATES	EMPLOYER	POSITION	REASON FOR LEAVING
Sept. 1961 to present	Ariz. State Univ. Radio-TV Bureau	Student Engineer Trainee	* * *
Sept. 1961 to present	Ariz. State Univ. M.O. Best Hall "A"	Assistant Head Resident/Counselor	* * *
Jan. 1957 to present	U.S. Army Reserve	Communications Sergeant	* * *
Summer mos. 1959–1961	Midwest Builders, Inc. Des Moines, Iowa	Carpenter's helper	Return to college
Oct. 1958– July 1959	Various Arizona contractors	Apprentice Carpenter	Return to college
Jan.–Oct. 1958	Osmundson Mfg. Co. Perry, Iowa	Shipping Clerk	For better paying job

REFERENCES

Rod Gelatt, Dept. of Journalism, S.U.I., Iowa City, Iowa
Don Bruce, Vice Pres., Osmundson Mfg. Co., Inc., Perry, Iowa
M.J. Bassman, Pres., Midwest Builders, Inc., Des Moines, Iowa
Lynn E. Dryer, Chief Engr., KAET-TV, A.S.U., Tempe, Arizona
R.E. Ditzler, 2926 E. Mariposa St., Phoenix, Arizona

1634 N. 52nd Street
Phoenix 8, Arizona
January 7, 1962

Mr. Orville J. Smith
Coast Oil Company
420 N. 5th Street
Baton Rouge, Louisiana

Dear Mr. Smith:

Dr. James C. Jones of the Arizona State University Geology Department has informed me that you are interested in hiring young men with a Bachelor of Science degree in Geology.

While reading your annual expansion report I was surprised to learn that you are going to do some exploration work in Chile in the hope of discovering new oil fields. Since I will be graduating in May with a B.S. in Geology, have an overall A— average, and am especially interested in petroleum exploration work, I believe I would fit in well with your plans.

I am available most of the time for an interview and can arrange my schedule to see you at your convenience. I am attaching a résumé of my education and experience and the names of people who have expressed a willingness to speak for me.

Yours truly,

Richard L. Soforth

Richard L. Soforth

RÉSUMÉ

Personal Data

NAME: Richard L. Soforth
RACE: Caucasian
MARITAL STATUS: Married
DRAFT STATUS: 4F   PHOTO
BIRTH DATE   1/11/40
CITIZENSHIP: U.S.
DEPENDENT: One

Education

A full transcript will be sent upon request. I have had these courses that bear directly upon the job I am seeking.

Structural Geology   Paleontology (2 courses)
Field Geology   Stratigraphy
Mineralogy (2 courses)   Optical Mineralogy

Work History

Present Employment: Part-time lab assistant and general helper with Arizona State University Geology Department, Tempe, Arizona.
Previous Job: None.

References

Dr. James C. Jones   Ralph Kearny
Geology Department   420 E. Hayden Road
Arizona State University   Phoenix 12, Arizona

Dr. George M. Peterson   Peter M. Swite
Geology Department   1200 N. Scottsdale Road
Arizona State University   Scottsdale, Arizona

A Geological Survey

GEOLOGICAL SURVEY

OF

TEMPE BUTTE

Technical Communication
Arizona State University
Tempe, Arizona

by

Richard L. Cooley
Senior Geology Student

and

John B. Sloan
Senior Geology Student
December 11, 1961

TABLE OF CONTENTS

LIST OF FIGURES

ABSTRACT

Tempe Butte, two low hills trending northwest-southeast, on the north edge of Tempe, Arizona, consists of layers of sandstone, siltstone, and shale, overlain by basalt and andesite flows that have been faulted and tilted to form a block fault mountain. A detailed stratigraphic section, a study of the structure, and an interpretation of the geologic history are made.

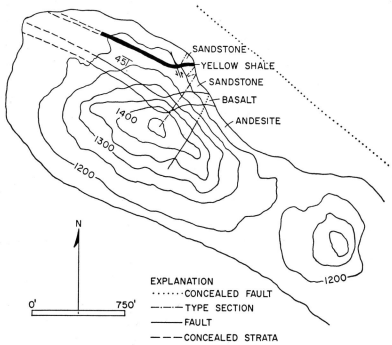

Fig. 1. Geologic map of Tempe Butte. Contours traced from enlargement of the 1912 edition of the Tempe Quadrangle published by the U.S.G.S.

I. Introduction

Tempe Butte (Fig. 1) is located at the north edge of Tempe, Arizona, on the south bank of the Salt River, Section 15, TIN, R4E, Salt and Gila River Base Line and Meridian. It consists of two hills trending northwest-southeast, the larger being about 340 feet high and the smaller almost 200 feet high, covering an area of approximately one-quarter of a square mile. Although not shown in Fig. 1, the Arizona State University football stadium is located in the saddle between the two hills.

All fieldwork was done by reconnaissance. The topographic map used for illustrations was enlarged from the 1912 Tempe Quadrangle published by the U.S.G.S.

The authors wish to extend their thanks to Dr. Raymond L. Ethington and Charles G. Evensen for their help in the preparation of this report.

II. Geography

The relief and size of the area have been discussed in the introduction.

All exposures of sedimentary rocks occur on the north side of the larger hill. The best of these exposures occurs as a small overhanging cliff along the base of the hill where the river has undercut. In most places the sediments are buried in caliche-cemented talus above this small cliff. A few of the ridges and gullies that extend up the side of the hill have good exposures in places; however, only one, which was chosen for the type section, has a continuous outcrop to the top of the hill.

The smaller hill and the south side and top of the larger hill are andesite.

A bed of yellow shale trending east-west forms a zone of weakness that is expressed at the surface as a linear depression almost parallel to the base of the larger hill. The base of the andesite on the larger hill is marked by an 8 to 12 foot cliff that extends parallel to the linear depression. The rest of the rocks have no distinctive topographic expression.

The butte is completely surrounded by alluvium.

Hereafter, when the term "the butte" is used, it will refer to the larger of the two hills.

III. Stratigraphy

All of the sedimentary rocks are sandstone, siltstone, and shale. Mud cracks were observed on many of the exposed bedding planes of the siltstone. Great

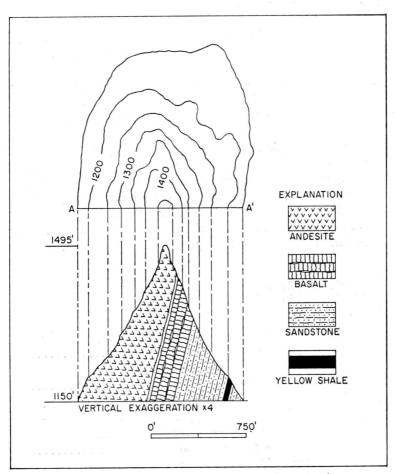

Fig. 2. Section through Tempe Butte along A-A'.

difficulty was encountered in dividing these rocks into units, because very few beds could be traced laterally for any distance. The beds were either thin or split into smaller ones, and colors and textures change laterally in short distances. The most significant division in these sediments occurs as a bed of yellow shale. All of the rest of the sediments are much alike.

Lying above the sediments is a basalt flow and an andesite flow separated from each other by a bed of red sandstone. The basalt is well weathered, but the andesite is relatively fresh. Occurring in the well-weathered basalt are zones of apparently similar composition but much less altered. Possibly these are more acidic zones within the basalt which were less susceptible to weathering. The basalt contains inclusions of the underlying sandstone, whereas the andesite contains inclusions of what possibly was a schist or a gneiss derived from some unknown locality.

The type section is taken from three different outcrops because no continuous sequence up the side of the hill could be found. The first seven units, starting at the river bed, were taken from the cliff directly below a power line tower that stands just above the yellow shale. Unit #8 was taken from the place where the yellow shale disappears under the river bed. The remaining units were taken about 20 yards east on the east side of a small ridge extending up the hill. The location of these sections is shown on Fig. 1. The section is shown on Fig. 2.

Detailed Stratigraphic Section

Rock Strata:

Andesite porphyry, gray; phenocrysts of biotite, hornblende, and sodic
    phagioclase composing about 10 percent of rock 70

Sandstone, red; fine to medium grained; thickness inferred because of
    talus covering in most places 6–7

Basalt, weathering green to black; lower half very well weathered,
    upper half less well weathered; amygduloidal with zeolite amyg-
    dules; no sharp contact between two parts; zones of less-
    weathered basalt located in the well-weathered basalt 89

Sandstone and siltstone, red-brown; sandstone mostly fine-grained and
    silty, few thin layers of coarse-grained sandstone; alternately thick
    and thin bedded; contact alteration on upper contact with basalt
    turns upper 1–2 feet gray 170

Sandstone, gray and red-brown; fine-grained, silty, gray beds tending
    to be shaly; few interbedded layers of coarse-grained sandstone 41

– 2 –

Fig. 3. Drag fold in yellow shale. Hammer is 12 inches long.

Fig. 4. Fault displacing yellow shale bed. Yellow shale (Y) contacts red sandstone (T).

Shale, first 2.5 feet gray-green, remainder yellow weathering brown;
   silty; an interbed about 4 feet thick of thick-bedded red-brown
   medium-grained sandstone near top   19
Sandstone, basal 4 feet a greenish-gray; next 20 feet the greenish-
   gray material present as particles in a matrix of red-brown sandstone; remainder of unit a red-brown fine-grained sandstone; thick
   to thin bedded   38
Sandstone, red-brown alternately thick and thin bedded; some lower
   layers exhibit graded bedding, upper layers medium to fine
   grained   15
Conglomerate, red-brown, average particle size about 2 mm in diameter; thick bedded; grades laterally to medium-grained sandstone, then back to conglomerate   3
Sandstone, red-brown; silty; alternately thick and thin bedded; first 1.5
   feet cross bedded   12
Sandstone, gray-green; fine-grained, silty; thin bedded   4
Sandstone, light red-brown; fine-grained, silty; bedding obscured by
   contemporaneous deformations   3
         Total rock strata   305

IV. Geologic Structure

The Tempe Butte is a tilted fault block with the major fault extending north-west-southeast somewhere in the Salt River bed, where it is covered by alluvium. The same strata that occur on the butte are also exposed to the north across the river, indicating a repetition of beds produced by the faulting. The average attitude (N35°–45°W, 45°SW) of these beds is similar to the average attitude (N65°–70°W, 45°SW) of the beds on the butte.

Dips and strikes taken in the sediments on the north side of the butte show less than 5° variation, indicating no appreciable warping accompanying faulting. However, small folds and crenulations in some beds probably indicate slumping at the time of deposition. One fold of this type observed in the type section about 25 yards below the basalt is overturned and is about three feet high. The other observed folds and crenulations are much smaller. The yellow shale bed showed small overturned folds with their axial planes all inclined west. These could be drag folds caused by differential movement during faulting or another example of slumping during deposition (see Fig. 3).

Two normal faults were found in the butte. One having a strike of N20°W was observed in the yellow shale just west of a power line tower (see Fig. 4). It

– 3 –

has an apparent dip slip of about seven feet. However, no exact computations on displacement can be made because the exposure is very poor. Also, the fault seems to die out about 20 to 30 yards above and below the yellow shale. The relative positions of the yellow shale beds to either side of the fault showed that the east block moved down relative to the west block.

The other fault was observed in the andesite toward the east end of the butte. This fault can be traced over the top of the butte, but it disappears under talus about halfway down both the north and south sides. Since no reference plane to either side of the fault in the andesite could be found, no displacement figures could be obtained. The brecciated zone produced by the fault is in places more than a yard wide.

Numerous small normal and reverse faults of a displacement of six inches to a foot were found in the sediments. They all trend in a north-south direction.

Fractured and brecciated zones were found in the andesite. These zones separated large blocks from the main mass of andesite. Therefore, it could not be determined whether these can be attributed to faults or slumping.

Covering of the structures by caliche-cemented talus prevented complete study of the faults. No doubt other minor faults are present, but they would be very difficult to detect in the sandstone because no beds could be traced laterally.

V. Geologic History

The splitting, thickening, thinning, and dividing of beds; the lenses of sandstone; the graded bedding and the slumping—all seem to indicate that the sediments are of continental floodplain origin. Some fossil palm leaf inprints were found, but they were too fragmentary for age assignment. In superficial appearance, strata of the butte resemble the Recreation red beds (Cretaceous) of the Tucson area (C.G. Evensen, personal communication, 1961)

The history of the butte seems to be: (1) deposition of the floodplain deposits; (2) extrusion of basalt; (3) deposition of sandy sediment; (4) extrusion of andesite; and (5) faulting and tilting of the butte.

This sequence is supported by two facts. First, there is at least one large fault through the andesite, indicated by slickensided surfaces in the fault described above and by brecciated zones. Although the fault is buried by talus at the point where it should intersect the sediments, it is presumed to cross them too, because of some brecciation observed lower in the sediments but in line with the fault.

Second, there is no angular unconformity between the sediments and basalt, because the basalt was not observed to have crossed the strata in any place. Also,

– 4 –

the line of outcrop of the base of the andesite is parallel to the surface expression of the bedding of the sediments, indicating no angular unconformity here either.

VI. Summary

Tempe Butte is actually two low hills trending northwest-southeast, located on the south bank of the Salt River at the north edge of Tempe, Arizona. It consists of layers of sandstone, siltstone, and shale overlain by a basalt and an andesite flow. The basalt and andesite are separated by a bed of red sandstone.

The butte is a tilted fault block, with the major fault trending northwest-southeast in the river bed. Other than small folds produced by slumping during deposition and some possible drag folds in a yellow shale, there is no folding; however, two normal faults were located. One displaces the bed of yellow shale about seven feet but dies out about 30 yards above and below it, and one crosses the andesite (displacement unknown). Numerous small normal and thrust faults were observed.

The geologic history of the butte seems to be: (1) deposition of floodplain deposits; (2) extrusion of basalt; (3) deposition of sandy sediments; (4) extrusion of andesite; and (5) faulting and tilting.

BIBLIOGRAPHY

Billings, M.P. Structural Geology (Englewood Cliffs, N.J.: Prentice-Hall, Inc., 1954)

Dunbar, C.O., and John Rogers. Principles of Stratigraphy (New York: John Wiley & Sons, Inc., 1957)

Lahee, F.L. Field Geology (New York: McGraw-Hill Book Company, 1952)

13
Professional Literacy

The previous twelve chapters concerning oral and written communication complete the body of the text. The present chapter offers a five-year reading program beginning with graduation. It is included here as a convenience and an encouragement to those who want to read but who are not quite sure where to start. The plan suggested will not help the few already literate technical students who know quite well what to read. Nor is it expected to be of much help to another small group of technically trained people who have little interest in developing professional standing. This group will be too busy with current reading, movies, television programs, and other diversional activities. But for the average technical student somewhat detached from humanity by his long voyage into mathematics and science unknowns, this plan may prove a godsend. The correlation between technical men who read and who become successful, and between technical men who do not read and who do not become successful, is very high. In fact, it is believed to be nearly 100 percent.

The greater success and prestige of the man who reads may be traced to several effects of reading. One of the more direct effects is the increased ability to understand the written word and to communicate with those other members of the human race who have not specialized in mathematics and science. This number is considerably larger than the young graduate may realize. The ability to understand others (not just another technically trained person) and the ability to make oneself understood are qualifications the professional man may improve by reading.

Another positive effect of wide reading on the technical man is to heighten his imagination. There is a widespread belief that men with imagination are better problem solvers. They do not give up when all the known formulas fail. Reading also increases the understanding of personality traits, and this knowledge makes it easier to work harmoniously with others. But even if there were not professional reasons for improving literacy, the personal rewards would make a reading program worthwhile. Sharing the experience of great writers broadens the individual's own experience and makes him wiser. These are only a few of the stimulating effects of reading.

But reading takes time—more than most people will give even in exchange for these effects. Perhaps the strongest motive should be found in the personal pleasures of reading rather than in any professional returns which one may observe. Reading is like an adventure without the physical exertion. It is the one remaining champagne bargain for the price of beer. One good book can change the ennui of everyday facts and figures to productive and interesting work. Once the reading program is begun, it will find its own place in a person's schedule. Authors of great books have a skill of their own for catching and holding the reader's interest. It is getting started that takes the will power.

One way to become interested in reading is to own a few books. A small personal collection may be started while one is still in college, maybe even before. The possession of books is a sign of budding literacy. It does not really matter what books are collected, just so they are books which people have not been willing to forget. Copies of such books can sometimes be bought at secondhand stores for as little as twenty-five cents. Old books, well worn and penciled, may be worth many times more to the owner than a bestseller in the show window. The books one personally buys are more useful in improving one's literacy than borrowed ones. Personally owned books can be read now or later; they can be marked or scribbled in along the margins. These marginal notes, indicating the stage of mental development of the reader, can be as revealing and amusing to the owner on the second or third reading in five, ten, or twenty years as the text itself. The kind of book obviously being discussed here for the personal library is the one which is worth reading well. A really great book reread and re-reread can do more to improve professional literacy than a hundred scanned.

One's personal library can be started with the books on the study desk during the last year in college. Advanced courses textbooks should be kept. These can serve as reference works for several years after the student has accepted employment. The student will, of course, keep and replace as necessary his collegiate dictionary and his English handbook. He will continue to receive the journal or technical magazine he subscribed for when he joined the student chapter of his technical society. These books, dusted off regularly and kept within sight, will soon attract other books.

After graduation, or as soon as they can be afforded, other professional tools should be added to the personal library: technical handbooks as needed to cover the field of specialization, a one-volume encyclopedia (the Columbia is excellent), a world atlas, a technical dictionary, a one-volume history of the United States, Bartlett's *Familiar Quotations,* and a copy of the Bible (the authoritative version of one's own church, with concordance). These books may not sound imposing, but the man who possesses them and makes use of them is a man marked for distinction, whatever his professional occupation.

Just what literary works a technical man should select and purchase for his library will depend upon his personal tastes. These works, however, will not differ a great deal from those any intelligent person would read. Technical people, it may safely be assumed, are also capable of thinking and feeling. They, too, can enjoy great men's thoughts and emotions in the forms now loosely called literature. The collective judgment of many people in more than one generation is needed, though, to establish what is literature. What is actually the best literature cannot be unanimously decided, even by the experts. Any suggested "list" is sure to contain a few books that seem of doubtful value to some individuals and to fail to contain someone's favorite book. But on one thing all experts would agree: technical people should read, and technical people have time to read only the very best.

On the other hand, judging what is best for oneself by its tendency to survive is not necessarily a safe guide, either. An indiscriminate reading of a five-foot shelf of classics would strain the capacity of some professors of literature. Reading of this type is not recommended for a beginner, at least not until he has cut his second molars on something a lot easier to read.

The best reading plan, then, for a technical man is one which starts simply and moves gradually toward the works which require more sustained effort. Books unified by character, time, and place—novels, biographies, and autobiographies—have built-in narrative suspense for holding the reader's attention; and they are long enough to give the reader, even a pretty dull one, the author's interpretation of life. For these reasons, the first-year suggested reading plan which follows contains mostly the longer narrative forms.

Some of the biographical narrative forms suggested for the first year of reading are quite old, going back to the beginnings of Western civilization, but they are well-known works in the language, and they have a strong time sequence which enables the beginner to read them easily. The novels in the first year are those which are of proven worth but still close enough to present-day writing to be read easily. The narrative works of fiction and nonfiction included in other years of the reading plan are somewhat more difficult to read and understand. Some titles encountered in high school will sound familiar, but they really are not. These books are beyond most high school students. If a novel such as *Huckleberry Finn* or *The Scarlet Letter* was read in high school, a second or third reading in more mature years will reveal that either of these books has a great deal more to say than a high school student is ready to understand. Both authors champion the freedom of the human spirit and cry out against conventions and falseness and hypocrisy in all its forms. *Huckleberry Finn* should be reread now, *The Scarlet Letter* next year. For the fifth year more difficult literary works can be read, including the great classics of world literature. In the fifth year there may also be opportunity for some reading of current works which time has not yet honored by the name of literature.

FIVE-YEAR READING PROGRAM

Note: N=novel, B=biography or autobiography, NF=nonfiction, PL=plays, P= poetry, S=short story, and E=essays.

First Year

Author	Type	Title
Angle, Paul McClelland	B	*The Lincoln Reader*
Austen, Jane	N	*Pride and Prejudice*
Bliven, Bruce	NF	*The Men Who Make the Future*
Brontë, Charlotte	N	*Jane Eyre*
Casanova, Giacomo	B	*Memoirs*
Cellini, Benvenuto	B	*Autobiography*
Churchill, Winston (American novelist)	N	*The Inside of the Cup*
Conrad, Joseph	N	*Lord Jim*
Crowther, J. G.	B	*Famous American Men of Science*
Defoe, Daniel	N	*Robinson Crusoe*
Du Maurier, Daphne	N	*Rebecca*
Forester, C. S.	N	*Captain Horatio Hornblower*
Franklin, Benjamin	B	*The Autobiography of Benjamin Franklin*
Hardy, Thomas	N	*The Return of the Native*
Howells, William Dean	N	*The Rise of Silas Lapham*
Kipling, Rudyard	N	*Kim*

Author	Type	Title
Rawlings, Marjorie Kinnan	N	*The Yearling*
Stefferud, Alfred	NF	*The Wonderful World of Books*
Steinbeck, John	N	*The Grapes of Wrath*
Stuart, Jesse	S	*Beyond Dark Hills*
Twain, Mark	N	*Huckleberry Finn*
West, Jessamyn	N	*The Friendly Persuasion*
Wouk, Herman	N	*The Caine Mutiny*
	B	*Gospel of St. Mark* (New Testament)
	B	*The Acts of the Apostles* (New Testament)

SECOND YEAR

Author	Type	Title
Anderson, Sherwood	N	*Winesburg, Ohio*
Barzun, Jacques	NF	*God's Country and Mine*
Benét, Stephen Vincent	S	*The Devil and Daniel Webster*
Brontë, Emily	N	*Wuthering Heights*
Buck, Pearl	N	*The Good Earth*
Bunyan, John	N	*The Pilgrim's Progress*
Carson, Rachel	NF	*The Sea Around Us*
Cather, Willa Sibert	N	*Death Comes for the Archbishop*
Clarke, Arthur C.	NF	*The Exploration of Space*
Cooper, James Fenimore	N	*The Last of the Mohicans*
Costain, Thomas	N	*The Conquerors*
Crane, Stephen	N	*The Red Badge of Courage*
Davenport, William H., Lowry C. Wimberly, and Harry Shaw	P	*Dominant Types in British and American Literature* (vol. 1: Poetry and Drama)
Davis, Elmer	E	*But We Were Born Free*
De Voto Bernard	NF	*Across the Wide Missouri*
Dickens, Charles	N	*A Tale of Two Cities*
Eliot, George	N	*Silas Marner*
Forester, C. S.	N	*The African Queen*
Forster, E. M.	N	*A Passage to India*
Guthrie, A. B., Jr.	N	*The Big Sky*
Hammett, Dashiell	N	*The Thin Man*
Hardy, Thomas	N	*Tess of the D'Urbervilles*
Harte, Bret	S	*The Luck of Roaring Camp*, and other sketches
Hawthorne, Nathaniel	N	*The Scarlet Letter*
Hugo, Victor	N	*Les Misérables*
Huxley, Aldous	N	*Brave New World*
Kaufman, George S., and Moss Hart	P	*You Can't Take It with You*
Lardner, Ring	S	*Hair-cut*
Lord, Walter	NF	*Day of Infamy*
Merejkowski, Dmitri	B	*The Romance of Leonardo da Vinci*
Milton, John	P	*Paradise Lost*
Morley, Christopher	N	*Thunder on the Left*
Porter, Katherine Anne	S	*Pale Horse, Pale Rider*
Saroyan, William	N	*The Human Comedy*

Schulberg, Budd	N	*Waterfront*
Shakespeare, William	PL	*The Comedies of Shakespeare*
Sheridan, Richard Brinsley	PL	*The Rivals*
Steinbeck, John	N	*Of Mice and Men*
Stout, Rex	N	*The Red Box*
Strachey, Lytton	B	*Portraits in Miniature*
Stuart, Jesse	N	*Taps for Private Tussie*
Twain, Mark	B	*Autobiography of Mark Twain*
	NF	*The Innocents Abroad*
	S	*The Man That Corrupted Hadley-burg*
	S	*The Mysterious Stranger*
	N	*A Connecticut Yankee in King Arthur's Court*
Wallace, Lew	N	*Ben Hur*
Wells, H. G.	N	*Tono Bungay*
Wilder, Thornton	N	*The Bridge of San Luis Rey*
	B	*Gospel of St. John* (New Testament)
		Ruth, Esther, Job (Old Testament)

THIRD YEAR

Adams, Henry	B	*The Education of Henry Adams*
Allen, Frederick Lewis	NF	*Only Yesterday*
Anderson, Maxwell	PL	*Key Largo*
Austen, Jane	N	*Sense and Sensibility*
Barry, Philip	PL	*The Animal Kingdom*
Bennett, Arnold	N	*The Old Wives' Tale*
Bowen, Catherine Drinker	B	*John Adams and the American Revolution*
Bradley, Sculley, Richard Beatty, and E. Hudson Long	P	*The American Traditions in Literature* (vols. 1, 2)
Brush, Katherine	S	*Night Club*
Catton, Bruce	NF	*A Stillness at Appomattox*
Ceram, C. W.	NF	*Gods, Graves, and Scholars*
Churchill, Sir Winston	NF	*The Gathering Storm*
	NF	*Their Finest Hour*
	NF	*The Grand Alliance*
Congreve, William	PL	*The Way of the World*
Conrad, Joseph	N	*Victory*
Cottrell, Leonard	NF	*The Anvil of Civilization*
De Voto, Bernard	NF	*The Year of Decision*
Dos Passos, John	N	*U.S.A.*
Dreiser, Theodore	S	*Free,* and other stories
Faulkner, William	S	*A Rose for Emily*
Fielding, Henry	N	*The History of Tom Jones*
Galsworthy, John	N	*The Forsyte Saga*
Guthrie, A. B., Jr.	N	*The Way West*
Hagedorn, Hermann	B	*The Roosevelt Family of Sagamore Hill*

Author	Type	Title
Hall, James Norman	N	*Men Against the Sea*
Hawthorne, Nathaniel	S	*The Portable Hawthorne* (ed. by Malcolm Cowley)
Hemingway, Ernest	N	*The Old Man and the Sea*
Henderson, G. F. R.	B	*Stonewall Jackson and the American Civil War*
Hugo, Victor	N	*The Hunchback of Notre Dame*
Jefferson, Thomas	B	*Life and Selected Writings of Jefferson*
Kantor, MacKinlay	N	*Andersonville*
Masters, Edgar Lee	P	*Spoon River Anthology*
Maugham, W. Somerset	N	*The Moon and Sixpence*
Melville, Herman	N	*Moby Dick*
Miller, Arthur	PL	*Death of a Salesman*
Namer, Emile	B	*Galileo, Searcher of the Heavens*
O'Neill, Eugene	PL	*The Hairy Ape*
Paton, Alan	N	*Cry, the Beloved Country*
Pepys, Samuel	B	*Diary* (abridged)
Sandburg, Carl	B	*Abraham Lincoln: the War Years*
Saroyan, William	PL	*The Time of Your Life*
	S	*My Name Is Aram*
Scott, Sir Walter	N	*The Heart of Midlothian*
Shakespeare, William	PL	*The Tragedies of Shakespeare*
Shaw, George Bernard	PL	*The Devil's Disciple*
Steinbeck, John	N	*East of Eden*
Strachey, Lytton	B	*Eminent Victorians*
Toynbee, Arnold Joseph	NF	*A Study of History* (abridged)
Wells, H. G.	N	*The War of the Worlds*
Wharton, Edith	N	*Ethan Frome*
Whitman, Walt	P	*Leaves of Grass*
	B	*Gospel of St. Luke* (New Testament) *Psalms, Proverbs, Isaiah* (Old Testament)

FOURTH YEAR

Author	Type	Title
Bacon, Francis	E	*Selected Essays of Francis Bacon*
Balzac, Honoré de	N	*Eugénie Grandet*
Bowen, Catherine Drinker	B	*Yankee from Olympus*
Butler, Samuel	N	*The Way of All Flesh, Erewhon*
Camus, Albert	N	*The Stranger*
Cervantes, Miguel de	N	*Don Quixote*
Chaucer, Geoffrey	P	*Troilus and Criseyde* (rendered into modern prose by R. M. Lumiansky)
Chesterton, G. K.	S	*The Father Brown Stories*
Churchill, Sir Winston	NF	*The Hinge of Fate*
	NF	*Closing the Ring*
	NF	*Triumph and Tragedy*
Cottrell, Leonard	NF	*Lost Cities*

Crane, Stephen	S, P	*Selected Prose and Poetry*
Dickens, Charles	N	*David Copperfield*
	N	*Oliver Twist*
	N	*Pickwick Papers*
Dostoevsky, Feodor	N	*Crime and Punishment*
Eliot, George	N	*Adam Bede*
Fielding, Henry	N	*The History of Joseph Andrews*
Fitzgerald, F. Scott	N	*The Great Gatsby*
Flaubert, Gustave	N	*Madame Bovary*
Galsworthy, John	PL	*Justice*
Goethe, Johann Wolfgang von	PL	*Faust*
Goldsmith, Oliver	PL	*She Stoops to Conquer*
Graves, Robert	N	*I, Claudius*
Hamsun, Knut	N	*Growth of the Soil*
Hayakawa, S. I.	NF	*Language in Thought and Action*
Homer	P	*The Iliad*
	P	*The Odyssey* (trans. by Robert Fitzgerald)
Irving, Washington	E, S	*Selected Writings of Washington Irving*
James, Henry	N	*The American*
Joyce, James	N	*Portrait of the Artist as a Young Man*
Lamb, Charles	E	*Essays of Elia*
Lewis, Sinclair	N	*Arrowsmith*
Ludwig, Emil	B	*Napoleon*
Marlowe, Christopher	PL	*Doctor Faustus*
Maugham, W. Somerset	N	*Of Human Bondage*
Meredith, George	N	*The Ordeal of Richard Feverel*
	N	*The Egoist*
More, Thomas	E	*Utopia*
Michener, James A.	N	*The Bridges at Toki-Ri*
Poe Edgar Allan	S, P	*Great Tales and Poems*
	S, P	*The Portable Poe* (ed. Philip van Doren Stern)
Ray, Gordon N., ed.	P	*Masters of British Literature* (vols. 1, 2)
Rostand, Edmond	PL	*Cyráno de Bergerac*
Sandberg, Carl	P	*The People, Yes*
Shakespeare, William	PL, P	*The Histories and Poems of Shakespeare*
Shaw, George Bernard	PL	*Caesar and Cleopatra*
Sitwell, Edith	B	*Alexander Pope*
Smollett, Tobias	N	*The Expedition of Humphry Clinker*
Stephens, James	N	*The Crock of Gold*
Sterne, Laurence	N	*The Life and Opinions of Tristram Shandy*
Swift, Jonathan	N	*Gulliver's Travels*
Thackeray, William M.	N	*Vanity Fair*
Toynbee, Arnold Joseph	NF	*Civilization on Trial*
Van Loon, Hendrik	NF	*The Story of Mankind*

Author	Type	Title
Veblen, Thorstein	NF	*The Theory of the Leisure Class*
Walpole, Hugh	N	*The Cathedral*
Waltari, Mika	N	*The Egyptian*
Wharton, Edith	N	*The Age of Innocence*
Wolfe, Thomas	N	*Look Homeward, Angel*
	B	*Gospel of St. Matthew* (New Testament)
	B	*Epistles of St. Paul* (New Testament)
		Genesis, Deuteronomy, and the Minor Prophets (Old Testament)

FIFTH YEAR

Author	Type	Title
Brown, Calvin S. (General Editor)	NF	*The Reader's Companion to World Literature* (a Mentor Book)
Carlyle, Thomas	NF	*The French Revolution*
Cecil, David, and Allen Tate, eds.	P	*Modern Verse in English*
Dostoevsky, Feodor	N	*The Brothers Karamazov*
Durant, Will	NF	*The Life of Greece*
	NF	*The Age of Reason Begins*
Frazer, Sir James G.	NF	*The Golden Bough* (one volume, abridged)
Gibbon, Edward	NF	*Decline and Fall of the Roman Empire*
Lamb, Harold	B	*Genghis Khan*
Oates, W. J., and Eugene O'Neill, Jr., eds.	PL	*Seven Famous Greek Plays*
Thucydides	NF	*Complete Writings* (tr. by Richard Crawley)
Tolstoy, Leo	N	*Anna Karenina*
		The Great Book Series (anything not previously read) Henry Regnery Company, Chicago
		The Harvard Classics (anything not previously read) ed. by Charles W. Eliot
		Current popular books from any source
		The Bible: Old and New Testaments (any parts not previously read)

appendix

Abbreviations

AMERICAN STANDARD ABBREVIATIONS FOR SCIENTIFIC AND ENGINEERING TERMS

(Extracted from American Standard Abbreviations for Scientific and Engineering Terms, ASA Z 10.1-1941, with permission of publisher, The American Society of Mechanical Engineer, 345 East 47th Street, New York 17, New York.)

absolute ....abs
acre ....spell out
acre-foot ....acre-ft
air horsepower ....air hp
alternating current (as adjective ....a-c
ampere ....amp
ampere-hour ....amp-hr
amplitude, an elliptic function ....am.
Angstrom unit ....A
antilogarithm ....antilog
atmosphere ....atm
atomic weight ....at. wt
average ....avg
avoirdupois ....avdp
azimuth ....az or α

barometer ....bar.
barrel ....bbl
Baumé ....Bé
board feet (feet board
   measure) ....fbm
boiler pressure ....spell out
boiling point ....bp
brake horsepower ....bhp
brake horsepower-hour ......bhp-hr
Brinell hardness number ......Bhn
British thermal unit ......Btu or B
bushel ....bu

calorie ....cal
candle c
candle-hour ....c-hr
candlepower ....cp
cent ....c or ¢

center to center ....c to c
centigram ....cg
centiliter cl
centimeter ....cm
centimeter-gram-second
   (system) ....cgs
chemical ....chem
chemically pure ....cp
circular ....cir
circular mils ....cir mils
coefficient ....coef
cologarithm ....colog
concentrate ....conc
conductivity ....cond
constant ....const
continental horsepower ....cont hp
cord ....cd
cosecant ....csc
cosine ....cos
cosine of the amplitude, an
   elliptic function ....cn
cost, insurance, and freight ....cif
cotangent ....cot
coulomb ....spell out
counter electromotive force ....cemf
cubic ....cu
cubic centimeter .....cu cm, cm³
   (liquid, meaning milliliter, ml)
cubic feet per minute ....cfm
cubic feet per second ....cfs
cubic foot ....cu ft
cubic inch ....cu in.
cubic meter ....cu m or m³
cubic micron .....cu μ or cu mu or μ³
cubic millimeter ....cu mm or mm³
cubic yard ....cu yd

current density .... spell out
cycles per second ...... spell out or c
cylinder .... cyl

day .... spell out
decibel .... db
degree .... deg or °
degree centigrade C
degree Fahrenheit .... F
degree Kelvin .... K
degree Réaumur .... R
delta amplitude, an elliptic
    function .... dn
diameter .... diam
direct-current (as adjective) ...... d-c
dollar .... $
dozen .... doz
dram .... dr

efficiency .... eff
electric .... elec
electromotive force .... emf
elevation .... el
equation .... eq
external .... ext

farad .... spell out or f
feet board measure (board
    feet) .... fbm
feet per minute .... fpm
feet per second .... fps
fluid .... fl
foot .... ft
foot-candle .... ft-c
foot-Lambert .... ft-L
foot-pound .... ft-lb
foot-pound-second (system) .... fps
foot-second (see cubic feet per
    (second)
franc .... fr
free aboard ship .... spell out
free alongside ship .... spell out
free on board .... fob
freezing point .... fp
frequency .... spell out
fusion point .... fnp

gallon .... gal
gallons per minute .... gpm
gallons per second .... gps
grain .... spell out
gram .... g

gram-calorie .... g-cal
greatest common divisor .... gcd

haversine .... hav
hectare .... ha
henry .... h
high-pressure (adjective) ...... h-p
hogshead .... hhd
horsepower .... hp
horsepower-hour .... hp-hr
hour .... hr
hour (in astronomical tables) ..... h
hundred C
hundredweight (112 lb) ...... cwt
hyperbolic cosine .... cosh
hyperbolic sine .... sinh
hyperbolic tangent .... tanh

inch .... in.
inch-pound .... in-lb
inches per second .... ips
indicated horsepower .... ihp
indicated horsepower-hour ... ihp-hr
inside diameter .... ID
intermediate-pressure (adjec-
    tive) .... i-p
internal .... int

joule .... j

kilocalorie .... kcal
kilocycles per second .... kc
kilogram .... kg
kilogram-calorie .... kg-cal
kilogram-meter .... kg-m
kilograms per cubic
    meter ..... kg per cu m or kg/m³
kilograms per second .... kgps
kiloliter .... kl
kilometer .... km
kilometers per second .... kmps
kilovolt .... kv
kilovolt-ampere .... kva
kilowatt .... kw
kilowatthour .... kwhr

Lambert L
latitude .... lat or φ
least common multiple .... lcm
linear foot .... lin ft
liquid .... liq
lira .... spell out

liter l
logarithm (common) ....log
logarithm (natural) ....log$_e$ or ln
longitude ....long. or λ
low-pressure (as adjective) .....l-p
lumen l
lumen-hour ....l-hr
lumens per watt ....lpw

mass ....spell out
mathematics (ical) ....math
maximum ....max
mean effective pressure ....mep
mean horizontal candlepower ..mhcp
megacycle ....spell out
megohm ....spell out
melting point ....mp
meter ....m
meter-kilogram ....m-kg
mho. ....spell out
microampere ....μa or mu a
microfarad ....μf
microinch ....μin.
micromicrofarad ....μμf
micromicron ....μμ or mu mu
micron ....μ or mu
microvolt ....μv
microwatt ....μw or mu w
mile ....spell out
miles per hour ....mph
miles per hour per second ...mphps
milliampere ....ma
milligram ....mg
millihenry ....mh
millilambert ....mL
milliliter ....ml
millimeter ....mm
millimicron ....mμ or m mu
million ....spell out
million gallons per day ....mgd
millivolt ....mv
minimum ....min
minute ....min
minute (angular measure) ....′
minute (time) (in astronomical
   tables) ....m
mole ....spell out
molecular weight ....mol. wt
month ....spell out

National Electrical Code ......NEC

ohm .... spell out or Ω
ohm-centimeter ....ohm-cm
ounce ....oz
ounce-foot ....oz-ft
ounce-inch ....oz-in.
outside diameter ....OD

parts per million ....ppm
peck ....pk
penny (pence) ....d
pennyweight ....dwt
peso ....spell out
pint ....pt
potential ....spell out
potential difference ....spell out
pound ....lb
pound-foot ....lb-ft
pound-inch ....lb-in.
pound sterling ....£
pounds per brake horsepower-
   hour ....lb per bhp-hr
pounds per cubic foot ..lb per cu ft
pounds per square foot ....psf
pounds per square inch ....psi
pounds per square inch
   absolute ....psia
power factor ....spell out or pf

quart ....qt

radian ....spell out
reactive kilovolt-ampere ....kvar
reactive volt-ampere ....var
revolutions per minute ....rpm
revolutions per second ....rps
rod ....spell out
root mean square ....rms

secant ....sec
second ....sec
second (angular) ....″
second-foot (see cubic feet
   per second)
second (time) (in astronomical
   tables) ....s
shaft horsepower ....shp
shilling ....s
sine ....sin
sine of the amplitude, an elliptic
   function ....sn
specific gravity ....sp gr
specific heat ....sp ht
spherical candle power ....scp

square ....sq

square centimeter .... sq cm or cm²

square foot ....sq ft

square inch ....sq in.

square kilometer ......sq km or km²

square meter ....sq m or m²

square micron ....sq μ or sq mu or μ²

square millimeter .... sq mm or mm²

square root of mean square .... rms

standard ....std

stere ....s

tangent ....tan

temperature ....temp

tensile strength ....ts

thousand ....M

thousand foot-pounds ....kip-ft

thousand pound ....kip

ton ....spell out

ton-mile ....spell out

versed sine ....vers

volt v

volt-ampere ....va

volt-coulomb ....spell out

watt ....w

watthour ....whr

watts per candle ....wpc

week ....spell out

weight ....wt

yard ....yd

year ....yr

Word List

107 Words Often Misspelled by Technical Students

accelerate
accommodate
accurate
achieve
acquire
advantageous
affect—effect
align
analysis
approximate
article
auxiliary
available
bulletin
capacitance
category
challenge
characteristic
choose—chose
comparative
complement— compliment
component
conceivable
convenient
correlation
cylinder
dependability
dependent
describe
desirable
device—devise
dimension
divide

donor
efficiency
empirical
equipped
existence
Fahrenheit
fission
fluorescent
foreseen
fourth
gases
gauge
hazard
height
homogeneous
impedance
indispensable
inductance
inherent
initiative
loose—lose
maintenance
metallic
mileage
miniature
missile
necessity
neutralize
nickel
noticeable
nuclear
occurred
parallel
particle

particular
performance
permanent
permeable
persistent
personnel
phenomenon
possess
precede
precision
preferred
principal—principle
propel
quantity
recommend
referred
requirement
resistance
resonance
rivet
safety
satellite
schedule
schematic
separate
significance
soluble
surveillance
susceptible
symmetrical
technical
temperature
tolerance
vicinity

Index